ST Publi

C000180317

UK Com

2022
(22nd edition)

Researched & Updated by:	Martin Hall & Stephen Jones 5 Sunninghill Close, West Hallam, Ilkeston DE7 6LS
Printed & Distributed by:	ST Publications 51 Kendal Street, Wigan WN6 7DJ

Front Cover:	60062 'Stainless Pioneer' having arrived earlier in the morning with 6V15 20.18(MO) Boston Sleaford Sidings to Swindon Stores loaded BYA steel carriers, is splitting the train for unloading. Tuesday 22nd June 2021. (Chris Perkins)
Rear Cover:	Southern 377411 enters East Croydon Station, 20th May 2021 (Daniel Jones)

Introduction

Welcome to the 2022 edition of the Loco, Unit, Light Rail and Passenger Stock Combined Volume of the UK and Ireland.

This book features all registered Loco's, Units and Passenger Stock registered to operate on Network Rail along with stock in the Isle of Man and Ireland. It also features Tram and Light Rail systems including the Underground Systems of London and Glasgow plus Internal Users, Track Machines and MPV's.

To help you identify Units we have also included tables of Unit Car Numbers against Set Numbers, This section does not now include all vehicle numbers that do match up with the units running numbers e.g 58711 - 159 107 would be included but 52403 - 156 403 would not be included.

For Isle of Man information visit website www.manx.electric.co.uk.

Martin Hall
5, Sunninghill Close
West Hallam
Ilkeston
Derbyshire
DE7 6LS

November 2021

Email - stpub1@gmail.com or martin.hall47@outlock.com

Contents

How to use this Publication

All entry headings are in the format -
Locomotives   *Class - Wheel Configuration - Type*
Units   *Class - Brand Name*
Coaching Stock *Type - Description*

Codes

o/o   **On Order**
S   **stored**
W   **withdrawn**
X   **Cross Country**

Allocation Codes

Code	Location	Code	Location
AD	Ashford (Hitachi)	CP	Crewe Carriage Sheds-LNWR
AFR	Appleby Frodingham Railway	CPRR	Chinnor & Princes Risborough R-way
AIR	Airedale Hospital	CRF	Cobra Railfreight, Middlesbrough
AK	Ardwick, Manchester	CS	Carnforth, WCRC
AL	Aylesbury	CVR	Colne Valley Railway
ALN	Aln Valley Railway	CWR	Cholsey & Wallingford Railway
AM	Ambronay (France, Eurostar)	CZ	Central Rivers
AN	Allerton		
AR	Attero Recycling, Rossington	DAG	Dagenham
ATC	Asfordby Technical Centre	DCP	Dovesite Caravan Park. Derbyshire
AVD	A V Dawson, Middlesbrough	DF	Derby Loram (RTC)
AVDC	Abbey View Day Centre, Port Talbot	DFR	Dean Forest Railway
AVR	Avon Valley Railway	DI	Didcot (Great Western Society)
		DIT	Daventry (Freightliner)
BA	Basford Hall (Freightliner)	DL	Dollands Moor
BAC	Croft Quarry	DMJR	Denbigh & Mold Junction Railway
BAR	Barry Rail Centre	DMR	Dartmoor Railway
BAT	Battlefield Railway (Shackerstone)	DR	Doncaster Carr (Azuma)
BC	MoD Bicester	DSB	Dales School, Blyth
BD	Birkenhead	DSR	Dartmouth Steam Railway
BH	Barrow Hill	DTG	Deanside Transit, Glasgow
BI	Brighton Lovers Walk	DUD	AB FAN Services. Dudley
BIR	Birmingham Railway Museum	DVL	Derwent Valley Light Railway
BK	Bristol Barton Hill	DY	Derby Etches Park
BM	Bournemouth		
BN	Bounds Green	EAR	East Anglian Railway Museum
BOS	Boston Docks	EBA	Embsay & Bolton Abbey Railway
BOU	Boulby Mine	EC	Edinburgh, Craigentinny
BR	Bluebell Railway	ECVR	Ecclesbourne Valley Railway
BRC	Buckinghamshire Railway Centre	EGS	E.G. Steel, Hamilton
BRE	Boden Rail (Nottingham)	EH	Eastleigh, LNWR
BS	Bescot	EHY	Eastleigh Yards
BSM	Bressingham Steam Museum	EKR	East Kent Light Railway
BSS	Corus, Scunthorpe	ELR	East Lancashire Railway
BT	Bo'ness	EM	East Ham
BU	Burton-on-Trent (Nemesis Rail)	EMRA	European Metal Recycling, Attercliffe
BWR	Bodmin & Wenford Railway	EMRK	European Metal Recycling, Kingsbury
		EOR	Epping Ongar Railway
CAM-L	Cambrian Railway Trust, Llynclys	ESR	East Somerset Railway
CAM	Cambrian Railway Trust, Gobowen	EVR	Eden Valley Railway
CD	Crewe LSL	EX	Exeter
CDR	Caledonian Railway, Brechin	EY	Ely Papworth
CE	Crewe Electric		
CES	Crossley Evans, Shipley	FB	Ferrybridge (W H Davies)
CF	Cardiff Canton	FF	Forest, Belgium
CFB	C.F.Booth, Rotherham	FHR	Fawley Hill Railway, Bucks
CFSW	Cardiff Celsa Steelworks	FR	Foxfield Railway
CH	Chester	FRA(A)	France - Alizay (ECR)
CHC	Crewe Heritage Centre	FX	Felixstowe Docks
CHR	Chasewater Light Railway		
CHV	Churnet Valley Railway	GAH	Garden Art, Hungerford
CK	Corkerhill, Glasgow	GCR	Great Central Railway, Loughborough
CL	Collyhurst St, Manchester (GBRF)	GCT	Garston Car Terminal
CMR	Corby Model Railway	GD	MoD Glen Douglas
CO	Coquelles	GR	Gwilli Railway

Allocation Codes

Code	Location	Code	Location
GS	Grantown-on-Spey	LUL	London Underground (West Ruislip)
GV	Garw Valley Railway	LWR	Lincolnshire Wolds Railway
GVR	Gwendraeth Valley Railway, Kidwelly	LY	Le Landy, France
GW	Glasgow Shields Road	MAN	Museum of Science & Ind, Manchester
GWR	Gloucester & Warwickshire Railway	MAR	Margate
GY	Great Yarmouth	MD	Merehead
		MH	Millerhill (Scotrail)
HA	Haymarket, Edinburgh	MHR	Mid Hants Railway
HCB	Heritage Centre, Bellingham	ML	Motherwell (Scotrail)
HDH	Sutton Bridge, Lincolnshire	MMR	Mizen Miniature Rail, Woking
HE	Hornsey	MN	Machynlleth
HEL	Hellifield	MNR	Mid Norfolk Railway
HH	Hams Hall (Freightliner)	MPR	Moreton Park Railway
HM	Healey Mills	MR	March, Whitemoor Yard
HOP	Hope Farm, Le Farge Cement	MRC	Midland Railway Centre
HPM	Hartlepool Pipe Mill	MRM	Mangapps Railway Museum
HQ	Unallocated / Off Lease	MTT	Merseyside Transport, Burscough
HR	Helston Railway	MW	MoD Marchwood
HSK	Hever Station		
HSW	Hartlepool Steel Works	NA	Newton Aycliffe (Hitachi)
HT	Heaton	NC	Norwich Crown Point
HUD	Huddersfield Station	NG	New Cross Gate
		NH	Newton Heath, Manchester
IL	Ilford	NHC	Nottingham Heritage Cent, Ruddington
IMG	Imerys, Goonbarrow	NIRT	Northamptonshire Ironstone Railway
IOW	Isle of Wight Steam Railway	NL	Neville Hill, Leeds
IP	Ipswich (Freightliner)	NLR	Northampton & Lamport Railway
IS	Inverness	NM	Nottingham Eastcroft
		NN	Northampton
KDR	Keith & Dufftown Railway	NNR	North Norfolk Railway
KESR	Kent & East Sussex Railway	NP	North Pole IEP
KET	Ketton Cement, Stamford	NRM	National Railway Museum, York
KIL	Killingholme	NRS	National Railway Museum, Shildon
KLR	Kirklees Light Railway	NT	Northam, Southampton
KM	Carlisle Kingmoor (DRS)	NVR	Nene Valley Railway
KT	MoD Kineton	NYM	North Yorkshire Moors Railway
KWVR	Keighley & Worth Valley Railway		
KY	Knottingley	OC	Old Oak Common (Crossrail)
		OS	Stravithie Station
LA	Laira	OWG	Olympic Way, Greenwich
LAC	Lackenby Steel Works	OY	Oxley
LAV	Lavender Line		
LB	Loughborough, Brush Traction	PBO	Portobello, Edinburgh
LD	Leeds Midland Road (Freightliner)	PBR	Pontypool & Blaenavon Railway
LG	Longsight, Manchester	PDP	PD Ports, Middlesbrough
LGST	Llanelli Goodshed Trust	PEA	Peak Rail
LH	LH Group, Barton under Needwood	PG	Peterborough (GBRF)
LHR	Lakeside & Haverthwaite Railway	PM	Bristol St Phillips Marsh
LL	Edge Hill, Liverpool	PO	Polmadie, Glasgow
LM	Long Marston	PSK	Private Site, Kinsley
LMMR	Llanelli & Mynydd Mawr Railway	PVR	Plym Valley Railway
LP	Longport	PWR	Poulton & Wyre Railway
LR	Llangollen Railway	PZ	Penzance Long Rock
LSS	Longstowe Station		
LT	MoD Longtown	RDR	Royal Deeside Railway
LU	MoD Ludgershall	RF	Reid Freight, Longton

Allocation Codes

RG	Reading		**TJS**	Titley Junction Station
RIB	Ribble Steam Railway		**TM**	Tyseley Museum
RM	Ramsgate		**TO**	Toton
RR	Roberts Road, Doncaster		**TP**	Trafford Park (Freightliner)
RTM	Rushden Transport Museum		**TPT**	TATA Steel, Port Talbot
RU	Rugby Rail Plant (Colas)		**TS**	Tyseley
RVR	Rother Valley Railway		**TSR**	Telford Steam Railway
RY	Ryde, IOW		**TSW**	Trostre Steel Works
			TT	Toton Training Compound
SA	Salisbury		**TWS**	TWS, North Side Works, Malton Road,
SCR	Swindon & Cricklade Railway			Leavening, North Yorkshire
SDR	South Devon Railway			
SDRT	Somerset & Dorset Railway Trust		**UKR**	UK Rail Leasing, Leicester
SE	St Leonards, Hastings			
SG	Slade Green		**VBR**	Vale of Berkeley Railway, Sharpness
SHP	Summerlee Heritage Park, Coatbridge			
SH	Strawberry Hill		**WA**	Wishaw (RSS)
SI	Soho, Birmingham		**WB**	Wembley, Alstom
SJ	Stourbridge Junction		**WD**	Wimbledon
SL	Stewarts Lane		**WE**	Willesden Brent
SO	Southall		**WEA**	Weardale Railway
SP	Springs Branch, Wigan		**WI**	Widnes, Alstom
SPA	Spa Valley Railway		**WH**	Whatley Quarry
SRC	Sellindge Rail Centre		**WN**	Willesden, London
SRHC	Sandford Station Rail Heritage Centre		**WP**	Worksop HNRC
SRM	Stephenson Railway Museum		**WR**	Wensleydale Railway
STR	Strathspey Railway		**WRH**	Waverley Route Heritage Centre
SU	Selhurst		**WRS**	Whitwell & Reepham Station
SUW	SembCorp Utilities, Wilton		**WSR**	West Somerset Railway
SVR	Severn Valley Railway			
SWR	Swanage Railway		**YRC**	Yeovil Rail Centre
SZ	Southampton Maritime (Freightliner)		**YK**	York
TAL	Talybont-on-Usk		**ZB**	Doncaster, Wabtec
TAT	Tata Steel, Shotton		**ZG**	Eastleigh, Arlington
TAVR	Tanat Valley Light Railway		**ZI**	Ilford, Bombardier
TB	Three Bridges E.M.U		**ZJ**	Stoke, Marcroft
TI	Temple Mills (Eurostar)		**ZK**	Kilmarnock, Brodies
TJ	Tavistock Jnc		**ZN**	Wolverton, Railcare

Notes

Shunting Locomotives

Class 01/5

01507	CES	Venom	01525	BC	Draper	01550	BC	Storeman
01508	ZG		01526	WR		01551	AK	Lancelot
01509	AL	Lesley	01527	LH		01552	LM	
01510	LT		01528	KT		01555	HSW	James
01511	LT		01529	WR		01560	HPM	
01512	BC	Conductor	01530	EKR		01565	CFB	
01513	KT	Greensleeves	01541	MW		01567	CRF	Elizabeth
01514	LT		01542	MW		01568	ZJ	
01515	FB		01543	FB		01569	LAC	Emma
01520	FB		01544	LM		01570	HOP	Blue John
01521	BC		01545	WR	River Annan	01571	IMG	Alex (P405D)
01522	MW		01547	KT		01572	BAC	Kathryn
01523	MW		01548	GD		01573	WR	(15)
01524	LU		01549	MW				

Class 07   0-6-0   DM

07007	ZG

Class 08   0-6-0   DE

08296	MD	(001)	08536	WA(s)		08653	LM(s)		D3948	CD	(08780)
08308	WEA	(23)	08567	ZG		08663	DF		08782	BH(s)	
08375	BOS	(No 21)	08568	WA		08669	ZB		08783	EMRK(s)	
08389	CFSW		08571	DIT		08670	BS		08784	LP	
08401	HH		08573	WEA		08676	EKR(s)		08785	IP	
08405	NL		08575	BU(s)		08678	CS		08786	BH(s)	
08410	AVD		08578	WP(s)		08682(s)	HOP	(D3849)	08788	PDP	
08411	WA(s)		08580	GCT		08683	EHY		08790	LG	
08417	PEA(s)		08585	SZ		08685	EKR(s)		08798	BH(s)	
08418	CS		08588	ZI		08690	NL		08799	BAT(s)	
08423	PDP	(H011)	08593	WA(s)		08691	BA		08802	WA(s)	
08428	BH		08596	EC	(H006)	08696	WB		08804	EKR(s)	
08441	NC		08598	AVD		08700	ZI		08805	TS	
08442	EH(s)		08600	AVD		08701	LM(s)		08809	KET	(24)
08445	DIT		08602	WP(s)	(004)	08703	WN		08810	EH	
08447	DTG		08605	KY		08704	KY		08818	WP	(4)
08451	LG		08611	WB		08706	WA(s)		08822	PM	
08454	WI		08613	WEA		08709	WA(s)		08823	TAT	
08460	FX		08615	TAT		08711	BU(s)		IEMD01	BH(s)	(08824)
08472	EC		08616	TS	(3783)	08714	HOP(s)		08834	AN	
08480	KIL		08617	OY		08721	WI		08836	LA	
08483	CD		08622	KET		08724	ZB		08846	MR	(003)
08484	NC		08623	HOP(s)		08730	TS		08847	PDP	
08485	CS		08624	TP		08735	EH		08853	ZB	
08499	CF		08629	UKR		D3905	SO	(08737)	08865	CZ	
08500	WP(s)		08630	CFSW		08738	WA		08868	CP	
08502	EKR		08632	WA		08742	BH		08870	GY	
08507	ZG		08641	LA		08743	SUW		08871	WEA	(H074)
08511	EHY		08643	LH		08752	CP		08872	EMRA(s)	
08516	BK		08644	LA		08754	ZN		08874	WEA	
08523	WEA		08645	PZ		08756	WEA(s)		08877	CFSW	
08525	NL		08648	IS		08762	GY		08879	HOP(s)	
08527	AR		08649	DUD(s)		08764	PO		08885	WEA(s)	
08530	LH		08650	WA		08765	BH(s)		08887	PO	
08531	LH		08652	WA		08774	AVD		08891	LH(s)	

Class 08 — 0-6-0 — DE

08892 WP	08912 AVD(s)	D4157 BS (08927)	08947 WH
08899 DY	08918 BU(s)	08933 WH	08948 TI
08903 SUW	08921 WA(s)	08934 MR	08950 NL
08904 WP	08922 ATC	08936 WEA(s)	08954 ZG
08905 HOP(s)	08924 CFSW	08939 SP	08956 BH
08908 NL	08925 WP	08943 BH	08994 BU(s)

Named Locomotives

08451 Longsight TMD	08691 Terri
08460 Spirit of the Oak	08701 Tyne 100
08483 Bungle	08703 Jermaine
08484 Captain Nathaniel Darell	08730 The Caley
08499 Redlight	08735 Geoff Hobbs 42
08525 Duncan Bedford	08743 Bryan Turner
08568 St Rollox	08752 Lenny
08585 Vicky	08774 Arthur Vernon Dawson
08598 Hercules	08780 Zippy
08615 Uncle Dai	08810 Richard J Wenham Eastleigh Depot December 1989 - July 1999
08616 Tyseley 100	
08617 Steve Purser	08818 Molly
08624 Rambo - Paul Ramsey	08822 Dave Mills
08630 Celsa 3 / Celsa Endeavour	08823 Kevla
08641 Pride of Laira	08865 Gilly
08644 Laira Diesel Depot 50 Years 1962-2012	08899 Midland Counties Railway175 1839-2014
08645 St Piran	08903 John W Antill
08649 Bradwell	08924 Celsa 2
08669 Bob Machin	08947 Howie
08682 Lionheart	08950 David Lightfoot
08690 David Thirkell	

Class 09 — 0-6-0 — DE

09002 BH	09014 BU(s)	09023 EMRA(s)	09201 HOP(s)
09006 BU(s)	09022 BOS	09106 CFSW (6)	09204 CP
09009 CL			

Class 18 — Bo-Bo — Clayton Hybrid

Note: The first two locos are at Chasewater Railway for testing and running trials.

18001	18003	18005	18007	18009	18011	18013	18015
18002	18004	18006	18008	18010	18012	18014	

Private Owner Diesel Shunting Locomotives

1 (pres)	BSS	63(s)	BSS	DH50-1	TSW	504	TPT	930	TPT
2 (pres)	BSS	70	BSS	DH50-2	LH	801	TPT	931	TPT
4	BSS	71	BSS	8.701	BSS	802	TPT	932	TPT
5	BSS	72	BSS	8.702	BSS	803	TPT	934	TPT
6	BSS	73	BSS	8.703	BSS	804	TPT	951	TPT
07	TPT	74	BSS	8.704	BSS	805	TPT	323-539-7	ZG
08	TPT	75	BSS	8.708	BSS	806	TPT	No 1 [4618-1]WA	
29	BSS	76	BSS	8.711(s)	LAC	820	BSS	No 2 [4618-2]WA	
30	BSS	90(s)	BSS	8.712	BSS	901	TPT	No 3 [4618-2]ATC	
44(s)	BSS	91(s)	BSS	8.716	BSS	903	TPT	No 4 [4618-4]ATC	
44	MD	92(s)	BSS	817	BSS	905	TPT	No 5 [4618-5]LU	
51	BSS	93	BSS	8.718	BSS	906	TPT	No 6 [4618-6]WA	
58	BSS	94(s)	BSS	8.719	BSS	907	TPT	No 7 [4618-7]BOU	
61(s)	BSS	95(s)	BSS	501	TPT	921	TPT		

Mainline Diesel Locomotives

Class 20 — Bo-Bo — DE

20007	HQ	20189	HQ	20305	BT(s)	20903	BU(s)
D8096	CD	20205	HQ	20308	BH(s)	20904	BU(s)
D8107	CD	20227	HQ	20309	BH(s)	20905	BH
20118	WP	20301	BH(s)	20311	WP	2	HOP
20121	BH(s)	20302	BT(s)	20312	BH(s)	3	HOP
20132	WP	20303	HQ(s)	20314	WP	81	BSS(s)
20142	HQ	20304	BH(s)	20901	BH	82	HOP

Named Locomotives

2	Sir George Earle	20166	River Fowey
D8107	Jocelyn Fielding 1940 - 2020	20227	Sherlock Holmes
20118	Saltburn by the Sea	20303	Max Joule 1958-1999
20132	Barrow Hill Depot	20905	Dave Darwin
20142	Sir John Betjeman		

Class 31 — A1A-A1A — DE

31128	BU	Charybdis	31461	BU(s)

Class 33 — Bo-Bo — DE

33025	CS		33030	CS(s)
33029	CS		33207	CS	Jim Martin

Class 37 — Co-Co — DE

37038	HQ(s)	37401	KM	37517	CS(s)	37612	BRE	
37057	BRE	37402	KM	37518	CS	D6851	CD	(37667)
37059	KM	37405	KM(s)	D6817	CD (37521)	37668	CS	
37069	KM	37407	KM	37601	UKR	37669	CS	
37099	BRE	37409	KM(s)	37602	ZG(s)	37676	CS	
37116	BRE	37418	BRE	37603	LT(s)	37685	CS	
37165	CS(s)	37419	KM	37604	LT(s)	37706	CS	
37175	BRE	37421	BRE	37605	DF(s)	37712	CS(s)	
37207	DUD(s)	37422	KM	37606	KM(s)	37716	KM	
37218	KM	37423	KM	37607	BH(s)	37800	UKR	
37219	BRE	37558	KM (37424)	37608	UKR	37884	UKR	
37240	BRE	37425	KM	37609	LT(s)	37901	UKR(s)	
37254	BRE	37510	UKR	37610	BRE	37905	UKR(s)	
37259	KM(s)	37516	CS	37611	UKR			

Named Locomotives

37057	Barbara Arbon	37424	Avro Vulcan XH558
37099	Merl Evans 1947 - 2016	37425	Concrete Bob / Sir Robert McAlpine
37219	Jonty Jarvis 8-12-1998 to 18-03-2006	37510	Orion
37254	Cardiff Canton	37516	Loch Laidon
37401	Mary Queen of Scots	37518	Fort William / An Gearasdan
37402	Stephen Middlemore 23.12.54-8.6.13	37601	Perseus
37407	Blackpool Tower	37608	Andromeda
37409	Lord Hinton	37611	Pegasus
37418	An Comuun Gaidrealach	37676	Loch Rannoch
37419	Carl Haviland 1954-2012	37685	Loch Arkaig
37422	Victorious	37800	Cassiopeia
37423	Spirit of the Lakes	37901	Mirrlees Pioneer

Class 43 (HST) — Bo-Bo — DE

43003 HA	43040 LA	43086 LA(s)	43144 HA	43179 HA	43285 LAx
43004 LA	43041 LA	43087 LA(s)	43145 HA	43180 LA(s)	43290 DF
43005 LA	43042 LA	43088 LA	43146 HA	43181 HA	43295 EY(s)
43009 LA	43043 LM(s)	43091 LA(s)	43147 HA	43182 HA	43299 DF
43010 LA	43045 LM(s)	43092 LA	43148 HA	43183 HA	43300 NL(s)
43012 HA	43046 CD	43093 LA	43149 HA	43185 ZK(s)	43301 LAx
43013 DF	43047 CD(s)	43094 LA	43150 HA	43186 LA	43303 LAx
43014 DF	43049 CD(s)	43097 LA	43151 HA	43187 LA	43304 LAx
43015 HA	43050 UKR(s)	43098 LA	43152 HA	43188 LA	43305 EY(s)
43016 LA	43052 UKR(s)	43122 LA	43153 LA	43189 LA	43306 EY(s)
43017 EY(s)	43053 LM(s)	43124 HA	43154 LA	43190 EY(s)	43307 EY(s)
43020 EY(s)	43054 UKR(s)	43125 HA	43155 LA	43191 EY(s)	43309 EY(s)
43021 HA	43055 CD	43126 HA	43156 LA	43192 LA	43310 EY(s)
43022 LA	43056 LA(s)	43127 HA	43158 LA	43193 LA(s)	43311 EY(s)
43023 EY(s)	43058 CD	43128 HA	43160 LA	43194 LA	43312 EY(s)
43024 EY(s)	43059 CD	43129 HA	43161 LA(s)	43195 LA(s)	43313 LA(s)
43025 EY(s)	43060 LM(s)	43130 HA	43162 LA	43196 LA(s)	43314 EY(s)
43026 HA	43062 DF	43131 HA	43163 HA	43197 LA(s)	43315 EY(s)
43027 LA	43063 LA(s)	43132 HA	43164 HA	43198 LA	43316 EY(s)
43028 HA	43064 LM(s)	43133 HA	43165 EY(s)	43206 EY(s)	43317 EY(s)
43029 LA	43066 UKR(s)	43134 HA	43168 HA	43207 LAx	43318 EY(s)
43030 HA(s)	43069 LA(s)	43135 HA	43169 HA	43208 LAx	43319 EY(s)
43031 HA	43070 LM(s)	43136 HA	43170 LA	43238 EY(s)	43320 EY(s)
43032 HA	43071 LM(s)	43137 HA	43171 LA	43239 LAx	43321 LAx
43033 HA	43073 LM(s)	43138 HA	43172 LA	43251 DF	43357 LAx
43034 HA	43076 UKR(s)	43139 HA	43174 EY(s)	43257 DF	43366 LAx
43035 HA	43078 LA(s)	43141 HA	43175 HA	43272 DF	43367 EY(s)
43036 HA	43079 LM(s)	43142 HA	43176 HA	43274 DF	43378 LAx
43037 HA	43083 ZG(s)	43143 HA	43177 HA	43277 svr(s)	43384 LAx

Class 43 — Rail Adventure Power Cars

43296	[92 70 0043 296-7]	43465	[92 70 0043 465-8]	43480	[92 70 0043 480-7]
43308	[92 70 0043 308-0]	43467	[92 70 0043 467-4]	43484	[92 70 0043 484-9]
43423	[92 70 0043 423-7]	43468	[92 70 0043 468-2]		

Named Locomotives

43004	Caerphilly Castle	43122	Dunster Castle
43013	Mark Carne CBE	43134	Gordon Aikman BEM MND Campaigner
43014	The Railway Observer		1985 - 2017
43041	St Catherines Castle	43153	Chun Castle
43042	Tregenna Castle	43154	Compton Castle
43046	Geoff Drury 1930 - 1999	43155	Rougemont Castle
43049	Neville Hill	43158	Kingswear Castle
43062	John Armitt	43170	Chepstow Castle
43073	Neville Hill Depot 42 Years	43186	Taunton Castle
43092	Cromwell's Castle	43188	Newport Castle
43093	Old Oak Common HST Depot	43189	Launceston Castle
	1976 - 2018	43192	Trematon Castle
43094	St Mawes Castle	43194	Okehampton Castle
43097	Castle Drogo	43198	Driver Stan Martin / Driver Brian Cooper
43098	Walton Castle		

Class 47 — Co-Co — DE

47194	CS(s)	47703	ZB(s)	47776	CS(s)	47816	CD(s)
47237	CS	47714	WP(s)	47786	CS	47818	ZG(s)
47245	CS	47715	WP	47787	CS(s)	47826	CS
47270	CS	47727	PG	47802	CS	47828	CD
47355	CS(s)	47739	PG	47804	CS	47830	LD
47368	CS(s)	47744	BU(s)	D1935	CD (47805)	47832	CS
47488	BU(s)	47746	CS	D1924	CD (47810)	47843	UKR(s)
47492	CS(s)	47749	PG	47811	CD(s)	47847	UKR(s)
D1944	CD (47501)	47760	CS	47812	CS	47848	CS
47526	CS(s)	47768	CS(s)	47813	CS	47851	CS
47593	CD (47790)	47769	BH(s)	47815	CS	47854	CS
47614	CD (47853)	47772	CS				

Named Locomotives

47245 V.E Day 75th Anniversary	47772 Carnforth TMD
D1944 Craftsman	47786 Roy Castle OBE
47593 Galloway Princess	D1935 Roger Hosking MA 1925-2013
47727 Edinburgh Castle/Caisteal Dhun Eideann	D1924 Crewe Diesel Depot
47746 Chris Fudge 29.7.70 - 22.6.10	47830 Beechings Legacy
47749 City of Truro	47854 Diamond Jubilee
47769 Resolve	

Class 56 — Co-Co — DE

56007	LP(s)	56065	LP(s)	56091	HQ	56106	UKR(s)
56009	LP(s)	56069	LP(s)	56094	BRE	56113	BRE
56032	LP(s)	56077	LP(s)	56096	BRE	56128	LP(s)
56037	LP(s)	56078	BRE	56098	HQ	56301	UKR
56038	LP(s)	56081	HQ	56103	HQ	56302	BRE
56049	BRE	56087	BRE	56104	UKR(s)	56303	HQ
56051	BRE	56090	BRE	56105	BRE	56312	HQ
56060	LP(s)						

Named Locomotives

56049 Robin of Templecombe 1938 - 2013	56302 PECO The Railway Modeller
56051 Survival	2016 70 Years
56091 Driver Wayne Gaskell, The Godfather	

Class 57 — Co-Co — DE

57001	CS	57008	LT(s)	57303	UKR	57310	UKR	57316	CS
57002	KM	57009	LT(s)	57304	KM	57311	ZG(s)	57601	CS
57003	KM	57010	LT(s)	57305	UKR	57312	UKR	57602	PZ
57004	LT(s)	57011	KM(s)	57306	KM	57313	CS	57603	PZ
57005	CS(s)	57012	LT(s)	57307	KM	57314	CS	57604	PZ
57006	CS	57301	UKR	57308	KM	57315	CS	57605	PZ
57007	KM(s)	57302	ZG(s)	57309	KM				

Named Locomotives

57002 Rail Express	57309 Pride of Crewe
57007 John Scott 12.5.45/22.5.12	57310 Pride of Cumbria
57301 Goliath	57311 Thunderbird
57302 Chad Varah	57313 Scarborough Castle
57303 Pride of Carlisle	57601 Windsor Castle
57304 Pride of Cheshire	57602 Restormel Castle
57306 Her Majesty's Railway Inspectorate 175	57603 Tintagel Castle
57307 Thunderbirds Lady Penelope	57604 Pendennis Castle
57308 Jamie Ferguson	57605 Totnes Castle

Class 58 — Co-Co — DE

58001	FRA(A)(s)	58011	FRA(A)(s)	58032	FRA(A)(s)	58039	FRA(A)(s)
58004	FRA(A)(s)	58012	BAT(s)	58033	FRA(A)(s)	58040	FRA(A)(s)
58005	FRA(A)(s)	58013	FRA(A)(s)	58034	FRA(A)(s)	58042	FRA(A)(s)
58006	FRA(A)(s)	58018	FRA(A)(s)	58035	FRA(A)(s)	58044	FRA(A)(s)
58007	FRA(A)(s)	58021	FRA(A)(s)	58036	FRA(A)(s)	58046	FRA(A)(s)
58009	FRA(A)(s)	58023	UKR	58038	FRA(A)(s)	58049	FRA(A)(s)
58010	FRA(A)(s)	58026	FRA(A)(s)				

Class 59 — Co-Co — DE

59001	MD	Yeoman Endeavour	59104	WH	Village of Great Elm
59002	MD	Alan J Day	59201	MD	
59003	PG	Yeoman Highlander	59202	MD	
59004	MD	Paul A Hammond	59203	MD	
59005	MD	Kenneth J Painter	59204	MD	
59101	WH	Village of Whatley	59205	MD	
59102	WH	Village of Chantry	59206	MD	John F Yeoman Rail Pioneer
59103	WH	Village of Mells			

Class 60 — Co-Co — DE

60001	TO	60019	TO	60035	TO(s)	60052	TO(s)	60069	TO(s)	60085	PG
60002	PG	60020	TO	60036	TO(s)	60053	TO(s)	60070	TO(s)	60087	PG
60003	TO(s)	60021	PG	60037	TO(s)	60054	TO	60071	TT(s)	60088	TO(s)
60004	TT(s)	60022	TT(s)	60038	TO(s)	60055	TO	60072	TO(s)	60089	TO(s)
60005	TO(s)	60023	TO(s)	60039	TO	60056	PG	60073	TO(s)	60090	TO(s)
60007	TO	60024	TO	60040	TO	60057	TT(s)	60074	TO	60091	TO
60008	TT(s)	60025	TO(s)	60041	TO(s)	60058	TO(s)	60075	TO(s)	60092	TO
60009	TO(s)	60026	PG	60042	TO(s)	60059	TO	60076	PG	60093	TO(s)
60010	TO	60027	TO(s)	60043	TO(s)	60061	TT(s)	60077	TO(s)	60094	TO(s)
60011	TO	60028	TO	60044	TO	60062	TO	60078	TO(s)	60095	PG
60012	TO(s)	60029	TO	60045	TO(s)	60063	TO	60079	TO(s)	60096	PG
60013	TT(s)	60030	TO(s)	60046	TO	60064	T0(s)	60080	TO(s)	60097	TO(s)
60014	TT(s)	60031	TO(s)	60047	PG	60065	TO	60081	TT(s)	60098	TT(s)
60015	TO	60032	TO(s)	60048	TO(s)	60066	TO	60082	CE(s)	60099	TT(s)
60017	TO	60033	TO(s)	60049	TO(s)	60067	TO(s)	60083	TO(s)	60100	TO
60018	TT(s)	60034	TO(s)	60051	TO(s)	60068	TO(s)	60084	TO(s)	60500	TO(s)

Named Locomotives

60002	Graham Farish 50th Anniversary 1970 - 2020	60045	The Permanent Way Institution
60003	Freight Transport Association	60046	William Wilberforce
60007	The Spirit of Tom Kendell	60047	Faithful
60008	Sir William McAlpine	60052	Glofa Twr-The last deep mine in Wales
60013	Robert Boyle	60055	Thomas Barnado
60019	Port of Grimsby & Immingham	60059	Swinden Dalesman
60020	The Willows	60062	Stainless Pioneer
60021	Penyghent	60065	Spirit of Jaguar
60024	Clitheroe Castle	60071	Ribblehead Viaduct
60026	Helvellyn	60072	Cairn Toul
60029	Ben Nevis	60074	Luke
60033	Tees Steel Express	60076	Dunbar
60034	Carnedd Llewelyn	60085	Adept
60036	GEFCO	60087	Bountiful
60039	Dove Holes	60091	Barry Needham
60040	The Territorial Army Centenary	60094	Rugby Flyer
60044	Dowlow	60096	Impetus
		60100	Midland Railway, Butterley

Class 66 (*European Mods) Co-Co DE

66001 TO	66041 TO	66082 TO	66120 TO	66164 TO	66208* TO
66002 TO	66042* TO	66083 TO	66121 TO	66165 TO	66209* TO
66003 TO	66043 TO(s)	66084 TO	66122 KM	66167 TO	66210* TO
66004 TO	66044 TO	66085 TO	66123* TO	66168 TO	66211* TO
66005 TO	66045* TO	66086 TO	66124 TO	66169 TO	66212* TO
66006 TO	66047 TO	66087 TO	66125 TO	66170 TO	66213* TO
66007 TO	66048 LP(s)	66088 TO	66126 KM	66171 TO	66214* TO
66009 TO	66049* TO	66089 TO	66127 TO	66172 TO	66215* TO
66010 TO	66050 TO	66090 TO	66128 TO	66174 TO	66216* TO
66011 TO	66051 TO	66091 KM	66129 TO	66175 TO	66217* TO
66012 TO	66052* TO	66092 TO	66130 TO	66176 TO	66218* TO
66013 TO	66053 TO	66093 TO	66131 TO	66177 TO	66219* TO
66014 TO	66054 TO	66094 TO	66133 TO	66179* TO	66221 TO
66015 TO	66055 TO	66095 TO	66134 TO	66181 TO	66222* TO
66017 TO	66056 TO	66096 TO	66135 TO	66182 TO	66223* TO
66018 TO	66057 TO	66097 TO	66136 TO	66183 TO	66224* TO
66019 TO	66059 TO	66098 TO	66137 TO	66185 TO	66225* TO
66020 TO	66060 TO	66099 TO	66138 TT(s)	66186 TO	66226* TO
66021 TO	66061 TO	66100 TO	66139 TO	66187 TO	66228* TO
66022* TO	66062* TO	66101 TO	66140 TO	66188 TO	66229* TO
66023 TO	66063 TO	66102 TO	66142 TO	66190 TO	66230 TO(s)
66024 TO	66064* TO	66103 TO	66143 TO	66191* TO	66231* TO
66025 TO	66065 TO	66104 TO	66144 TO	66192 TO	66232* TO
66026* TO	66066 TO	66105 TO	66145 TO	66193* TO	66233* TO
66027 TO	66067 TO	66106 TO	66147 TO	66194 TO	66234* TO
66028 TO	66068 TO	66107 TO	66148 TO	66195* TO	66235* TO
66029* TO	66069 TO	66108 KM	66149 TO	66197 TO	66236* TO
66030 TO	66070 TO	66109 TO	66150 TO	66198 TO	66239* TO
66031 KM	66071* TO	66110 TO	66151 TO	66199 TO	66240* TO
66032 TO	66072* TO	66111 TO	66152 TO	66200 TO	66241* TO
66033* TO	66073 TO	66112 TO	66154 TO	66201* TO	66242* TO
66034 TO	66074 TO	66113 TO	66155 TO	66202* TO	66243* TO
66035 TO	66075 TO	66114 TO	66156 TO	66203* TO	66244* TO
66036* TO	66076 TO	66115 TO	66158 TO	66204* TO	66245* TO
66037 TO	66077 TO	66116 TO	66160 TO	66205 TO	66246* TO
66038* TO	66078 TO	66117 TO	66161 TO	66206 TO	66247* TO
66039 TO	66079 TO	66118 TO	66162 TO	66207 TO	66249* TO
66040 TO	66080 TO	66119 TO			

Named Locomotives

66005	Maritime Intermodel One	66100	Armistice 100 1918 - 2018
66035	Resourceful	66109	Teesport Express
66047	Maritime Intermodel Two	66142	Maritime Intermodel Three
66050	EWS Energy	66148	Maritime Intermodel Seven
66051	Maritime Intermodel Four	66152	Derek Holmes Railway Operator
66055	Alain Thauvette	66162	Maritime Intermodel Five
66066	Geoff Spencer	66172	Paul Melleny
66077	Benjamin Gimbert GC	66175	Rail Riders Express
66079	James Nightall GC	66185	DP World London Gateway
66090	Maritime Intermodel Six		

Class 66   Co-Co   DE

Note: * Allocated to Heavyhaul traffic

66301 KM	66430 KM	66517 LD	66542 LD	66563 LD	66598 LD
66302 KM	66431 KM	66518 LD	66543 LD	66564 LD	66599 LD
66303 KM	66432 KM	66519 LD	66544 LD	66565 LD	66601 LD*
66304 KM	66433 KM	66520 LD	66545 LD	66566 LD	66602 LD*
66305 KM	66434 KM	66522 LD	66546 LD	66567 LD	66603 LD*
66413 LD	66501 LD	66523 LD	66547 LD	66568 LD	66604 LD*
66414 LD	66502 LD	66524 LD	66548 LD	66569 LD	66605 LD*
66415 LD	66503 LD	66525 LD	66549 LD	66570 LD	66606 LD*
66416 LD	66504 LD	66526 LD	66550 LD	66571 LD	66607 LD*
66418 LD	66505 LD	66528 LD	66551 LD	66572 LD	66610 LD*
66419 LD	66506 LD	66529 LD	66552 LD	66585 LD	66613 LD*
66420 LD	66507 LD	66531 LD	66553 LD	66587 LD	66614 LD*
66421 KM	66508 LD	66532 LD	66554 LD	66588 LD	66615 LD*
66422 KM	66509 LD	66533 LD	66555 LD	66589 LD	66616 LD*
66423 KM	66510 LD	66534 LD	66556 LD	66590 LD	66617 LD*
66424 KM	66511 LD	66536 LD	66557 LD	66591 LD	66618 LD*
66425 KM	66512 LD	66537 LD	66558 LD	66592 LD	66619 LD*
66426 KM	66513 LD	66538 LD	66559 LD	66593 LD	66620 LD*
66427 KM	66514 LD	66539 LD	66560 LD	66594 LD	66621 LD*
66428 KM	66515 LD	66540 LD	66561 LD	66596 LD	66622 LD*
66429 KM	66516 LD	66541 LD	66562 LD	66597 LD	66623 LD*

Named Locomotives

66301 Kingmoor TMD	66532 P&O Nedlloyd Atlas
66302 Endeavour	66533 Hanjin Express / Senator Express
66303 Rail Riders 2020	66534 OOCL Express
66413 Lest We Forget	66540 Ruby
66415 You Are Never Alone	66552 Maltby Raider
66418 Patriot - In Memory of Fallen Railway Employees	66587 As One We Can
	66592 Johnson Stevens Agencies
66421 Gresty Bridge TMD	66593 3MG Mersey Multimodal Gateway
66428 Carlisle Eden Mind	66594 NYK Spirit of Kyoto
66501 Japan 2001	66597 Viridor
66502 Basford Hall Centenary 2001	66601 The Hope Valley
66503 The Railway Magazine	66614 1916 POPPY 2016
66506 Crewe Regeneration	66618 Railways Illustrated Annual Photographic Awards - Alan Barnes
66522 East London Express	
66526 Driver Steve Dunn (George)	66619 Derek W. Johnson MBE
66528 Madge Elliot M.B.E	

Class 66 (GBRF)   Co-Co   DE

66701	PG		66715	PG	Valour
66702	PG	Blue Lightning	66716	PG	Locomotive & Carriage Institution Centenary 1911-2011
66703	PG	Doncaster PSB 1981 - 2002			
66704	PG	Colchester Power Signalbox	66717	PG	Good Old Boy
66705	PG	Golden Jubilee	66718	PG	Sir Peter Hendy CBE
66706	PG	Nene Valley	66719	PG	METRO-LAND
66707	PG	Sir Sam Fay Great Central Railway	66720	PG	
66708	PG	Jayne	66721	PG	Harry Beck
66709	PG	Sorrento	66722	PG	Sir Edward Watkin
66710	PG	Phil Packer BRIT	66723	PG	Chinook (ZA723)
66711	PG	Sence	66724	PG	Drax Power Station
66712	PG	Peterborough Power Signalbox	66725	PG	Sunderland
66713	PG	Forest City	66726	PG	Sheffield Wednesday
66714	PG	Cromer Lifeboat	66727	PG	Maritime One

Class 66 (GBRF) (cont)

Number	Code	Name	Number	Code	Name
66728	PG	Institution of Railway Operators	66762	PG	
66729	PG	Derby County	66763	PG	Severn Valley Railway
66730	PG	Whitemoor	66764	PG	Major John Poyntz Engineer & Railwayman
66731	PG	Capt Tom Moore A True British Inspiration	66765	PG	
66732	PG	GBRf The First Decade 1999-2009 John Smith MD	66766	PG	
			66767	PG	Kings Cross PSB 1971 - 2021
66733	PG	Cambridge PSB	66768	PG	
66734			66769	PG	LMA-League Managers Association
66735	PG	Peterborough United	66770	PG	
66736	PG	Wolverhampton Wanderers	66771	PG	Amanda
66737	PG	Lesia	66772	PG	Maria
66738	PG	Huddersfield Town	66773	PG	Pride of GB Railfreight
66739	PG	Bluebell Railway	66774	PG	
66740	PG	Sarah	66775	PG	F231 HMS Argyll
66741	PG	Swanage Railway	66776	PG	Joanne
66742	PG	ABP Port of Immingham Centenary 1912-2012	66777	PG	Annette
			66778	PG	Cambois Depot 25 Years
66743	PG		66779	PG	Evening Star
66744	PG	Crossrail	66780	PG	The Cemex Express
66745	PG	Modern Railways The First 50 Years	66781	PG	
			66782	PG	
66746	PG		66783	PG	The Flying Dustman
66747	PG	Made in Sheffield	66784	PG	Keighley & Worth Valley Railway 50th Anniversary 1968-2018
66748	PG	West Burton 50			
66749	PG	Christopher Hopcroft MBE	66785	PG	
66750	PG	Bristol Panel Signal Box	66786	PG	
66751	PG	Inspiration Delivered Hitatchi Rail Europe	66787	PG	
			66788	PG	Locomotion 15
66752	PG	The Hoosier State	66789	PG	British Rail 1948-2018
66753	PG	EMD Roberts Road	66790	PG	
66754	PG	Northampton Saints	66791	PG	
66755	PG	Tony Berkeley O.B.E	66792	PG	
66756	PG	Royal Corps of Signals	66793	PG	
66757	PG	West Somerset Railway	66794	PG	Steve Hannam
66758	PG	The Pavior	66795	PG	Bescot LDC
66759	PG	Chippy	66796	PG	The Green Progressor
66760	PG	David Gordon Harris	66797	PG	
66761	PG	Wensleydale Railway Association 25 Years 1990-2015	66798	PG	
			66799	PG	

Class 66 (Colas)   Co-Co   DE

66846	RU	66847	RU	66848	RU	66849	RU	66850	RU

Class 66 (Freightliner)   Co-Co   DE

66951	LD	66952	LD	66953	LD	66955	LD	66956	LD	66957	LD

Named Locomotives

66847   Terry Baker
66849   Wylam Dilly
66850   David Maidment OBE - www.Railwaychildren.org.uk
66957   Stephenson Locomotive Society 1909 - 2009

Class 67   Bo-Bo   DE

67001 CE	67006 CE	67011 CE(s)	67016 CE	67021 CE	67026 CE(s)
67002 CE	67007 CE	67012 CE	67017 CE	67022 CE(s)	67027 RU
67003 TO(s)	67008 CE	67013 CE	67018 CE(s)	67023 RU	67028 CE
67004 TO(s)	67009 CE(s)	67014 CE	67019 TO(s)	67024 CE	67029 CE(s)
67005 CE	67010 CE	67015 CE	67020 CE	67025 CE	67030 CE(s)

Named Locomotives		
67005 Queen's Messenger	67023 Stella	67027 Charlotte
67006 Royal Sovereign	67026 Diamond Jubilee	67029 Royal Diamond
67018 Keith Heller		

Class 68 (Vossloh Type E 4000)   Bo-Bo   DE

68001	KM	Evolution	68013	KM		68024	LG	Centaur
68002	KM	Intrepid	68014	KM		68025	LG	Superb
68003	KM	Astute	68015	KM		68026	LG	Enterprise
68004	KM	Rapid	68016	KM	Fearless	68027	LG	Splendid
68005	KM	Defiant	68017	KM	Hornet	68028	LG	Lord President
68006	KM	Daring	68018	KM	Vigilant	68029	LG	Courageous
68007	KM	Valiant	68019	LG	Brutus	68030	LG	Black Douglas
68008	KM	Avenger	68020	LG	Reliance	68031	LG	Felix
68009	KM	Titan	68021	LG	Tireless	68032	LG	Destroyer
68010	KM	Oxford Flyer	68022	LG	Resolution	68033	KM	The Poppy
68011	KM		68023	LG	Achilles	68034	KM	
68012	KM							

Class 69   Co-Co   DE

69001 ex 56031 PG	69005	69009	69013
69002 ex 56311 PG	69006	69010	69014
69003 ex 56018 PG	69007	69011	69015
69004	69008	69012	69016

Named Locomotives	
69001 Mayflower	69002 Bob Tiller CM&EE

Class 70   Co-Co   DE

70001 LD	70007 LD	70014 LD	70020 LD	70806 RU	70812 RU
70002 LD	70008 LD	70015 LD	70801 RU	70807 RU	70813 RU
70003 LD	70009 LD(s)	70016 LD	70802 RU	70808 RU	70814 RU
70004 LD	70010 LD	70017 LD	70803 RU	70809 RU	70815 RU
70005 LD	70011 LD	70018 LD(s)	70804 RU	70810 RU	70816 RU
70006 LD	70013 LD(s)	70019 LD	70805 RU	70811 RU	70817 RU

Named Locomotives	
70001 PowerHaul	70004 The Coal Industry Society

Class 97/3   Co-Co   DE

97301 DF	97303 DF
97302 DF Ffestiniog and Welsh Highland Railway	97304 DF John Tiley

DC Electric Locomotives

Class 73		Bo-Bo				ED
73101	ZG(s)	The Royal Alex	73213	SE		Rhodalyn
73107	SE	Tracy	73235	BM		
73109	SE	Battle of Britain 80th Anniversary	73951	DF	[73104]	Malcolm Brinded
E6016	ZG(s)	(73110)	73952	DF	[73211]	Janice Kong
73119	SE	Borough of Eastleigh	73961	SE	[73209]	Alison
73128	SE	OVS Bullied C.B.E.	73962	SE	[73204]	Dick Mabbutt
73133	ZG		73963	SE	[73206]	Janice
73134	LB(s)	Woking Homes 1885-1985	73964	SE	[73205]	Jeanette
73136	SE	Mhairi	73965	SE	[73208]	Des O'Brien
73138	PEA(s)		73966	EC	[73005]	
73139	ZG(s)		73967	EC	[73006]	
73141	SE	Charlotte	73968	EC	[73117]	
73201	SE	Broadlands	73969	EC	[73105]	
73202	SL	Graham Stenning	73970	EC	[73103]	
73212	SE	Fiona	73971	EC	[73207]	

AC Electric Locomotives

Class 86				Bo-Bo				E	
86101	CD	86604	BA(s)	86609	BA(s)	86613	BA(s)	86627	BA(s)	86637	BA(s)
86251	BA(s)	86605	BA(s)	86610	BA(s)	86614	BA(s)	86628	BA(s)	86638	BA(s)
86259	HQ	86607	BA(s)	86612	BA(s)	86622	CHC(s)	86632	BA(s)	86639	BA(s)
86401	CS	86608	BA(s)						

Named Locomotives	
86101 Sir William A Stanier FRS	86401 Mons Meg
86259 Les Ross / Peter Pan	

Class 87		Bo-Bo		E
87002	CD	Royal Sovereign		

Class 88			Bo-Bo				ED	
88001	KM	Revolution	88005	KM	Minerva	88008	KM	Ariadne
88002	KM	Prometheus	88006	KM	Juno	88009	KM	Diana
88003	KM	Genesis	88007	KM	Electra	88010	KM	Aurora
88004	KM	Pandora						

Class 90		Bo-Bo			E
90001	CD	Royal Scot	90014	CE	Over The Rainbow
90002	CD	Wolf of Badenoch	90015	CE	
90003	CE		90016	CE	
90004	CE	City of Chelmsford	90017	CE(s)	
90005	CE	Vice-Admiral Lord Nelson	90018	CE	The Pride of Bellshill
90006	CE	Modern Railways Magazine/ Roger Ford	90019	CE	Multimodal
			90020	CE	
90007	CE	Sir John Betjeman	90021	CE	
90008	CE	The East Anglian	90022	CE(s)	Freightconnection
90009	CE		90023	CE(s)	
90010	CE		90024	CE	
90011	CE	East Anglian Daily Times	90025	CE(s)	
90012	CE		90026	CE	
90013	CE		90027	CE(s)	

Class 90 — Bo-Bo — E

Number	Code	Name		Number	Code	Name
90028	CE	Sir William McAlpine		90039	CE	
90029	CE			90040	CE	The Railway Mission
90030	CE(s)			90041	CE	
90031	CE(s)	The Railway Children Partnership Working for Street Children Worldwide		90042	CE	
				90043	CE	
90032	CE(s)			90044	CE	
90033	CE(s)			90045	CE	
90034	CE			90046	CE	
90035	CE			90047	CE	
90036	CE	Driver Jack Mills		90048	CE	
90037	CE	Christine		90049	CE	
90038	CE(s)			90050	BA(s)	

Class 91 — Bo-Bo — E

Number	Code	Number	Code	Number	Code	Number	Code	Number	Code	Number	Code
91101	NL	91107	NL	91112	HQ(s)	91117	UKR(s)	91121	HQ(s)	91127	NL
91103	ZB(s)	91108	ZB(s)	91114	NL	91118	HQ(s)	91122	UKR	91128	UKR
91104	ZB(s)	91109	NL	91115	HQ(s)	91119	NL	91124	NL	91130	NL
91105	NL	91110	NL	91116	HQ(s)	91120	UKR(s)	91125	HQ(s)	91131	HQ(s)
91106	NL	91111	NL								

Named Locomotives

Number	Name		Number	Name
91101	Flying Scotsman		91111	For The Fallen
91107	Skyfall		91114	Durham Cathedral
91109	Sir Bobby Robson		91115	Blaydon Races
91110	Battle of Britain Memorial Flight Spitfire, Hurricane, Lancaster, Dakota		91119	Bounds Green Intercity Depot 1977-2016
			91130	Lord Mayor of Newcastle

Class 92 — Co-Co — EE

Number	Code	Name		Number	Code	Name
92004	CE(s)	Jane Austen		92028	WN	
92006	WN			92029	CE(s)	Dante
92007	CE(s)	Schubert		92031	CE(s)	
92008	CE(s)	Jules Verne		92032	WN	IMechE Railway Division
92009	CE(s)	Marco Polo		92033	WN	
92010	WN			92035	CE(s)	Mendelssohn
92011	CE	Handel		92036	CE	Bertolt Brecht
92013	CE(s)	Puccini		92037	CE(s)	Sullivan
92014	WN			92038	WN	
92015	CE			92040	LB(s)	Goethe
92016	CE(s)			92041	CE	Vaughan Williams
92017	CE(s)	Bart the Engine		92042	CE	
92018	WN			92043	WN	
92019	CE	Wagner		92044	WN	Couperin
92020	WN			92045	LB(s)	Chaucer
92021	LB(s)	Purcell		92046	LB(s)	Sweelinck
92023	WN					

Class 93 — Bo-Bo — on order

Note: Locos are in production, the first one is due 2022-23 and owned by ROG.

93001	93006	93011	93016	93021	93026
93002	93007	93012	93017	93022	93027
93003	93008	93013	93018	93023	93028
93004	93009	93014	93019	93024	93029
93005	93010	93015	93020	93025	93030

Channel Tunnel Locomotives

Class 0 — Bo-Bo

0001	CO	0003	CO	0005	CO	0007	CO	0009	CO
0002	CO	0004	CO	0006	CO	0008	CO	0010	CO

Class 0 — 0-4-0

0031	CO	Frances	0037	CO	Lydie
0032	CO	Elisabeth	0038	CO	Jenny
0033	CO	Silke	0039	CO	Pacita
0034	CO	Amanda	0040	CO	Jill
0035	CO	Mary	0041	CO	Kim
0036	CO	Lawrence	0042	CO	Nicole

Class 9/0 — Bo-Bo-Bo — E

9005	CO	Jessye Norman	9024	CO	Gotthard 1882
9007	CO	Dame Joan Sutherland	9026	CO	Furkatunnel 1982
9011	CO	Jose Van Dam	9029	CO	Thomas Allen
9013	CO	Maria Callas	9033	CO	Montserrat Cabelle
9015	CO	Lotschberg 1913	9036	CO	Alain Fondary
9018	CO	Wilhelmena Fernandez	9037	CO	Gabriel Bacquier
9022	CO	Dame Janet Baker			

Class 9/7 — Bo-Bo-Bo — E

9701	CO		9706	CO		9714	CO	[9104]	9719	CO	[9109]
9702	CO		9707	CO		9715	CO	[9105]	9720	CO	[9110]
9703	CO		9711	CO	[9101]	9716	CO	[9106]	9721	CO	[9111]
9704	CO		9712	CO	[9102]	9717	CO	[9107]	9722	CO	[9112]
9705	CO		9713	CO	[9103]	9718	CO	[9108]	9723	CO	[9113]

Class 9/8 — Bo-Bo-Bo — E

9801	CO	Lesley Garrett	9821	CO	Teresa Berganza
9802	CO	Stuart Burrows	9823	CO	Dame Elisabeth
9803	CO	Benjamin Luxon			Legge-Schwarzkoff
9804	CO	Victoria De Los Angeles	9825	CO	
9806	CO	Regine Crespin	9827	CO	Barbara Hendricks
9808	CO	Elisabeth Soderstrom	9828	CO	Dame Kiri Te Kanawa
9809	CO	Francois Pollet	9831	CO	Placido Domingo
9810	CO	Jean-Philippe Courtis	9832	CO	Renata Tebaldi
9812	CO	Luciano Pavarotti	9834	CO	Mirella Freni
9814	CO	Lucia Popp	9835	CO	Nicolai Gedda
9816	CO	Willard White	9838	CO	Hildegard Behrens
9819	CO	Maria Ewing	9840	CO	
9820	CO	Nicolai Ghiaurov			

Preserved Diesel & Electric Locos

Note: in this section each loco is listed by current number, allocation and then any previous numbers.

Class 323 (Ex-DB)		DM 0-4-0
323 674-2	NVR	

Class 01	Andrew Barclay	DM 0-4-0
01531	PEA	[7018, H4323]
01546	EKR	
01558	RIB	
01562	DCP	
01583	LAV	
01585	BRC	
D2953	PEA	[11503]
D2956	ELR	[11506]

Class 02	Yorkshire Engine Co	DH 0-4-0
02003	BH	[D2853]
D2854	PEA	
D2858	MRC	
D2860	NRM	
D2866	PEA	
D2867	BAT	
D2868	BH	

Class 03	Doncaster/Swindon	DM 0-6-0
D2018	MRM	[11205, 03018]
03020	MRM	[11207, D2020]
D2022	SCR	[11209, 03022]
D2023	KESR	[11210]
D2024	KESR	[11211]
03027	PEA	[D2027]
D2037	RDR	[03037]
D2041	CVR	
D2046	PVR	
D2051	NNR	
D2059	IOW	[03059]
D2062	ELR	[03062]
D2063	NNR	[03063]
03066	BH	[D2066]
03069	DFR	[D2069]
D2072	LHR	[03072]
03073	CHC	[D2073]
03078	SRM	[D2078]
03079	DVL	[D2079]
03081	MRM	[D2081]
D2084	CS	[03084]
03089	MRM	[D2089]
D2090	NRS	[03090]
D2094	RDR	[03094]
03099	PEA	[D2099]
D2112	RVR	[03112]
03113	PEA	[D2113]
D2117	LHR	
03118	NHC	[D2118]
03119	EOR	[D2119]
D2120	FHR	[03120]
03901	SDRT	[03128, D2128]

D2133	WSR	
D2134	RDR	[03134]
D2138	MRC	
D2139	PEA	[D2000]
03141	GVR	[D2141]
03144	WR	[D2144]
03145	MPR	[D2145]
D2148	RIB	
D2152	SCR	[03152]
D2158	MRM	[03158]
03162	LR	[D2162]
D2170	EOR	[03170]
D2178	GR	
03179	RTM	[D2179]
03180	PEA	[D2180]
D2182	GWR	
D2184	CVR	
D2189	RIB	[03189]
D2192	DSR	
03196	CS	[D2196]
03197	MRM	[D2197]
D2199	PEA	
03371	DSR	[Dept 92, D2371]
03381	CS	[03381]
03399	MRM	[D2399]

Class 04	Drewry	DM 0-6-0
D2203	EBA	[11103]
D2205	PEA	[11106]
D2207	NYM	[11108]
D2229	PEA	[11135]
D2245	DVR	[11215]
D2246	SDR	[11216]
D2271	SDR	
D2272	PEA	
D2279	EAR	[11249]
D2280	GWR	
D2284	PEA	
D2289	PEA	
D2298	BRC	
D2302	MPR	
04110	BAT	[D2310]
D2324	BU	
D2325	MRM	
D2334	MNR	
D2337	PEA	

Unclassified	Hudswell-Clarke	0-6-0
D2511	KWVR	

Class 05	Hunslet	DM 0-6-0
D2554	IOW	[11140, 05001, 97803]
D2578	MPR	
D2587	PEA	
D2595	RIB	

Preserved Diesel & Electric Locos

Class 06   Andrew Barclay   DM   0-4-0
D2420	PEA	[06003, 97804]

Unclassified   North British   0-4-0
| D2767 | BT | |
D2774	STR	

Class 07   Ruston & Hornsby   DE   0-6-0
07001	PEA	[D2985]
D2989	GCR	[07005]
07010	AVR	[D2994]
D2995	SE	[07011]
07012	BH	[D2996]
07013	ELR	[D2997]

Class 08   English Electric   DE   0-6-0
D3000	WP	[13000]
13002	PVR	[D3002]
D3014	DSR	[13014]
08011	CPRR	[13018, D3018]
D3019	CAM-L	[13019, 08012]
D3022	SVR	[13022, 08015]
08016	PEA	[13023, D3023]
13029	TM	[08021, D3029]
D3030	CWR	[13030, 08022]
08032	MHR	[13044, D3044]
13059	CDR	[08046, 03059]
08054	EBA	[13067, D3067]
08060	CWR	[13074, D3074]
13079	NRS	[08064, D3079]
13101	GCR	[D3101]
D3167	LWR	[13167, 08102]
D3174	KESR	[13174, 08108]
08114	NHC	[13180, D3180]
D3190	CWR	[13190, 08123]
D3201	SVR	[13201, 08133]
08164	ELR	[13232, D3232]
D3236	BU	[08168, 13236]
D3255	TWS	[13255]
13261	SCR	[D3261]
13265	LR	[08195, D3265]
08202	AVR	[13272, D3272]
08220	NHC	[D3290]
08238	DFR	[13308, D3308]
08266	KWVR	[13336, D3336]
08288	MHR	[D3358]
08331	MRC	[D3401]
08359	CHR	[D3429]
08377	MHR	[D3462]
08436	SWR	[D3551]
D3558	BT	[08443]
08444	BWR	[D3559]
D3586	SVR	[08471]
D3591	SWR	[08476]
13594	ELR	[08479, D3594]
D3605	STR	[08490]
08495	NYM	[D3610]

08503	TS	[D3658]
08528	DVL	[D3690]
08556	NYM	[D3723]
08590	MRC	[D3757]
604	DI	[08604, D3771]
08631	WEA	[D3798]
D3800	CHV	[08633]
08635	SVR	[D3802]
08694	NHC	[D3861]
08757	TSR	[D3925]
D3935	NNR	[08767]
D3937	DFR	[08769]
D3940	NNR	[08772]
D3941	EBA	[08773]
08795	LE	[D3963]
08825	CPRR	[D3993]
08830	PEA	[D3998]
08850	NYM	[D4018]
D4095	SDRT	[08881]
D4118	AVR	[08888]
08896	SVR	[D4126]
D4137	GCR	[08907]
08911	NRS	[D4141]
08915	SRM	[D4145]
D4167	DMR	[08937]
08944	ELR	[D4174]
08993	KWVR	[08592, D3759]
08995	GVR	[08687, D3854]

Class 09   English Electric   DE   0-6-0
09001	PEA	[D3665]
D3668	SCR	[09004]
D3671	WN	[09007]
D3721	SDR	[09010]
D4100	SVR	[09012]
09015	AVR	[D4103]
09017	NRM	[D4105]
D4106	BR	[09018]
D4107	WSR	[09019]
09024	ELR	[D4112]
D4113	LAV	[09025]
09026	SPA	[D4114]
09107	SVR	[08845, D4013]

Class 10   Lister Blackstone   DE   0-6-0
D3452	BWR	
D3489	SPA	
10119	GCR	[D4067]
D4092	BH	

BR Class 11   DE   0-6-0
12049	MHR	[12082]
12052	CDR	[MP228]
12077	MRC	
12083	BAT	
12088	ALN	[01564]
12093	CDR	[MP229]

12099	SVR
12131	NNR
12139	NYM

Class 12		**DE**	**0-6-0**
15224	SPA

Class 14	**Swindon**	**DH**	**0-6-0**
D9500	PEA
D9502	ELR
D9504	KESR
D9513	EBA	[NCB 38]
D9516	DI
D9518	WSR	[NCB 7]
D9520	MNR	[45]
D9521	DFR
D9523	WR
14901	PEA	[D9524]
D9525	PEA
D9526	KESR
D9529	NVR	[14029]
D9531	ELR
D9537	ECVR
D9539	RIB
D9551	SVR
D9553	WA
D9555	DFR

Class 15	**BTH/Clayton**	**DE**	**Bo-Bo**
D8233	ELR	[ADB968001]

Class 17	**Clayton**	**DE**	**Bo-Bo**
D8568	CPRR

Gas Turbine	**Brown-Boveri**	**A1A-A1A**
18000	DI	[Gas Turbine]

Class 20	**English Electric**	**DE**	**Bo-Bo**
8001	EOR	[20001]
20016	CDR	[D8016]
20020	BT	[D8020]
20031	KWVR	[D8031]
20048	MRC	[D8048]
D8000	NRM	[20050]
D8057	CHV	[20057]
D8059	CPRR	[20059]
2002	BAT	[20063, D8063]
D8069	WP	[20069]
2008I	CDR	[D8081]
20087	BAT	[D8087]
20088	CDR	[D8088]
D8098	GCR	[20098]
D8110	BAT	[20110]
D8137	GWR	[20137]
D8154	NHC	[20154]
20166	WR	[D8166]
20169	WR	[D8169]

D8188	SPA	[20188]
20214	LHR	[D8314]
2004	GWR	[20228, D8328]

Class 24	**Sulzer**	**DE**	**Bo-Bo**
D5032	NYM	[24032]
D5054	ELR	[24054, ADB968008]
D5061	NYM	[24061, RDB968007, 97201]
5081	GWR	[24081]

Class 25	**Sulzer**	**DE**	**Bo-Bo**
D5185	GCR	[25035]
25057	WP	[D5207]
25059	KWVR	[D5209]
D5217	BU	[25067]
25072	CDR	[D5222]
25083	CDR	[D5233]
D7523	EOR	[25173]
D7535	SDR	[25185]
25191	SDR	[D7541]
25235	BT	[D7585]
25244	KESR	[D7594]
D7612	MHR	[25262, 25901]
25265	BU	[D7615]
D7628	NYM	[25278]
25279	ELR	[D7629]
D7633	RF	[25283, 25904]
D7659	PEA	[25309, 25909]
25313	WP	[D7663]
D7671	MRC	[25321]
25322	CHV	[25912, D7672]

Class 26	**BRC&W Co**	**DE**	**Bo-Bo**
D5301	CDR	[26001]
26002	STR	[D5302]
26004	BU	[D5304]
26007	BH	[D5300]
D5310	LR	[26010]
26011	BU	[D5311]
D5314	CDR	[26014]
26024	BT	[D5324]
26025	STR	[D5325]
26035	CDR	[D5335]
26038	BT	[D5338]
26040	WRH	[D5340]
D5343	GWR	[26043]

Class 27	**BRC&W Co**	**DE**	**Bo-Bo**
27001	BT	[D5347]
27005	BT	[D5351]
D5353	CDR	[27007]
D5370	CDR	[27024, ADB968028]
5394	STR	[27050, 27106]
D5401	GCR	[27056, 27112]
D5410	UKR	[27059, 27123, 27205]
27066	BH	[27103, 27212, D5386]

Preserved Diesel & Electric Locos

Class 28   Metrovick   DE   Co-Bo

D5705	ELR	[S15705,TDB968006]

Class 31   Brush   DE   A1A-A1A

31018	NRM	[D5500]
D5518	AVR	[31101]
31105	MRM	[D5523]
31106	ELR	[D5524]
31108	NVR	[D5526]
31119	EBA	[D5537]
31130	AVR	[D5548]
5580	MRC	[31162]
97205	CPRR	[31163, D5581]
D5600	EBA	[31179, 31435]
31190	PVR	[D5613]
D5627	PBR	[31203]
31206	ECVR	[D5630]
D5631	NNR	[31207]
31210	DFR	[D5634]
31233	MRM	[D5660]
31235	DFR	[D5662]
31255	MNR	[D5683]
31270	BU	[D5800]
31271	NVR	[D5801]
31285	WEA	[D5817]
31289	NLR	[D5821]
D5830	NHC	[31297, 31463, 31563]
D5862	STR	[31327]
31514	MRC	[31414, D5814]
31418	MRC	[31104, D5522]
31430	SPA	[31265, 31530, D5695]
31438	EOR	[31139, 31538, D5557]
31452	GY	[31279, D5809]
31454	BU	[31228, D5654]
31459	WR	[31256, D5684]
31465	WEA	[31213, D5637]
31466	SVR	[31115, D5533]
31601	EBA	[31186, D5609]

Class 33   BRC&W Co   DE   Bo-Bo

D6501	SDR	[33002]
D6508	BAT	[33008]
D6515	SWR	[33012]
33018	MRM	[D6530]
33019	BU	[D6531]
33021	CHV	[D6539]
33035	WR	[D6553]
33046	ELR	[D6564]
D6566	WSR	[33048]
D6570	BR	[33052]
33053	NLR	[D6571]
D6575	WSR	[33057]
33063	SPA	[D6583]
33065	SPA	[D6585]
33102	CHV	[D6513]
33103	BU	[D6514]
33108	SVR	[D6521]
33109	ELR	[D6525]
33110	MRM	[D6527]
33111	SWR	[D6528]
D6535	GCR	[33116]
D6536	ELR	[33117]
33201	BAT	[D6586]
33202	MNR	[D6587]
D6593	BAT	[33208]

Class 35   Hymek   DH   Bo-B

D7017	WSR
D7018	WSR
D7029	SVR
D7076	ELR

Class 37   English Electric   DE   Co-Co

37003	UKR	[37360, D6703]
37009	NHC	[37340, D6709]
37023	PBR	[D6723]
37025	BT	[D6725]
D6729	EOR	[37029]
D6732	NNR	[37353, 37032]
6737	SDR	[37321, 37037]
37042	EVR	[D6742]
37067	BT	[37703, D6767]
37075	KWVR	[D6775]
37097	CDR	[D6797]
37108	CHC	[37325, D6808]
37109	ELR	[D6809]
37142	BWR	[D6842]
37190	MAR	[37314, D6890]
D6898	SRM	[37198]
37214	BT	[D6914]
37215	GWR	[D6915]
D6916	PBR	[37216]
D6948	GWR	[37248]
37250	WR	[D6950]
37255	BU	[D6955]
37261	BT	[D6961]
37263	TSR	[D6963]
37264	NYM	[D6964]
6975	DSR	[37275]
37294	EBA	[D6994]
37308	SVR	[37274, D6608]
37310	PEA	[37152, D6852]
D6700	NRM	[37350, 37119]
D5910	BH	[37372, 37159, D6859]
37403	BT	[37307, D6607]
37503	PSK	[37017, D6717]
37674	ALY	[37169, D6869]
37679	WA	[37123, D6823]
37688	CD	[37205, D6905]
37714	GCR	[37024, D6724]
37906	BAT	[37206, D6906]

Preserved Diesel & Electric Locos

Class 40 **English Electric** **DE 1Co-Co1**

D200	NRM	[40122]
D212	BH	[40012, 97407]
D213	CD	[40013]
40106	SVR	[D306]
40118	TM	[D318, 97408]
40135	ELR	[97406, D335]
40145	CD	[D145]

Class 41 **Prototype HST Power Car**

41001	NHC	[43000, ADB975812]

Class 42 **Warship DH Bo-Bo**

D821	SVR	
D832	ELR	also carries 818

Class 43 **HST Power Car**

43002	NRM
43018	CHC
43044	NHC
43048	MRC
43081	CHC
43082	CVR
43089	MRC
43102	NRS
43159	NHC

Class 44 **Peak DE 1Co-Co1**

D4	MRC	[44004]
D8	PEA	[44008]

Class 45 **Sulzer DE 1Co-Co1**

45015	BAT	[D14]
45041	NVR	[D53]
45060	BH	[D100]
45105	BH	[D86]
45108	ELR	[D120]
45112	BU	[D61]
45118	BH	[D67]
D123	GCR	[45125]
45132	EOR	[D22]
45133	MNR	[D40]
45135	ELR	[D99]
45149	GWR	[D135]

Class 46 **Sulzer DE 1Co-Co1**

46010	NHC	[D147]
46035	PEA	[97403, D172]
D182	MRC	[46045, 97404]

Class 47 **Brush DE Co-Co**

D1524	EBA	[47004]
47077	NYM	[47840, 47613, D1661]
D1693	GWR	[47105]
1705	GCR	[47117]
1842	CHC	[47192]
47292	NHC	[D1994]
47306	BWR	[D1787]
47367	MNR	[D1886]
47376	GWR	[D1895]
47395	NLR	[47205, D1855]
47401	MRC	[D1500]
D1501	ELR	[47402]
D1516	MRC	[47417]
1566	LR	[47449]
47484	WA	[D1662]
47579	MRM	[47793, 47183, D1778]
47580	TM	[47732 ,47167, D1762]
D1933	MNR	[47596, 47255]
47635	EOR	[47029, D1606]
47640	BAT	[47244, D1921]
47643	BT	[47269, D1970]
47701	BU	[47493, D1932]
47712	CD	[47505, D1948]
47761	MRC	[47564, 47038, D1619]
47765	ELR	[47631, 47059, D1643]
47771	ZG	[47503, D1946]
47773	TM	[47541, D1755]
47785	WR	[47665, 47232, D1909]
47798	NRM	[47834,47609,47072,D1656]
47799	EVR	[47620, 47070, D1654]
47841	MAR	[47622, 47134, D1726]

Class 50 **English Electric DE Co-Co**

50002	SDR	[D402]
50007	SVR	[D407] also carries 50034
50008	HQ	[D408]
50015	ELR	[D415]
50017	GCR	[D417]
50019	MNR	[D419]
50021	ZG	[D421]
50026	ZG	[D426]
50027	MHR	[D427]
50029	PEA	[D429]
50030	PEA	[D430]
50031	SVR	[D431]
50033	SVR	[D433] also carries 50024
50035	SVR	[50135, D435]
50042	BWR	[D442]
50044	SVR	[D444]
50049	SVR	[50149, D449]
50050	BRE	[D400]

Class 52 **Western DH Co-Co**

D1010	WSR
D1013	SVR
D1015	SVR
D1023	NRM
D1041	ELR
D1048	MRC
D1062	SVR

Preserved Diesel & Electric Locos

Class 55	English Electric	DE	Co-Co
D9002	NRM	[55002]	
D9009	BH	[55009]	
55015	BH	[D9015]	
D9016	MAR	[55016]	
55019	BH	[D9019]	
55022	CD	[D9000] also carries 55018	

Class 56	BREL	DE	Co-Co
56006	ELR		
56097	NHC		

Class 58	BREL	DE	Co-Co
58016	UKR		
58022	ECVR		
58048	BAT		

Class 60	Brush	DE	Co-Co
60050	PSK		
60060	UKR		
60086	PSK		

Class 97/6	Ruston & Hornsby		0-6-0
97650	PEA	[PWM650]	
97651	SCR	[PWM651]	
97654	PEA	[PWM654]	

	Prototype Deltic		Co-Co
DELTIC	NRS		

Prototype English Electric Shunter			0-6-0
D0226	KWVR	[2345]	

Prototype North British Shunter			0-4-0
27414	TSR		
27415	BT		

Class 71	Doncaster		Bo-Bo
E5001	NRS	[71001]	

Class 73	Eastleigh	Bo-Bo	ED
73001	CD	[73901, E6001]	
73002	ZG	[73902, E6002]	
E6003	SCR	[73003]	
73114	BU	[E6020]	
73118	BAR	[E6024]	
E6036	CAM	[73129]	
73130	BC	[E6037]	
E6047	SPA	[73140]	
73210	ECVR	[73116, E6022]	

Class 76 (EM1)	Gorton		Bo-Bo
76020	NRM	[E26020, 26020]	

Class 77 (EM2)	Gorton		Co-Co
27000	MRC	[E27000, 1502]	
1505	MAN	[E27001]	

Class 81	AEI/BRC&W	AL1	Bo-Bo
81002	BH	[E3003]	

Class 82	AEI/Metro Vickers/BP	AL2	Bo-Bo
82008	BH	[E3054]	

Class 83	English Electric	AL3	Bo-Bo
E3035	BH	[83012]	

Class 84	GEC/North British	AL4	Bo-Bo
84001	BT	[E3036]	

Class 85	British Railways	AL5	Bo-Bo
85006	BH	[85101, E3061]	

Class 87	BREL		Bo-Bo
87001	NRM		
87035	CHC		

Class 89	GEC/BREL		Co-Co
89001	BH		

Notes

Preserved Steam Locomotives on the Main Line

Note: 45699 is currently numbered 45627 Sierra Leone

825		34092	City of Wells	46521	
1450		35018	British India Line	48151	
1466		35028	Clan Line	60007	Sir Nigel Gresley
1744		43106		60009	Union of South Africa
2857		44871		60019	Bittern
4936	Kinlet Hall	44932		60103	Flying Scotsman
4965	Rood Ashton Hall	45212		60163	Tornado
5043	Earl of Mount Edgcumbe	45231	Sherwood Forester	61264	
9466		45305	Alderman A.E. Draper	61306	Mayflower
9600		45407	Lancashire Fusilier	62005	
13065		45596	Bahamas	70000	Britannia
30850	Lord Nelson	45690	Leander	70013	Oliver Cromwell
31806		45699	Galatea	71000	Duke of Gloucester
34027	Taw Valley	46100	Royal Scot	75029	
34046	Braunton	46115	Scots Guardsman	76079	
34067	Tangmere	46201	Princess Elizabeth	76084	
34070	Manston	46233	Duchess of Sutherland		

Notes

Diesel Multiple Units

Class 139 — Parry People Mover

139 001	SJ	39001	139 002	SJ	39002

Class 142 — Pacer

142 003	ZG(s)	55544	55594	142 078	WR(s)	55728	55774
142 007	ZG(s)	55548	55598	142 087	WR(s)	55737	55783
142 014	ZG(s)	55555	55605	142 089	ZG(s)	55739	55785
142 032	ZG(s)	55573	55623	142 090	WR(s)	55740	55786
142 047	HQ(s)	55588	55638	142 095	HQ(s)	55745	55791
142 056	ZG(s)	55706	55752				

Class 143 — Pacer

143 617	PM(s)	55644	55683	143 619	PM(s)	55660	55685
143 618	PM(s)	55659	55684				

Class 144 — Pacer

144 005	DF(s)	55805	55828	144 015	LM(s)	55815	55851	55838
144 012	LM(s)	55812	55835	144 021	LM(s)	55821	55857	55844

Class 150 — Sprinter

150 001	NH	55200	55400	55300	150 004	NH	52112	57212	57112
150 002	NH	55201	55401	55301	150 005	NH	52117	52223	57117
150 003	NH	52116	57209	57116	150 006	NH	52147	57223	57147

Class 150 — Sprinter

150 101	NH	52101	57101	150 132	NH	52132	57132	150 213	CF	52213	57213
150 102	NH	52102	57102	150 133	NH	52133	57133	150 214	NL	52214	57214
150 103	NH	52103	57103	150 134	NH	52134	57134	150 215	NL	52215	57215
150 104	NH	52104	57104	150 135	NH	52135	57135	150 216	EX	52216	57216
150 105	NH	52105	57105	150 136	NH	52136	57136	150 217	CF	52217	57217
150 106	NH	52106	57106	150 137	NH	52137	57137	150 218	NL	52218	57218
150 107	NH	52107	57107	150 138	NH	52138	57138	150 219	EX	52219	57219
150 108	NH	52108	57108	150 139	NH	52139	57139	150 220	NH	52220	57220
150 109	NH	52109	57109	150 140	NH	52140	57140	150 221	EX	52221	57221
150 110	NH	52110	57110	150 141	NH	52141	57141	150 222	NL	52222	57222
150 111	NH	52111	57111	150 142	NH	52142	57142	150 224	NH	52224	57224
150 113	NH	52113	57113	150 143	NH	52143	57143	150 225	NH	52225	57225
150 114	NH	52114	57114	150 144	NH	52144	57144	150 226	NH	52226	57226
150 115	NH	52115	57115	150 145	NH	52145	57145	150 227	CF	52227	57227
150 118	NH	52118	57118	150 146	NH	52146	57146	150 228	NL	52228	57228
150 119	NH	52119	57119	150 148	NH	52148	57148	150 229	CF	52229	57229
150 120	NH	52120	57120	150 149	NH	52149	57149	150 230	CF	52230	57230
150 121	NH	52121	57121	150 150	NH	52150	57150	150 231	CF	52231	57231
150 122	NH	52122	57122	150 201	NL	52201	57201	150 232	EX	52232	57232
150 123	NH	52123	57123	150 202	EX	52202	57202	150 233	EX	52233	57233
150 124	NH	52124	57124	150 203	NL	52203	57203	150 234	EX	52234	57234
150 125	NH	52125	57125	150 204	NL	52204	57204	150 235	CF	52235	57235
150 126	NH	52126	57126	150 205	NL	52205	57205	150 236	CF	52236	57236
150 127	NH	52127	57127	150 206	NL	52206	57206	150 237	CF	52237	57237
150 128	NH	52128	57128	150 207	PM	52207	57207	150 238	EX	52238	57238
150 129	NH	52129	57129	150 208	CF	52208	57208	150 239	EX	52239	57239
150 130	NH	52130	57130	150 210	NL	52210	57210	150 240	CF	52240	57240
150 131	NH	52131	57131	150 211	NL	52211	57211	150 241	CF	52241	57241

Class 150 — Sprinter

Unit	Depot			Unit	Depot			Unit	Depot		
150 242	CF	52242	57242	150 257	CF	52257	57257	150 272	NL	52272	57272
150 243	EX	52243	57243	150 258	CF	52258	57258	150 273	NL	52273	57273
150 244	EX	52244	57244	150 259	CF	52259	57259	150 274	NL	52274	57274
150 245	CF	52245	57245	150 260	CF	52260	57260	150 275	NL	52275	57275
150 246	EX	52246	57246	150 261	EX	52261	57261	150 276	NL	52276	57276
150 247	EX	52247	57247	150 262	CF	52262	57262	150 277	NL	52277	57277
150 248	EX	52248	57248	150 263	EX	52263	57263	150 278	CF	52278	57278
150 249	EX	52249	57249	150 264	CF	52264	57264	150 279	CF	52279	57279
150 250	CF	52250	57250	150 265	EX	52265	57265	150 280	CF	52280	57280
150 251	CF	52251	57251	150 266	EX	52266	57266	150 281	CF	52281	57281
150 252	CF	52252	57252	150 267	CF	52267	57267	150 282	CF	52282	57282
150 253	CF	52253	57253	150 268	NL	52268	57268	150 283	CF	52283	57283
150 254	CF	52254	57254	150 269	NL	52269	57269	150 284	CF	52284	57284
150 255	CF	52255	57255	150 270	NL	52270	57270	150 285	CF	52285	57285
150 256	CF	52256	57256	150 271	NL	52271	57271				

Named Unit

150 214 The Bentham Line - A Dementia Friendly Railway
150 275 Yorkshire Regiment / Yorkshire Warrior

Class 153 — Super Sprinter

Unit	Depot		Unit	Depot		Unit	Depot	
153 301	EY(s)	52301	153 334	LM(s)	52334	153 375	LM(s)	57375
153 303	CF	52303	153 351	EY(s)	57351	153 376	DF	57376
153 304	EY(s)	52304	153 352	EY(s)	57352	153 377	CK	57377
153 305	CK	52305	153 353	CF	57353	153 378	EY(s)	57378
153 307	NH	52307	153 354	LM(s)	57354	153 379	NM	57379
153 308	NM	52308	153 355	NM	57355	153 380	CK	57380
153 311	DF	52311	153 356	LM(s)	57356	153 381	BU(s)	57381
153 312	CF	52312	153 357	NM	57357	153 383	LM(s)	57383
153 315	EY(s)	52315	153 358	NH	57358	153 384	NM	57384
153 316	LM(s)	52316	153 359	NH	57359	153 385	DF	57385
153 317	EY(s)	52317	153 360	NH	57360	153 906	CF	52306
153 319	NM	52319	153 361	CF	57361	153 909	CF	52309
153 320	CF	52320	153 362	CF	57362	153 910	CF	52310
153 323	CF	52323	153 363	NH	57363	153 913	CF	52313
153 324	NH	52324	153 364	BU(s)	57364	153 914	CF	52314
153 325	CF	52325	153 365	LM(s)	57365	153 918	CF	52318
153 327	CF	52327	153 366	BU(s)	57366	153 921	CF	52321
153 328	NH	52328	153 367	CF	57367	153 922	CF	52322
153 329	CF	52329	153 369	CF	57369	153 926	CF	52326
153 330	NH	52330	153 370	CK	57370	153 935	CF	52335
153 331	NH	52331	153 371	LM(s)	57371	153 968	CF	57368
153 332	NH	52332	153 373	CK	57373	153 972	CF	57372
153 333	CF	52333	153 374	LE(s)	57374	153 982	CF	57382

Named Units

153 316 John 'Longitude' Harrison Inventor of the Marine Chronometer
153 361 Connecting Wiltshire
153 383 Ecclesbourne Valley Railway 150 years

Class 155 — Super Sprinter

Unit	Depot			Unit	Depot			Unit	Depot		
155 341	NL	52341	57341	155 344	NL	52344	57344	155 346	NL	52346	57346
155 342	NL	52342	57342	155 345	NL	52345	57345	155 347	NL	52347	57347
155 343	NL	52343	57343								

Class 156				Super Sprinter					
156 401	NM	52401	57401	156 447	HT	52447	57447	156 485	HT	52485	57485

156 401	NM	52401	57401	156 447	HT	52447	57447	156 485	HT	52485	57485
156 402	NM	52402	57402	156 448	HT	52448	57448	156 486	HT	52486	57486
156 403	NM	52403	57403	156 449	HT	52449	57449	156 487	HT	52487	57487
156 404	NM	52404	57404	156 450	CK	52450	57450	156 488	HT	52488	57488
156 405	NM	52405	57405	156 451	HT	52451	57451	156 489	HT	52489	57489
156 406	NM	52406	57406	156 452	NH	52452	57452	156 490	HT	52490	57490
156 408	NM	52408	57408	156 453	CK	52453	57453	156 491	HT	52491	57491
156 410	NM	52410	57410	156 454	HT	52454	57454	156 492	CK	52492	57492
156 411	NM	52411	57411	156 455	NH	52455	57455	156 493	CK	52493	57493
156 413	NM	52413	57413	156 456	CK	52456	57456	156 494	CK	52494	57494
156 414	NM	52414	57414	156 457	CK	52457	57457	156 495	CK	52495	57495
156 415	NM	52415	57415	156 458	CK	52458	57458	156 496	HT	52496	57496
156 420	NH	52420	57420	156 459	NH	52459	57459	156 497	DY	52497	57497
156 421	HT	52421	57421	156 460	NH	52460	57460	156 498	DY	52498	57498
156 423	NH	52423	57423	156 461	NH	52461	57461	156 499	CK	52499	57499
156 424	NH	52424	57424	156 462	CK	52462	57462	156 500	CK	52500	57500
156 425	NH	52425	57425	156 463	HT	52463	57463	156 501	CK	52501	57501
156 426	NH	52426	57426	156 464	NH	52464	57464	156 502	CK	52502	57502
156 427	NH	52427	57427	156 465	HT	52465	57465	156 503	CK	52503	57503
156 428	NH	52428	57428	156 466	NH	52466	57466	156 504	CK	52504	57504
156 429	NH	52429	57429	156 467	CK	52467	57467	156 505	CK	52505	57505
156 430	CK	52430	57430	156 468	HT	52468	57468	156 506	CK	52506	57506
156 431	CK	52431	57431	156 469	HT	52469	57469	156 507	CK	52507	57507
156 432	CK	52432	57432	156 470	DY	52470	57470	156 508	CK	52508	57508
156 433	CK	52433	57433	156 471	HT	52471	57471	156 509	CK	52509	57509
156 434	CK	52434	57434	156 472	HT	52472	57472	156 510	CK	52510	57510
156 435	CK	52435	57435	156 473	DY	52473	57473	156 511	CK	52511	57511
156 436	CK	52436	57436	156 474	CK	52474	57474	156 512	CK	52512	57512
156 437	CK	52437	57437	156 475	HT	52475	57475	156 513	CK	52513	57513
156 438	HT	52438	57438	156 476	CK	52476	57476	156 514	CK	52514	57514
156 439	CK	52439	57439	156 477	CK	52477	57477	156 907	NM	52407	57407
156 440	HT	52440	57440	156 478	CK	52478	57478	156 909	BH(s)	52409	57409
156 441	NH	52441	57441	156 479	HT	52479	57479	156 912	NM	52412	57412
156 442	CK	52442	57442	156 480	HT	52480	57480	156 916	NM	52416	57416
156 443	HT	52443	57443	156 481	HT	52481	57481	156 917	BH(s)	52417	57417
156 444	HT	52444	57444	156 482	HT	52482	57482	156 918	NM	52418	57418
156 445	CK	52445	57445	156 483	HT	52483	57483	156 919	NM	52419	57419
156 446	CK	52446	57446	156 484	HT	52484	57484	156 922	NM	52422	57422

Named Units	
156 480 Spirit of the Royal Air Force	156 483 William George Hardy

Class 158				Express Sprinter				
158 701	IS	52701		57701	158 766	EX	52766	57766
158 702	IS	52702		57702	158 767	EX	52767	57767
158 703	IS	52703		57703	158 769	EX	52769	57769
158 704	IS	52704		57704	158 770	NM	52770	57770
158 705	IS	52705		57705	158 773	NM	52773	57773
158 706	IS	52706		57706	158 774	NM	52774	57774
158 707	IS	52707		57707	158 777	NM	52777	57777
158 708	IS	52708		57708	158 780	NM	52780	57780
158 709	IS	52709		57709	158 782	NL	52782	57782
158 710	IS	52710		57710	158 783	NM	52783	57783
158 711	IS	52711		57711	158 784	NH	52784	57784
158 712	IS	52712		57712	158 785	NM	52785	57785
158 713	IS	52713		57713	158 786	NL	52786	57786
158 714	IS	52714		57714	158 787	NH	52787	57787
158 715	IS	52715		57715	158 788	NM	52788	57788
158 716	IS	52716		57716	158 789	NL	52789	57789
158 717	IS	52717		57717	158 790	HT	52790	57790
158 718	IS	52718		57718	158 791	HT	52791	57791
158 719	IS	52719		57719	158 792	HT	52792	57792
158 720	IS	52720		57720	158 793	HT	52793	57793
158 721	IS	52721		57721	158 794	NH	52794	57794
158 722	IS	52722		57722	158 795	NH	52795	57795
158 723	IS	52723		57723	158 796	NH	52796	57796
158 724	IS	52724		57724	158 797	NH	52797	57797
158 725	IS	52725		57725	158 798	PM	52798 58715	57798
158 726	CK	52726		57726	158 799	NM	52799	57799
158 727	CK	52727		57727	158 806	NM	52806	57806
158 728	CK	52728		57728	158 810	NM	52810	57810
158 729	CK	52729		57729	158 812	NM	52812	57812
158 730	CK	52730		57730	158 813	NM	52813	57813
158 731	CK	52731		57731	158 815	HT	52815	57815
158 732	CK	52732		57732	158 816	HT	52816	57816
158 733	CK	52733		57733	158 817	HT	52817	57817
158 734	CK	52734		57734	158 818	MN	52818	57818
158 735	CK	52735		57735	158 819	MN	52819	57819
158 736	CK	52736		57736	158 820	MN	52820	57820
158 738	CK	52738		57738	158 821	MN	52821	57821
158 739	CK	52739		57739	158 822	MN	52822	57822
158 740	CK	52740		57740	158 823	MN	52823	57823
158 741	CK	52741		57741	158 824	MN	52824	57824
158 745	EX	52745		57745	158 825	MN	52825	57825
158 747	EX	52747		57747	158 826	MN	52826	57826
158 749	EX	52749		57749	158 827	MN	52827	57827
158 750	EX	52750		57750	158 828	MN	52828	57828
158 752	NL	52752 58716	57752		158 829	MN	52829	57829
158 753	NL	52753 58710	57753		158 830	MN	52830	57830
158 754	NL	52754 58708	57754		158 831	MN	52831	57831
158 755	NL	52755 58702	57755		158 832	MN	52832	57832
158 756	NL	52756 58712	57756		158 833	MN	52833	57833
158 757	NL	52757 58706	57757		158 834	MN	52834	57834
158 758	NL	52758 58714	57758		158 835	MN	52835	57835
158 759	NL	52759 58713	57759		158 836	MN	52836	57836
158 760	EX	52760		57760	158 837	CF	52837	57837
158 762	EX(s)	52762		57762	158 838	CF	52838	57838
158 763	EX(s)	52763		57763	158 839	CF	52839	57839
158 765	EX	52765		57765	158 840	CF	52840	57840

Class 158 — Express Sprinter

Unit	Depot	Car	Car	Car
158 841	CF	52841	57841	
158 842	HT	52842	57842	
158 843	HT	52843	57843	
158 844	HT	52844	57844	
158 845	HT	52845	57845	
158 846	NM	52846	57846	
158 847	NM	52847	57847	
158 848	HT	52848	57848	
158 849	HT	52849	57849	
158 850	HT	52850	57850	
158 851	HT	52851	57851	
158 852	NM	52852	57852	
158 853	HT	52853	57853	
158 854	NM	52854	57854	
158 855	HT	52855	57855	
158 856	NM	52856	57856	
158 857	NM	52857	57857	
158 858	NM	52858	57858	
158 859	HT	52859	57859	
158 860	HT	52860	57860	
158 861	HT	52861	57861	
158 862	NM	52862	57862	
158 863	NM	52863	57863	
158 864	NM	52864	57864	
158 865	NM	52865	57865	
158 866	NM	52866	57866	
158 867	NL	52867	57867	
158 868	NL	52868	57868	
158 869	NL	52869	57869	
158 870	NL	52870	57870	
158 871	NL	52871	57871	
158 872	NL	52872	57872	
158 880	SA	52737	57737	
158 881	SA	52742	57742	
158 882	SA	52743	57743	
158 883	SA	52744	57744	
158 884	SA	52772	57772	
158 885	SA	52775	57775	
158 886	SA	52779	57779	
158 887	SA	52781	57781	
158 888	SA	52802	57802	
158 889	NM	52808	57808	
158 890	SA	52814	57814	
158 901	NL	52901	57901	
158 902	NL	52902	57902	
158 903	NL	52903	57903	
158 904	NL	52904	57904	
158 905	NL	52905	57905	
158 906	NL	52906	57906	
158 907	NL	52907	57907	
158 908	NL	52908	57908	
158 909	NL	52909	57909	
158 910	NL	52910	57910	
158 950	PM	57751	52761	57761
158 951	PM	52751	52764	57764
158 956	PM	52748	52768	57768
158 957	PM	57748	52771	57771
158 958	PM	57746	52776	57776
158 959	PM	52746	52778	57778

Named Units

158 791	County of Nottinghamshire	158 854	The Station Volunteer
158 847	Lincoln Castle Explorer	158 864	ELR 50 Visit Lincolnshire In 2020

Class 159 — South Western Turbo

Unit	Depot	Car	Car	Car
159 001	SA	52873	58718	57873
159 002	SA	52874	58719	57874
159 003	SA	52875	58720	57875
159 004	SA	52876	58721	57876
159 005	SA	52877	58722	57877
159 006	SA	52878	58723	57878
159 007	SA	52879	58724	57879
159 008	SA	52880	58725	57880
159 009	SA	52881	58726	57881
159 010	SA	52882	58727	57882
159 011	SA	52883	58728	57883
159 012	SA	52884	58729	57884
159 013	SA	52885	58730	57885
159 014	SA	52886	58731	57886
159 015	SA	52887	58732	57887
159 016	SA	52888	58733	57888
159 017	SA	52889	58734	57889
159 018	SA	52890	58735	57890
159 019	SA	52891	58736	57891
159 020	SA	52892	58737	57892
159 021	SA	52893	58738	57893
159 022	SA	52894	58739	57894
159 101	SA	52800	58717	57800
159 102	SA(s)	52803	58703	57803
159 103	SA	52804	58704	57804
159 104	SA	52805	58705	57805
159 105	SA	52807	58707	57807
159 106	SA	52809	58709	57809
159 107	SA	52811	58711	57811
159 108	SA	52801	58701	57801

Class 165 — Network Turbo

Unit						Unit				
165 001	AL	58801		58834		165 039	AL	58833	55414	58866
165 002	AL	58802		58835		165 101	RG	58916	55415	58953
165 003	AL	58803		58836		165 102	RG	58917	55416	58954
165 004	AL	58804		58837		165 103	RG	58918	55417	58955
165 005	AL	58805		58838		165 104	RG	58919	55418	58956
165 006	AL	58806		58839		165 105	RG	58920	55419	58957
165 007	AL	58807		58840		165 106	RG	58921	55420	58958
165 008	AL	58808		58841		165 107	RG	58922	55421	58959
165 009	AL	58809		58842		165 108	RG	58923	55422	58960
165 010	AL	58810		58843		165 109	RG	58924	55423	58961
165 011	AL	58811		58844		165 110	RG	58925	55424	58962
165 012	AL	58812		58845		165 111	RG	58926	55425	58963
165 013	AL	58813		58846		165 112	RG	58927	55426	58964
165 014	AL	58814		58847		165 113	RG	58928	55427	58965
165 015	AL	58815		58848		165 114	RG	58929	55428	58966
165 016	AL	58816		58849		165 116	RG	58931	55430	58968
165 017	AL	58817		58850		165 117	RG	58932	55431	58969
165 018	AL	58818		58851		165 118	RG	58933		58879
165 019	AL	58819		58852		165 119	RG	58934		58880
165 020	AL	58820		58853		165 120	RG	58935		58881
165 021	AL	58821		58854		165 121	RG	58936		58882
165 022	AL	58822		58855		165 122	RG	58937		58883
165 023	AL	58873		58867		165 123	RG	58938		58884
165 024	AL	58874		58868		165 124	RG	58939		58885
165 025	AL	58875		58869		165 125	RG	58940		58886
165 026	AL	58876		58870		165 126	RG	58941		58887
165 027	AL	58877		58871		165 127	RG	58942		58888
165 028	AL	58878		58872		165 128	PM	58943		58889
165 029	AL	58823	55404	58856		165 129	PM	58944		58890
165 030	AL	58824	55405	58857		165 130	PM	58945		58891
165 031	AL	58825	55406	58858		165 131	PM	58946		58892
165 032	AL	58826	55407	58859		165 132	PM	58947		58893
165 033	AL	58827	55408	58860		165 133	PM	58948		58894
165 034	AL	58828	55409	58861		165 134	PM	58949		58895
165 035	AL	58829	55410	58862		165 135	PM	58950		58896
165 036	AL	58830	55411	58863		165 136	PM	58951		58897
165 037	AL	58831	55412	58864		165 137	PM	58952		58898
165 038	AL	58832	55413	58865						

Class 166 — Network Express Turbo

Unit						Unit				
166 201	PM	58101	58601	58122		166 212	PM	58112	58612	58133
166 202	PM	58102	58602	58123		166 213	PM	58113	58613	58134
166 203	PM	58103	58603	58124		166 214	PM	58114	58614	58135
166 204	PM	58104	58604	58125		166 215	PM	58115	58615	58136
166 205	PM	58105	58605	58126		166 216	PM	58116	58616	58137
166 206	PM	58106	58606	58127		166 217	PM	58117	58617	58138
166 207	PM	58107	58607	58128		166 218	PM	58118	58618	58139
166 208	PM	58108	58608	58129		166 219	PM	58119	58619	58140
166 209	PM	58109	58609	58130		166 220	PM	58120	58620	58141
166 210	PM	58110	58610	58131		166 221	PM	58121	58621	58142
166 211	PM	58111	58611	58132						

Named Units

166 204	Norman Topsham MBE	166 220	Roger Watkins-The GWR Master Train Planner
166 221	Reading Train Care Depot		

Class 168 — Clubman

Unit	Depot				
168 001	AL	58151	58651	58451	58251
168 002	AL	58152	58652	58452	58252
168 003	AL	58153	58653	58453	58253
168 004	AL	58154	58654	58454	58254
168 005	AL	58155	58655	58455	58255
168 106	AL	58156	58756	58456	58256
168 107	AL	58157	58457	58757	58257
168 108	AL	58158	58458		58258
168 109	AL	58159	58459		58259
168 110	AL	58160	58460		58260
168 111	AL	58161	58461		58261
168 112	AL	58162	58462		58262
168 113	AL	58163	58463		58263
168 214	AL	58164	58464		58264
168 215	AL	58165	58465	58365	58265
168 216	AL	58166	58366	58466	58266
168 217	AL	58167	58467	58367	58267
168 218	AL	58168		58468	58268
168 219	AL	58169		58469	58269
168 321	AL	50301			79301
168 322	AL	50302			79302
168 323	AL	50303			79303
168 324	AL	50304			79304
168 325	AL	50305			79305
168 326	AL	50306			79306
168 327	AL	50307			79307
168 328	AL	50308			79308
168 329	AL	50399			79399

Class 170 — Turbostar

Unit	Depot			
170 101	TSx	50101	55101	79101
170 102	TSx	50102	55102	79102
170 103	TSx	50103	55103	79103
170 104	TSx	50104	55104	79104
170 105	TSx	50105	55105	79105
170 106	TSx	50106	55106	79106
170 107	TSx	50107	55107	79107
170 108	TSx	50108	55108	79108
170 109	TSx	50109	55109	79109
170 110	TSx	50110	55110	79110
170 111	TSx	50111		79111
170 112	TSx	50112		79112
170 113	TSx	50113		79113
170 114	TSx	50114		79114
170 115	TSx	50115		79115
170 116	TSx	50116		79116
170 117	TSx	50117		79117
170 201	CF	50201	56201	79201
170 202	CF	50202	56202	79202
170 203	CF	50203	56203	79203
170 204	CF	50204	56204	79204
170 205	CF	50205	56205	79205
170 206	CF	50206	56206	79206
170 207	CF	50207	56207	79207
170 208	CF	50208	56208	79208
170 270	CF	50270		79270
170 271	CF	50271		79271
170 272	CF	50272		79272
170 273	DY	50273		79273
170 393	HA	50393	56393	79393
170 394	HA	50394	56394	79394
170 395	HA	50395	56395	79395
170 396	HA	50396	56396	79396
170 397	TSx	50397	56397	79397
170 398	TSx	50398	56398	79398
170 401	HA	50401	56401	79401
170 402	HA	50402	56402	79402
170 403	HA	50403	56403	79403
170 404	HA	50404	56404	79404
170 405	HA	50405	56405	79405
170 406	HA	50406	56406	79406
170 407	HA	50407	56407	79407
170 408	HA	50408	56408	79408
170 409	HA	50409	56409	79409
170 410	HA	50410	56410	79410
170 411	HA	50411	56411	79411
170 412	HA	50412	56412	79412
170 413	HA	50413	56413	79413
170 414	HA	50414	56414	79414
170 415	HA	50415	56415	79415
170 416	DY	50416	56416	79416
170 417	DY	50417	56417	79417
170 418	DY	50418	56418	79418
170 419	DY	50419	56419	79419
170 420	DY	50420	56420	79420
170 425	HA	50425	56425	79425
170 426	HA	50426	56426	79426
170 427	HA	50427	56427	79427
170 428	HA	50428	56428	79428
170 429	HA	50429	56429	79429
170 430	HA	50430	56430	79430
170 431	HA	50431	56431	79431
170 432	HA	50432	56432	79432
170 433	HA	50433	56433	79433
170 434	HA	50434	56434	79434
170 450	HA	50450	56450	79450
170 451	HA	50451	56451	79451
170 452	HA	50452	56452	79452
170 453	NL	50453	56453	79453
170 454	NL	50454	56454	79454
170 455	NL	50455	56455	79455
170 456	NL	50456	56456	79456
170 457	NL	50457	56457	79457
170 458	NL	50458	56458	79458
170 459	NL	50459	56459	79459
170 460	NL	50460	56460	79460
170 461	NL	50461	56461	79461
170 470	HA	50470	56470	79470
170 471	HA	50471	56471	79471
170 472	NL	50472	56472	79472

Class 170 — Turbostar

Unit	Depot	Cars				Unit	Depot	Cars		
170 473	NL	50473	56473	79473		170 515	DY	50515	79515	
170 474	NL	50474	56474	79474		170 516	TS	50516	79516	
170 475	NL	50475	56475	79475		170 517	TS	50517	79517	
170 476	NL	50476	56476	79476		170 530	DY	50630	79630	
170 477	NL	50477	56477	79477		170 531	DY	50631	79631	
170 478	NL	50478	56478	79478		170 532	DY	50632	79632	
170 501	TS	50501	79501			170 533	TS	50633	79633	
170 502	TS	50502	79502			170 534	DY	50634	79634	
170 503	DY	50503	79503			170 535	TS	50635	79635	
170 504	TS	50504	79504			170 618	TSx	50518	56630	79518
170 505	TS	50505	79505			170 619	TSx	50519	56631	79519
170 506	TS	50506	79506			170 620	TSx	50520	56632	79520
170 507	TS	50507	79507			170 621	TSx	50521	56633	79521
170 508	TS	50508	79508			170 622	TSx	50522	56634	79522
170 509	TS	50509	79509			170 623	TSx	50523	56635	79523
170 510	TS	50510	79510			170 636	TSx	50636	56636	79636
170 511	DY	50511	79511			170 637	TSx	50637	56637	79637
170 512	TS	50512	79512			170 638	TSx	50638	56638	79638
170 513	TS	50513	79513			170 639	TSx	50639	56639	79639
170 514	TS	50514	79514							

Named Unit

170 417	The Key Worker		170 622	Pride of Leicester

Class 171 — Turbostar

Unit	Depot	Cars				Unit	Depot	Cars			
171 201	SU	50421			79421	171 727	SU	50727			79727
171 202	SU	50423			79423	171 728	SU	50728			79728
171 401	SU	50422	56421	56422	79422	171 729	SU	50729			79729
171 402	SU	50424	56423	56424	79424	171 730	SU	50392			79392
171 721	SU	50721			79721	171 801	SU	50801	56801	54801	79801
171 722	SU	50722			79722	171 802	SU	50802	56802	54802	79802
171 723	SU	50723			79723	171 803	SU	50803	56803	54803	79803
171 724	SU	50724			79724	171 804	SU	50804	56804	54804	79804
171 725	SU	50725			79725	171 805	SU	50805	56805	54805	79805
171 726	SU	50726			79726	171 806	SU	50806	56806	54806	79806

Class 172 — Turbostar

Unit	Depot	Cars				Unit	Depot	Cars		
172 001	TS	59311	59411			172 219	TS	50219	79219	
172 002	TS	59312	59412			172 220	TS	50220	79220	
172 003	TS	59313	59413			172 221	TS	50221	79221	
172 004	TS	59314	59414			172 222	TS	50222	79222	
172 005	TS	59315	59415			172 331	TS	50331	56331	79331
172 006	TS	59316	59416			172 332	TS	50332	56332	79332
172 007	TS	59317	59417			172 333	TS	50338	56333	79333
172 008	TS	59318	59418			172 334	TS	50334	56334	79334
172 101	TS	59111	59211			172 335	TS	50335	56335	79335
172 102	TS	59112	59212			172 336	TS	50336	56336	79336
172 103	TS	59113	59213			172 337	TS	50337	56337	79337
172 104	TS	59114	59214			172 338	TS	50333	56338	79338
172 211	TS	50211	79211			172 339	TS	50339	56339	79339
172 212	TS	50212	79212			172 340	TS	50340	56340	79340
172 213	TS	50213	79213			172 341	TS	50341	56341	79341
172 214	TS	50214	79214			172 342	TS	50342	56342	79342
172 215	TS	50215	79215			172 343	TS	50343	56343	79343
172 216	TS	50216	79216			172 344	TS	50344	56344	79344
172 217	TS	50217	79217			172 345	TS	50345	56345	79345
172 218	TS	50218	79218							

Class 175 — Coradia

Note: Several of these units are currently working out of formation

Unit					Unit				
175 001	CH	50701		79701	175 104	CH	50754	56754	79754
175 002	CH	50702		79702	175 105	CH	50755	56755	79755
175 003	CH	50703		79703	175 106	CH	50756	56756	79756
175 004	CH	50759		79759	175 107	CH	50757	56757	79757
175 005	CH	50705		79751	175 108	CH	50758	56758	79758
175 006	CH	50706		79765	175 109	CH	50704	56759	79705
175 007	CH	50707		79707	175 110	CH	50760	56760	79760
175 008	CH	50708		79708	175 111	CH	50761	56761	79761
175 009	CH	50709		79709	175 112	CH	50762	56762	79762
175 010	CH	50710		79710	175 113	CH	50763	56763	79763
175 011	CH	50711		79511	175 114	CH	50764	56764	79764
175 101	CH	50751	56751	79704	175 115	CH	50706	56765	79765
175 102	CH	50752	56752	79752	175 116	CH	50766	56766	79766
175 103	CH	50753	56753	79753					

Class 180 — Adelante

Unit							Name
180 101	HT	59901	56901	55901	54901	50901	
180 102	HT	59902	56902	55902	54902	50902	
180 103	HT	59903	56903	55903	54903	50903	
180 104	HT	59904	56904	55904	54904	50904	
180 105	HT	59905	56905	55905	54905	50905	The Yorkshire Artist Ashley Jackson
180 106	HT	59906	56906	55906	54906	50906	
180 107	HT	59907	56907	55907	54907	50907	Hart of the North
180 108	HT	59908	56908	55908	54908	50908	William Shakespeare
180 109	DY	59909	56909	55913	54909	50909	
180 110	DY	59910		55910	54910	50910	
180 111	DY	59911	56911	55911	54911	50911	
180 112	HT	59912	56912	55912	54912	50912	James Herriot Celebrating 100 Years 1916-2016
180 113	DY	59913	56913	55909	54913	50913	
180 114	HT	59914	56914	55914	54914	50914	Kirkgate Calling
Spare		56910					

Class 185 — Trans Pennine Express

Unit					Unit				
185 101	AK	51101	53101	54101	185 122	AK	51122	53122	54122
185 102	AK	51102	53102	54102	185 123	AK	51123	53123	54123
185 103	AK	51103	53103	54103	185 124	AK	51124	53124	54124
185 104	AK	51104	53104	54104	185 125	AK	51125	53125	54125
185 105	AK	51105	53105	54105	185 126	AK	51126	53126	54126
185 106	AK	51106	53106	54106	185 127	AK	51127	53127	54127
185 107	AK	51107	53107	54107	185 128	AK	51128	53128	54128
185 108	AK	51108	53108	54108	185 129	AK	51129	53129	54129
185 109	AK	51109	53109	54109	185 130	AK	51130	53130	54130
185 110	AK	51110	53110	54110	185 131	AK	51131	53131	54131
185 111	AK	51111	53111	54111	185 132	AK	51132	53132	54132
185 112	AK	51112	53112	54112	185 133	AK	51133	53133	54133
185 113	AK	51113	53113	54113	185 134	AK	51134	53134	54134
185 114	AK	51114	53114	54114	185 135	AK	51135	53135	54135
185 115	AK	51115	53115	54115	185 136	AK	51136	53136	54136
185 116	AK	51116	53116	54116	185 137	AK	51137	53137	54137
185 117	AK	51117	53117	54117	185 138	AK	51138	53138	54138
185 118	AK	51118	53118	54118	185 139	AK	51139	53139	54139
185 119	AK	51119	53119	54119	185 140	AK	51140	53140	54140
185 120	AK	51120	53120	54120	185 141	AK	51141	53141	54141
185 121	AK	51121	53121	54121	185 142	AK	51142	53142	54142

Class 185 — Trans Pennine Express

185 143	AK	51143	53143	54143	185 148	AK	51148	53148	54148
185 144	AK	51144	53144	54144	185 149	AK	51149	53149	54149
185 145	AK	51145	53145	54145	185 150	AK	51150	53150	54150
185 146	AK	51146	53146	54146	185 151	AK	51151	53151	54151
185 147	AK	51147	53147	54147					

Class 195 — Northern — CAF

195 001	NH	101001		103001	195 105	NH	101105	102105	103105
195 002	NH	101002		103002	195 106	NH	101106	102106	103106
195 003	NH	101003		103003	195 107	NH	101107	102107	103107
195 004	NH	101004		103004	195 108	NH	101108	102108	103108
195 005	NH	101005		103005	195 109	NH	101109	102109	103109
195 006	NH	101006		103006	195 110	NH	101110	102110	103110
195 007	NH	101007		103007	195 111	NH	101111	102111	103111
195 008	NH	101008		103008	195 112	NH	101112	102112	103112
195 009	NH	101009		103009	195 113	NH	101113	102113	103113
195 010	NH	101010		103010	195 114	NH	101114	102114	103114
195 011	NH	101011		103011	195 115	NH	101115	102115	103115
195 012	NH	101012		103012	195 116	NH	101116	102116	103116
195 013	NH	101013		103013	195 117	NH	101117	102117	103117
195 014	NH	101014		103014	195 118	NH	101118	102118	103118
195 015	NH	101015		103015	195 119	NH	101119	102119	103119
195 016	NH	101016		103016	195 120	NH	101120	102120	103120
195 017	NH	101017		103017	195 121	NH	101121	102121	103121
195 018	NH	101018		103018	195 122	NH	101122	102122	103122
195 019	NH	101019		103019	195 123	NH	101123	102123	103123
195 020	NH	101020		103020	195 124	NH	101124	102124	103124
195 021	NH	101021		103021	195 125	NH	101125	102125	103125
195 022	NH	101022		103022	195 126	NH	101126	102126	103126
195 023	NH	101023		103023	195 127	NH	101127	102127	103127
195 024	NH	101024		103024	195 128	NH	101128	102128	103128
195 025	NH	101025		103025	195 129	NH	101129	102129	103129
195 101	NH	101101	102101	103101	195 130	NH	101130	102130	103130
195 102	NH	101102	102102	103102	195 131	NH	101131	102131	103131
195 103	NH	101103	102103	103103	195 132	NH	101132	102132	103132
195 104	NH	101104	102104	103104	195 133	NH	101133	102133	103133

Named Units

195 104	Deva Victrix	195 116	Proud to be Northern
195 111	Keyworker	195 128	Calder Champion

Class 196/0 — CAF for West Midlands — built / on test*

196 001*	121001	124001	196 005*	121005	124005	196 009*	121009	124009
196 002*	121002	124002	196 006*	121006	124006	196 010*	121010	124010
196 003*	121003	124003	196 007*	121007	124007	196 011*	121011	124011
196 004*	121004	124004	196 008*	121008	124008	196 012*	121012	124012

Class 196/1 — CAF for West Midlands — built / on test*

196 101*	121101	122101	123101	124101	196 108*	121108	122108	123108	124108
196 102*	121102	122102	123102	124102	196 109*	121109	122109	123109	124109
196 103*	121103	122103	123103	124103	196 110*	121110	122110	123110	124110
196 104*	121104	122104	123104	124104	196 111*	121111	122111	123111	124111
196 105*	121105	122105	123105	124105	196 112*	121112	122112	123112	124112
196 106*	121106	122106	123106	124106	196 113	121113	122113	123113	124113
196 107*	121107	122107	123107	124107	196 114	121114	122114	123114	124114

Class 197 — Transport for Wales 2 car units — built / on test*

Unit			Unit			Unit		
197 001*	131001	133001	197 018	131018	133018	197 035	131035	133035
197 002*	131002	133002	197 019	131019	133019	197 036	131036	133036
197 003*	131003	133003	197 020	131020	133020	197 037	131037	133037
197 004	131004	133004	197 021	131021	133021	197 038	131038	133038
197 005	131005	133005	197 022	131022	133022	197 039	131039	133039
197 006	131006	133006	197 023	131023	133023	197 040	131040	133040
197 007	131007	133007	197 024	131024	133024	197 041	131041	133041
197 008	131008	133008	197 025	131025	133025	197 042	131042	133042
197 009	131009	133009	197 026	131026	133026	197 043	131043	133043
197 010	131010	133010	197 027	131027	133027	197 044	131044	133044
197 011	131011	133011	197 028	131028	133028	197 045	131045	133045
197 012	131012	133012	197 029	131029	133029	197 046	131046	133046
197 013	131013	133013	197 030	131030	133030	197 047	131047	133047
197 014	131014	133014	197 031	131031	133031	197 048	131048	133048
197 015	131015	133015	197 032	131032	133032	197 049	131049	133049
197 016	131016	133016	197 033	131033	133033	197 050	131050	133050
197 017	131017	133017	197 034	131034	133034	197 051	131051	133051

Class 197 — Transport for Wales 3 car units — built / on test*

Unit				Unit			
197 101*	131101	132101	133101	197 114	131114	132114	133114
197 102*	131102	132102	133102	197 115	131115	132115	133115
197 103	131103	132103	133103	197 116	131116	132116	133116
197 104	131104	132104	133104	197 117	131117	132117	133117
197 105	131105	132105	133105	197 118	131118	132118	133118
197 106	131106	132106	133106	197 119	131119	132119	133119
197 107	131107	132107	133107	197 120	131120	132120	133120
197 108	131108	132108	133108	197 121	131121	132121	133121
197 109	131109	132109	133109	197 122	131122	132122	133122
197 110	131110	132110	133110	197 123	131123	132123	133123
197 111	131111	132111	133111	197 124	131124	132124	133124
197 112	131112	132112	133112	197 125	131125	132125	133125
197 113	131113	132113	133113	197 126	131126	132126	133126

Class 220 — Voyager

Unit						Unit					
220 001	CZx	60301	60701	60201	60401	220 018	CZx	60318	60718	60218	60418
220 002	CZx	60302	60702	60202	60402	220 019	CZx	60319	60719	60219	60419
220 003	CZx	60303	60703	60203	60403	220 020	CZx	60320	60720	60220	60420
220 004	CZx	60304	60704	60204	60404	220 021	CZx	60321	60721	60221	60421
220 005	CZx	60305	60705	60205	60405	220 022	CZx	60322	60722	60222	60422
220 006	CZx	60306	60706	60206	60406	220 023	CZx	60323	60723	60223	60423
220 007	CZx	60307	60707	60207	60407	220 024	CZx	60324	60724	60224	60424
220 008	CZx	60308	60708	60208	60408	220 025	CZx	60325	60725	60225	60425
220 009	CZx	60309	60709	60209	60409	220 026	CZx	60326	60726	60226	60426
220 010	CZx	60310	60710	60210	60410	220 027	CZx	60327	60727	60227	60427
220 011	CZx	60311	60711	60211	60411	220 028	CZx	60328	60728	60228	60428
220 012	CZx	60312	60712	60212	60412	220 029	CZx	60329	60729	60229	60429
220 013	CZx	60313	60713	60213	60413	220 030	CZx	60330	60730	60230	60430
220 014	CZx	60314	60714	60214	60414	220 031	CZx	60331	60731	60231	60431
220 015	CZx	60315	60715	60215	60415	220 032	CZx	60332	60732	60232	60432
220 016	CZx	60316	60716	60216	60416	220 033	CZx	60333	60733	60233	60433
220 017	CZx	60317	60717	60217	60417	220 034	CZx	60334	60734	60234	60434

Named Units

220 009	Hixon January 6th 1968	220 016	VOYAGER 20

Class 221							Super Voyager

221 101	CZ	60351	60951	60851	60751	60451	101 Squadron
221 102	CZ	60352	60952	60852	60752	60452	
221 103	CZ	60353	60953	60853	60753	60453	
221 104	CZ	60354	60954	60854	60754	60454	
221 105	CZ	60355	60955	60855	60755	60455	
221 106	CZ	60356	60956	60856	60756	60456	
221 107	CZ	60357	60957	60857	60757	60457	
221 108	CZ	60358	60958	60858	60758	60458	
221 109	CZ	60359	60959	60859	60759	60459	
221 110	CZ	60360	60960	60860	60760	60460	
221 111	CZ	60361	60961	60861	60761	60461	
221 112	CZ	60362	60962	60862	60762	60462	
221 113	CZ	60363	60963	60863	60763	60463	
221 114	CZ	60364	60964	60864	60764	60464	
221 115	CZ	60365	60965	60865	60765	60465	
221 116	CZ	60366	60966	60866	60766	60466	City of Bangor / Dinas Bangor
221 117	CZ	60367	60967	60867	60767	60467	
221 118	CZ	60368	60968	60868	60768	60468	
221 119	CZx	60369	60769	60969	60869	60469	
221 120	CZx	60370	60770	60970	60870	60470	
221 121	CZx	60371	60771	60971	60871	60471	
221 122	CZx	60372	60772	60972	60872	60472	
221 123	CZx	60373	60773	60973	60873	60473	
221 124	CZx	60374	60774	60974	60874	60474	
221 125	CZx	60375	60775	60975	60875	60475	
221 126	CZx	60376	60776	60976	60876	60476	
221 127	CZx	60377	60777	60977	60877	60477	
221 128	CZx	60378	60778	60978	60878	60478	
221 129	CZx	60379	60779	60979	60879	60479	
221 130	CZx	60380	60780	60980	60880	60480	
221 131	CZx	60381	60781	60981	60881	60481	
221 132	CZx	60382	60782	60982	60882	60482	
221 133	CZx	60383	60783	60983	60883	60483	
221 134	CZx	60384	60784	60984	60884	60484	
221 135	CZx	60385	60785	60985	60885	60485	
221 136	CZx	60386	60786		60886	60486	
221 137	CZx	60387	60787	60987	60887	60487	
221 138	CZx	60388	60788	60988	60888	60488	
221 139	CZx	60389	60789	60989	60889	60489	
221 140	CZx	60390	60790		60890	60490	
221 141	CZx	60391	60791	60991		60491	
221 142	CZ	60392	60992	60986	60792	60492	
221 143	CZ	60393	60993	60994	60793	60493	
221 144	CZx	60394	60794	60990		60494	

Class 222 — Meridian

222 001	DY	60241	60445	60341	60621	60561	60551	60161	The Entrepreneur Express
222 002	DY	60242	60346	60342	60622	60562	60544	60162	The Cutler's Company
222 003	DY	60243	60446	60343	60623	60563	60553	60163	Tornado
222 004	DY	60244	60345	60344	60624	60564	60554	60164	Children's Hospital Sheffield
222 005	DY	60245	60347	60443	60625	60565	60555	60165	
222 006	DY	60246	60447	60441	60626	60566	60556	60166	The Carbon Cutter
222 007	DY	60247	60442	60627	60567	60167			
222 008	DY	60248	60918	60628	60545	60168			Derby Etches Park
222 009	DY	60249	60919	60629	60557	60169			
222 010	DY	60250	60920	60630	60546	60170			
222 011	DY	60251	60921	60631	60531	60171			
222 012	DY	60252	60922	60632	60532	60172			
222 013	DY	60253	60923	60633	60533	60173			
222 014	DY	60254	60924	60634	60534	60174			
222 015	DY	60255	60925	60635	60535	60175			175 Years of Derby's Railways 1839-2014
222 016	DY	60256	60926	60636	60536	60176			
222 017	DY	60257	60927	60637	60537	60177			Lions Clubs International Centenary 1917-2017
222 018	DY	60258	60928	60638	60444	60178			
222 019	DY	60259	60929	60639	60547	60179			
222 020	DY	60260	60930	60640	60543	60180			
222 021	DY	60261	60931	60641	60552	60181			
222 022	DY	60262	60932	60642	60542	60182			Invest In Nottingham
222 023	DY	60263	60933	60643	60541	60183			

Class 222/1 — Pioneer

222 101	DY	60271	60571	60681	60191	222 103	DY	60273	60573	60683	60193
222 102	DY	60272	60572	60682	60192	222 104	DY	60274	60574	60684	60194

Class 230 — Vivarail   *on test

Note: 230 002 is currently in the USA.

230 001	LM	300001	300201	300101	230 006*		300006	300206	300106
230 002		300002	300202	300102	230 007*		300007	300207	300107
230 003	BY	300003		300103	230 008*		300008	300208	300108
230 004	BY	300004		300104	230 009*		300009	300209	300109
230 005	BY	300005		300105	230 010*		300010	300210	300110

Class 231 — Transport for Wales on order

231 001	381001	381201	381401	381301	381101
231 002	381002	381202	381402	381302	381102
231 003	381003	381203	381403	381303	381103
231 004	381004	381204	381404	381304	381104
231 005	381005	381205	381405	381305	381105
231 006	381006	381206	381406	381306	381106
231 007	381007	381207	381407	381307	381107
231 008	381008	381208	381408	381308	381108
231 009	381009	381209	381409	381309	381109
231 010	381010	381210	381410	381310	381110
231 011	381011	381211	381411	381311	381111

Note: in this section each unit is listed by current number, allocation and previous number.

50015	MRC	[53015, 55929, 977775]	51339	CVR	
50019	MRC	[53019]	51342	EOR	
50160	NYM	[53160]	51347	GR	
50164	NYM	[53164]	51351	PBR	
50170	ECVR	[53170]	51352	SDR	
50193	GCR	[53193, 977898]	51353	WR	
50203	GCR	[53203, 977897]	51354	WSR	
50204	NYM	[53204]	51356	SWR	
50222	BAR	[53222, 977693]	51360	GWR	
50253	ECVR	[53253]	51363	GWR	
50256	WR	[53256]	51365	PVR	
50266	GCR	[53266]	51367	STR	
50321	GCR	[53321, 977900]	51370	MNR	
50338	BAR	[53338, 977694]	51371	ZG	[960301, 977987]
50413	HR	[carries 56168]	51372	GWR	
50416	LR	[DB975005]	51375	CPPR	[960301, 977992]
50437	ELR	[53437]	51376	SDR	
50447	LR	[53447]	51381	MRM	
50454	LR	[53454]	51382	CVR	
50455	ELR	[53455]	51384	EOR	
50479	NNR	[53479]	51388	SWR	
50494	ELR	[53494]	51392	SWR	
50517	ELR	[53517]	51396	GCR	
50528	LR	[53528]	51397	PBR	
50531	TSR	[53531]	51400	WR	
50599	ECVR	[53599]	51401	GR	
50619	DFR	[53619]	51402	STR	
50628	KDR	[53628]	51405	GWR	
50632	DFR	[53632]	51407	PVR	
50645	NHC	[53645]	51412	MNR	
50746	WR	[53746]	51413	ZG	[960301, 977988]
50926	NHC	[53926, 977814]	51427	GCR	[977899]
50928	KWVR	[53928]	51434	MNR	
50933	SVR	[53933]	51485	ELR	
50971	KESR	[53971]	51499	MNR	
50980	WEA	[53980]	51503	MNR	
51017	BT		51505	ECVR	
51043	BT		51511	NYM	
51073	ECVR		51512	CAM-L	
51074	SCR		51562	NRM	
51104	SCR		51565	KWVR	
51118	MRC		51566	DFR	
51131	BAT		51567	ECVR	[977854]
51138	NHC	[977921]	51568	KDR	
51151	NHC		51571	KESR	
51187	CAM-L		51572	WR	
51188	NNR		51591	MRC	[55966]
51189	KWVR		51610	MRC	[55967]
51192	NNR		51616	HR	
51205	CAM-L		51618	LR	
51210	WR		51622	HR	
51213	EAR		51625	MRC	[55976]
51226	MNR		51655	Private, Rosyth	
51228	NNR		51669	MRC	
51321	BAT	[977753]	51803	KWVR	

Preserved Diesel Multiple Units

51813	ELR		55033	CVR	[977826]
51842	ELR		55034	ECVR	[121034]
51849	MRC		56006	MRC	[54006]
51859	WSR		56015	MRC	[54015, 54904, 977776]
51880	WSR		56047	STR	[54047]
51886	BRC		56055	CAM-L	[54055]
51887	WSR		56062	NNR	[54062]
51899	BRC		56097	MRC	
51907	MRC		56121	ELR	
51909	ESR		56160	DMJR	[DB975228]
51914	DFR		56169	HR	
51919	GV		56171	LR	[DB975006]
51922	NRM		56182	NNR	[54182, 977554]
51933	LR		56207	AFR	[54207]
51937	PWR	[977806]	56208	SVR	[54208]
51941	SVR		56223	LR	[54223]
51942	MNR		56224	KDR	[54224]
51947	ESR		56270	MNR	[54270]
51950	TSR		56271	ESR	[54271]
51990	STR	[977830]	56274	WR	[54274]
51993	TAVR	[977834]	56279	LAV	[54279]
52005	TAVR	[977832]	56287	EOR	[54287]
52006	AVR		56289	ELR	[54289]
52008	STR		56301	MNR	
52012	TAVR	[977835]	56342	GCR	[54342, 042222]
52025	AVR	[977833]	56343	WR	[54343]
52029	GWR		56347	MNR	[54347]
52030	STR	[977831]	56352	NNR	[54352]
52031	TAVR		56356	BAR	[54356, 6300]
52044	DFR		56358	EAR	[54358]
52048	GV		56408	LAV	[54408]
52053	KDR	[977807]	56456	LR	[54456]
52054	WEA		56484	PWR	[56484]
52062	TSR		56490	MRC	[54490]
52064	SVR		56491	KDR	[54491]
52071	LHR		56492	DFR	[54492]
52077	LHR		56495	KLR	[54495]
54504	LR	[56504]	59003	DSR	
55000	SDR		59004	DSR	
55001	ELR	[DB975023]	59117	MNR	
55003	GWR		59137	ELR	
55005	BAT		59228	ELR	
55006	ECVR		59245	AFR	
55009	GCR		59250	SVR	
55012	WEA	[977941]	59276	GCR	
55019	LMMR	[DB975042, 960015]	59303	ECVR	
55020	BWR	[121020]	59387	DFR	
55022	SO	[977873]	59404	BT	
55023	CPRR		59444	CHR	
55024	CPRR	[977858, 960010]	59486	SWR	
55025	LM	[977859, 960011]	59488	DSR	
55027	ECVR	[977975, 960302]	59492	ZG	
55028	SWR	[977860, 960012]	59493	SDR	
55029	RTM	[977968]	59494	DSR	
55031	ECVR	[977976, 960303]	59500	WR	
55032	WR	[977842]	59501	NHC	

Preserved Diesel Multiple Units

59503	DSR		59678	WSR	
59505	GWR		59701	ELR	
59506	GCR		59719	DSR	
59507	DSR		59740	SDR	[9740]
59508	GR		59761	BRC	
59509	WR		59791	TAVR	
59510	GWR		79018	ECVR	[DB975007]
59511	STR		79443	BT	
59513	DSR		79612	ECVR	[DB975008]
59514	SCR		79900	ECVR	[DB975010]
59515	YRC		79960	RIB	
59517	DSR		79962	KWVR	
59520	DMR		79963	EAR	
59521	HR		79964	KWVR	
59539	NYM		79976	BU	
59575	GCR		79978	SCR	
59603	CHR		999507	LAV	[RDB999507]
59609	MRC		977091	GVR	[RDB977091]
59659	MRC	[9659]	NER 3170	EBA	
59664	TAL				

2nd Generation Preserved Diesel Multiple Units

LEV-1	WR	[RDB975874]	142 091	RTM	[55741, 55787]
RE 004	WRH	[RB004]	142 094	EBA	[55744, 55790]
55500	KDR	[140001]	143 601	TAVR	[55642, 55667]
55501	KDR	[140001]	143 602	NVR	[55651, 55668]
55508	ZG	[141108]	143 603	CHR	[55658, 55669]
55513	MRC	[141113]	143 606	LMMR	[55647, 55672]
55528	ZG	[141108]	143 607	LMMR	[55648, 55673]
55533	MRC	[141113]	143 612	WA	[55653, 55678]
142 001	NRM	[55542, 55592]	143 616	TAVR	[55657, 55682]
142 004	TSR	[55545, 55595]	143 622	LGST	[55663, 55688]
142 006	LMMR	[55547, 55597]	143 623	WR	[55664, 55689]
142 011	MRC	[55552, 55602]	143 625	WR	[55666, 55691]
142 013	MRC	[55554, 55604]	144 001	AIR	[55801]
142 017	EKR	[55558, 55608]	144 001	HUD	[55824]
142 018	WR	[55559, 55609]	144 002	DSB	[55802, 55825]
142 019	WRH	[55560, 55610]	144 003	NHC	[55803, 55826]
142 020	WRH	[55561, 55611]	144 004	ALN	[55804, 55827]
142 023	PVR	[55564, 55614]	144 006	CAM	[55806, 55829]
142 027	CHR	[55568, 55618]	144 007	CAM	[55807, 55830]
142 028	WR	[55569, 55619]	144 008	CMR	[55831]
142 029	CHR	[55570, 55620]	144 010	WEA	[55810, 55833]
142 030	CHR	[55571, 55621]	144 011	KWVR	[55811, 55834]
142 035	WR	[55576, 55626]	144 013	TSR	[55813, 55836]
142 036	EKR	[55577, 55627]	144 014	TM	[55814, 55850, 55837]
142 038	MNR	[55579, 55629]	144 016	ALN	[55816, 55852, 55839]
142 041	WR	[55582, 55632]	144 017	AFR	[55817, 55853, 55840]
142 055	FR	[55705, 55751]	144 018	MNR	[55818, 55854, 55841]
142 058	TSR	[55708, 55754]	144 019	TM	[55819, 55855, 55843]
142 060	WR	[55710, 55756]	144 020	WR	[55820, 55856, 55843]
142 061	MNR	[55711, 55757]	144 022	KDR	[55822, 55858, 55845]
142 084	RTM	[55734, 55780]	144 023	TM	[55823, 55859, 55846]

Preserved Diesel Electric Multiple Units

60000	SE	[1001, 201001]
60001	SE	[1001, 201001]
60019	SE	[1013, 202001]
60100	EKR	[60154, 1101, 205001]
60108	EVR	[1109, 205009]
60110	EOR	[1111, 205205]
60116	SE	[60016, 1012]
60117	LAV	[1118, 205018]
60118	SE	[60018, 1013, 202001]
60122	LAV	[1123, 205023]
60124	MHR	[1125, 205025]
60127	SCR	[1302, 207203]
60130	BC	[1305, 207202]
60142	SPA	[1317, 207017]
60145	SE	[977939, 1127, 205027]
60146	CDR	[1128, 205 028]
60149	SE	[977940, 1131, 205031]
60150	CDR	[1132, 205032]
60151	LAV	[1133, 205033]
60500	SE	[1001, 201001]
60501	SE	[1001, 201001]
60502	SE	[1001, 201001]
60527	SE	[1013, 202001]
60528	SE	[1013, 202001]
60529	SE	[1013, 202001]
60616	SPA	[1317, 207017]
60658	EVR	[1109, 205009]
60669	SCR	[1124, 205024]
60673	CDR	[1128, 205028]
60677	CDR	[1132, 205032]
60700	SE	[1001, 201001]
60708	SE	[1012]
60709	SE	[1013, 202004]
60750	BAT	[1032, 975386]
60800	EKR	[1101, 205001]
60808	EVR	[1109, 205009]
60810	EOR	[1111, 207205]
60820	LAV	[1121, 205008]
60822	SCR	[1123, 205023]
60824	MHR	[1125, 205025]
60827	CDR	[1128, 205028]
60828	LAV	[1118, 205018]
60831	CDR	[1132, 205032]
60832	LAV	[1133, 205033]
60904	BC	[1305, 207202]
60916	SPA	[1317, 207017]
67300	EKR	[54000, 60300, 210001, 7001]

DMU Car Index

Note:- From this edition we now only list the individual vehicle numbers that do not match the last three digits of the set number e.g. 58711 - 159 107 would be included but 52402 - 156 402 would

50301	168 321	50752	175 102	50913	180 113	52803	159 102	52892	159 020
50302	168 322	50753	175 103	50914	180 114	52804	159 103	52893	159 021
50303	168 323	50754	175 104	52116	150 003	52805	159 104	52894	159 022
50304	168 324	50755	175 105	52112	150 004	52807	159 105	54901	180 101
50305	168 325	50756	175 106	52117	150 005	52808	158 889	54902	180 102
50306	168 326	50757	175 107	52147	150 006	52809	159 106	54903	180 103
50307	168 327	50758	175 108	52223	150 005	52811	159 107	54904	180 104
50308	168 328	50759	175 004	52737	158 880	52814	158 890	54905	180 105
50309	168 329	50760	175 110	52742	158 881	52873	159 001	54906	180 106
50333	172 338	50761	175 111	52743	158 882	52874	159 002	54907	180 107
50338	172 333	50762	175 112	52744	158 883	52875	159 003	54908	180 108
50421	171 201	50763	175 113	52746	158 959	52876	159 004	54909	180 109
50422	171 401	50764	175 114	52748	158 956	52877	159 005	54910	180 110
50423	171 202	50765	175 006	52751	158 951	52878	159 006	54911	180 111
50424	171 402	50766	175 116	52761	158 950	52879	159 007	54912	180 112
50701	175 001	50901	180 101	52764	158 951	52880	159 008	54913	180 113
50702	175 002	50902	180 102	52768	158 956	52881	159 009	54914	180 114
50703	175 003	50903	180 103	52771	158 957	52882	159 010	55200	150 001
50704	175 109	50904	180 104	52772	158 884	52883	159 011	55201	150 002
50705	175 005	50905	180 105	52775	158 885	52884	159 012	55300	150 001
50706	175 006	50906	180 106	52776	158 958	52885	159 013	55301	150 002
50707	175 007	50907	180 107	52778	158 959	52886	159 014	55400	150 001
50708	175 008	50908	180 108	52779	158 886	52887	159 015	55401	150 002
50709	175 009	50909	180 109	52781	158 887	52888	159 016	55404	165 029
50710	175 010	50910	180 110	52800	159 101	52889	159 017	55405	165 030
50711	175 011	50911	180 111	52801	159 108	52890	159 018	55406	165 031
50751	175 101	50912	180 112	52802	158 888	52891	159 019	55407	165 032

DMU Car Index

55408	165 033	55901	180 101	57212	150 004	58108	166 208	58256	168 106
55409	165 034	55902	180 102	57223	150 006	58109	166 209	58257	168 107
55410	165 035	55903	180 103	57737	158 880	58110	166 210	58258	168 108
55411	165 036	55904	180 104	57742	158 881	58111	166 211	58259	168 109
55412	165 037	55905	180 105	57743	158 882	58112	166 212	58260	168 110
55413	165 038	55906	180 106	57744	158 883	58113	166 213	58261	168 111
55414	165 039	55907	180 107	57746	158 958	58114	166 214	58262	168 112
55415	165 101	55908	180 108	57748	158 957	58115	166 215	58263	168 113
55416	165 102	55909	180 113	57751	158 950	58116	166 216	58264	168 214
55417	165 103	55910	180 110	57761	158 950	58117	166 217	58265	168 215
55418	165 104	55911	180 111	57764	158 951	58118	166 218	58266	168 216
55419	165 105	55912	180 112	57768	158 956	58119	166 219	58267	168 217
55420	165 106	55913	180 109	57771	158 957	58120	166 220	58268	168 218
55421	165 107	55914	180 114	57772	158 884	58121	166 221	58269	168 219
55422	165 108	56421	171 401	57775	158 885	58122	166 201	58365	168 215
55423	165 109	56422	171 401	57776	158 958	58123	166 202	58366	168 216
55424	165 110	56423	171 402	57778	158 959	58124	166 203	58367	168 217
55425	165 111	56424	171 402	57779	158 886	58125	166 204	58451	168 001
55426	165 112	56630	170 618	57781	158 887	58126	166 205	58452	168 002
55427	165 113	56631	170 619	57800	159 101	58127	166 206	58453	168 003
55428	165 114	56632	170 620	57801	159 108	58128	166 207	58454	168 004
55430	165 116	56633	170 621	57802	158 888	58129	166 208	58455	168 005
55431	165 117	56634	170 622	57803	159 102	58130	166 209	58456	168 106
55544	142 003	56635	170 623	57804	159 103	58131	166 210	58457	168 107
55548	142 007	56751	175 101	57805	159 104	58132	166 211	58458	168 108
55555	142 014	56752	175 102	57807	159 105	58133	166 212	58459	168 109
55573	142 032	56753	175 103	57808	158 889	58134	166 213	58460	168 110
55588	142 047	56754	175 104	57809	159 106	58135	166 214	58461	168 111
55594	142 003	56755	175 105	57811	159 107	58136	166 215	58462	168 112
55598	142 007	56756	175 106	57814	158 890	58137	166 216	58463	168 113
55605	142 014	56757	175 107	57873	159 001	58138	166 217	58464	168 214
55623	142 032	56758	175 108	57874	159 002	58139	166 218	58465	168 215
55638	142 047	56759	175 109	57875	159 003	58140	166 219	58466	168 216
55644	143 617	56760	175 110	57876	159 004	58141	166 220	58467	168 217
55659	143 618	56761	175 111	57877	159 005	58142	166 221	58468	168 218
55660	143 619	56762	175 112	57878	159 006	58151	168 001	58469	168 219
55683	143 617	56763	175 113	57879	159 007	58152	168 002	58601	166 201
55684	143 618	56764	175 114	57880	159 008	58153	168 003	58602	166 202
55685	143 619	56765	175 115	57881	159 009	58154	168 004	58603	166 203
55706	142 056	56766	175 116	57882	159 010	58155	168 005	58604	166 204
55728	142 078	56901	180 101	57883	159 011	58156	168 106	58605	166 205
55737	142 087	56902	180 102	57884	159 012	58157	168 107	58606	166 206
55739	142 089	56903	180 103	57885	159 013	58158	168 108	58607	166 207
55740	142 090	56904	180 104	57886	159 014	58159	168 109	58608	166 208
55752	142 056	56905	180 105	57887	159 015	58160	168 110	58609	166 209
55774	142 078	56906	180 106	57888	159 016	58161	168 111	58610	166 210
55783	142 087	56907	180 107	57889	159 017	58162	168 112	58611	166 211
55785	142 089	56908	180 108	57890	159 018	58163	168 113	58612	166 212
55786	142 090	56909	180 109	57891	159 019	58164	168 214	58613	166 213
55805	144 005	56910	spare	57892	159 020	58165	168 215	58614	166 214
55812	144 012	56911	180 111	57893	159 021	58166	168 216	58615	166 215
55815	144 015	56912	180 112	57894	159 022	58167	168 217	58616	166 216
55821	144 021	56913	180 113	58101	166 201	58168	168 218	58617	166 217
55828	144 005	56914	180 114	58102	166 202	58169	168 219	58618	166 218
55835	144 012	57116	150 003	58103	166 203	58251	168 001	58619	166 219
55838	144 015	57112	150 004	58104	166 204	58252	168 002	58620	166 220
55844	144 021	57117	150 005	58105	166 205	58253	168 003	58621	166 221
55851	144 015	57147	150 006	58106	166 206	58254	168 004	58651	168 001
55857	144 021	57209	150 003	58107	166 207	58255	168 005	58652	168 002

DMU Car Index

58653	168 003	58816	165 016	58875	165 025	58952	165 137	60165	222 005
58654	168 004	58817	165 017	58876	165 026	58953	165 101	60166	222 006
58655	168 005	58818	165 018	58877	165 027	58954	165 102	60167	222 007
58701	159 108	58819	165 019	58878	165 028	58955	165 103	60168	222 008
58702	158 755	58820	165 020	58879	165 118	58956	165 104	60169	222 009
58703	159 102	58821	165 021	58880	165 119	58957	165 105	60170	222 010
58704	159 103	58822	165 022	58881	165 120	58958	165 106	60171	222 011
58705	159 104	58823	165 029	58882	165 121	58959	165 107	60172	222 012
58706	158 757	58824	165 030	58883	165 122	58960	165 108	60173	222 013
58707	159 105	58825	165 031	58884	165 123	58961	165 109	60174	222 014
58708	158 754	58826	165 032	58885	165 124	58962	165 110	60175	222 015
58709	159 106	58827	165 033	58886	165 125	58963	165 111	60176	222 016
58710	158 753	58828	165 034	58887	165 126	58964	165 112	60177	222 017
58711	159 107	58829	165 035	58888	165 127	58965	165 113	60178	222 018
58712	158 756	58830	165 036	58889	165 128	58966	165 114	60179	222 019
58713	158 759	58831	165 037	58890	165 129	58968	165 116	60180	222 020
58714	158 758	58832	165 038	58891	165 130	58969	165 117	60181	222 021
58715	158 798	58833	165 039	58892	165 131	59111	172 101	60182	222 022
58716	158 752	58834	165 001	58893	165 132	59112	172 102	60183	222 023
58717	159 101	58835	165 002	58894	165 133	59113	172 103	60191	222 101
58718	159 001	58836	165 003	58895	165 134	59114	172 104	60192	222 102
58719	159 002	58837	165 004	58896	165 135	59211	172 101	60193	222 103
58720	159 003	58838	165 005	58897	165 136	59212	172 102	60194	222 104
58721	159 004	58839	165 006	58898	165 137	59213	172 103	60201	220 001
58722	159 005	58840	165 007	58916	165 101	59214	172 104	60202	220 002
58723	159 006	58841	165 008	58917	165 102	59311	172 001	60203	220 003
58724	159 007	58842	165 009	58918	165 103	59312	172 002	60204	220 004
58725	159 008	58843	165 010	58919	165 104	59313	172 003	60205	220 005
58726	159 009	58844	165 011	58920	165 105	59314	172 004	60206	220 006
58727	159 010	58845	165 012	58921	165 106	59315	172 005	60207	220 007
58728	159 011	58846	165 013	58922	165 107	59316	172 006	60208	220 008
58729	159 012	58847	165 014	58923	165 108	59317	172 007	60209	220 009
58730	159 013	58848	165 015	58924	165 109	59318	172 008	60210	220 010
58731	159 014	58849	165 016	58925	165 110	59411	172 001	60211	220 011
58732	159 015	58850	165 017	58926	165 111	59412	172 002	60212	220 012
58733	159 016	58851	165 018	58927	165 112	59413	172 003	60213	220 013
58734	159 017	58852	165 019	58928	165 113	59414	172 004	60214	220 014
58735	159 018	58853	165 020	58929	165 114	59415	172 005	60215	220 015
58736	159 019	58854	165 021	58931	165 116	59416	172 006	60216	220 016
58737	159 020	58855	165 022	58932	165 117	59417	172 007	60217	220 017
58738	159 021	58856	165 029	58933	165 118	59418	172 008	60218	220 018
58739	159 022	58857	165 030	58934	165 119	59901	180 101	60219	220 019
58756	168 106	58858	165 031	58935	165 120	59902	180 102	60220	220 020
58757	168 107	58859	165 032	58936	165 121	59903	180 103	60221	220 021
58801	165 001	58860	165 033	58937	165 122	59904	180 104	60222	220 022
58802	165 002	58861	165 034	58938	165 123	59905	180 105	60223	220 023
58803	165 003	58862	165 035	58939	165 124	59906	180 106	60224	220 024
58804	165 004	58863	165 036	58940	165 125	59907	180 107	60225	220 025
58805	165 005	58864	165 037	58941	165 126	59908	180 108	60226	220 026
58806	165 006	58865	165 038	58942	165 127	59909	180 109	60227	220 027
58807	165 007	58866	165 039	58943	165 128	59910	180 110	60228	220 028
58808	165 008	58867	165 023	58944	165 129	59911	180 111	60229	220 029
58809	165 009	58868	165 024	58945	165 130	59912	180 112	60230	220 030
58810	165 010	58869	165 025	58946	165 131	59913	180 113	60231	220 031
58811	165 011	58870	165 026	58947	165 132	59914	180 114	60232	220 032
58812	165 012	58871	165 027	58948	165 133	60161	222 001	60233	220 033
58813	165 013	58872	165 028	58949	165 134	60162	222 002	60234	220 034
58814	165 014	58873	165 023	58950	165 135	60163	222 003	60241	222 001
58815	165 015	58874	165 024	58951	165 136	60164	222 004	60242	222 002

DMU Car Index

60243	222 003	60341	222 001	60409	220 009	60477	221 127	60630	222 010
60244	222 004	60342	222 002	60410	220 010	60478	221 128	60631	222 011
60245	222 005	60343	222 003	60411	220 011	60479	221 129	60632	222 012
60246	222 006	60344	222 004	60412	220 012	60480	221 130	60633	222 013
60247	222 007	60345	222 004	60413	220 013	60481	221 131	60634	222 014
60248	222 008	60346	222 002	60414	220 014	60482	221 132	60635	222 015
60249	222 009	60347	222 005	60415	220 015	60483	221 133	60636	222 016
60250	222 010	60351	221 101	60416	220 016	60484	221 134	60637	222 017
60251	222 011	60352	221 102	60417	220 017	60485	221 135	60638	222 018
60252	222 012	60353	221 103	60418	220 018	60486	221 136	60639	222 019
60253	222 013	60354	221 104	60419	220 019	60487	221 137	60640	222 020
60254	222 014	60355	221 105	60420	220 020	60488	221 138	60641	222 021
60255	222 015	60356	221 106	60421	220 021	60489	221 139	60642	222 022
60256	222 016	60357	221 107	60422	220 022	60490	221 140	60643	222 023
60257	222 017	60358	221 108	60423	220 023	60491	221 141	60681	222 101
60258	222 018	60359	221 109	60424	220 024	60492	221 142	60682	222 102
60259	222 019	60360	221 110	60425	220 025	60493	221 143	60683	222 103
60260	222 020	60361	221 111	60426	220 026	60494	221 144	60684	222 104
60261	222 021	60362	221 112	60427	220 027	60531	222 011	60701	220 001
60262	222 022	60363	221 113	60428	220 028	60532	222 012	60702	220 002
60263	222 023	60364	221 114	60429	220 029	60533	222 013	60703	220 003
60271	222 101	60365	221 115	60430	220 030	60534	222 014	60704	220 004
60272	222 102	60366	221 116	60431	220 031	60535	222 015	60705	220 005
60273	222 103	60367	221 117	60432	220 032	60536	222 016	60706	220 006
60274	222 104	60368	221 118	60433	220 033	60537	222 017	60707	220 007
60301	220 001	60369	221 119	60434	220 034	60541	222 023	60708	220 008
60302	220 002	60370	221 120	60441	222 006	60542	222 022	60709	220 009
60303	220 003	60371	221 121	60442	222 007	60543	222 020	60710	220 010
60304	220 004	60372	221 122	60443	222 005	60544	222 002	60711	220 011
60305	220 005	60373	221 123	60444	222 018	60545	222 008	60712	220 012
60306	220 006	60374	221 124	60445	222 001	60546	222 010	60713	220 013
60307	220 007	60375	221 125	60446	222 003	60547	222 019	60714	220 014
60308	220 008	60376	221 126	60447	222 006	60551	222 001	60715	220 015
60309	220 009	60377	221 127	60451	221 101	60552	222 021	60716	220 016
60310	220 010	60378	221 128	60452	221 102	60553	222 003	60717	220 017
60311	220 011	60379	221 129	60453	221 103	60554	222 004	60718	220 018
60312	220 012	60380	221 130	60454	221 104	60555	222 005	60719	220 019
60313	220 013	60381	221 131	60455	221 105	60556	222 006	60720	220 020
60314	220 014	60382	221 132	60456	221 106	60557	222 009	60721	220 021
60315	220 015	60383	221 133	60457	221 107	60561	222 001	60722	220 022
60316	220 016	60384	221 134	60458	221 108	60562	222 002	60723	220 023
60317	220 017	60385	221 135	60459	221 109	60563	222 003	60724	220 024
60318	220 018	60386	221 136	60460	221 110	60564	222 004	60725	220 025
60319	220 019	60387	221 137	60461	221 111	60565	222 005	60726	220 026
60320	220 020	60388	221 138	60462	221 112	60566	222 006	60727	220 027
60321	220 021	60389	221 139	60463	221 113	60567	222 007	60728	220 028
60322	220 022	60390	221 140	60464	221 114	60571	222 101	60729	220 029
60323	220 023	60391	221 141	60465	221 115	60572	222 102	60730	220 030
60324	220 024	60392	221 142	60466	221 116	60573	222 103	60731	220 031
60325	220 025	60393	221 143	60467	221 117	60574	222 104	60732	220 032
60326	220 026	60394	221 144	60468	221 118	60621	222 001	60733	220 033
60327	220 027	60401	220 001	60469	221 119	60622	222 002	60734	220 034
60328	220 028	60402	220 002	60470	221 120	60623	222 003	60751	221 101
60329	220 029	60403	220 003	60471	221 121	60624	222 004	60752	221 102
60330	220 030	60404	220 004	60472	221 122	60625	222 005	60753	221 103
60331	220 031	60405	220 005	60473	221 123	60626	222 006	60754	221 104
60332	220 032	60406	220 006	60474	221 124	60627	222 007	60755	221 105
60333	220 033	60407	220 007	60475	221 125	60628	222 008	60756	221 106
60334	220 034	60408	220 008	60476	221 126	60629	222 009	60757	221 107

DMU Car Index

60758	221 108	60794	221 144	60886	221 136	60966	221 116	79307	168 327
60759	221 109	60851	221 101	60887	221 137	60967	221 117	79308	168 328
60760	221 110	60852	221 102	60888	221 138	60968	221 118	79392	171 730
60761	221 111	60853	221 103	60889	221 139	60969	221 119	79399	168 329
60762	221 112	60854	221 104	60890	221 140	60970	221 120	79421	171 201
60763	221 113	60855	221 105	60918	222 008	60971	221 121	79422	171 401
60764	221 114	60856	221 106	60919	222 009	60972	221 122	79423	171 202
60765	221 115	60857	221 107	60920	222 010	60973	221 123	79424	171 402
60766	221 116	60858	221 108	60921	222 011	60974	221 124	79701	175 001
60767	221 117	60859	221 109	60922	222 012	60975	221 125	79702	175 002
60768	221 118	60860	221 110	60923	222 013	60976	221 126	79703	175 003
60769	221 119	60861	221 111	60924	222 014	60977	221 127	79704	175 101
60770	221 120	60862	221 112	60925	222 015	60978	221 128	79705	175 109
60771	221 121	60863	221 113	60926	222 016	60979	221 129	79706	175 115
60772	221 122	60864	221 114	60927	222 017	60980	221 130	79707	175 007
60773	221 123	60865	221 115	60928	222 018	60981	221 131	79708	175 008
60774	221 124	60866	221 116	60929	222 019	60982	221 132	79709	175 006
60775	221 125	60867	221 117	60930	222 020	60983	221 133	79710	175 010
60776	221 126	60868	221 118	60931	222 021	60984	221 134	79711	175 011
60777	221 127	60869	221 119	60932	222 022	60985	221 135	79751	175 005
60778	221 128	60870	221 120	60933	222 023	60986	221 142	79752	175 102
60779	221 129	60871	221 121	60951	221 101	60987	221 137	79753	175 103
60780	221 130	60872	221 122	60952	221 102	60988	221 138	79754	175 104
60781	221 131	60873	221 123	60953	221 103	60989	221 139	79755	175 105
60782	221 132	60874	221 124	60954	221 104	60990	221 144	79756	175 106
60783	221 133	60875	221 125	60955	221 105	60991	221 141	79757	175 107
60784	221 134	60876	221 126	60956	221 106	60992	221 142	79758	175 108
60785	221 135	60877	221 127	60957	221 107	60993	221 143	79759	175 004
60786	221 136	60878	221 128	60958	221 108	60994	221 143	79760	175 110
60787	221 137	60879	221 129	60959	221 109	79301	168 321	79761	175 111
60788	221 138	60880	221 130	60960	221 110	79302	168 322	79762	175 112
60789	221 139	60881	221 131	60961	221 111	79303	168 323	79763	175 113
60790	221 140	60882	221 132	60962	221 112	79304	168 324	79764	175 114
60791	221 141	60883	221 133	60963	221 113	79305	168 325	79765	175 115
60792	221 142	60884	221 134	60964	221 114	79306	168 326	79766	175 116
60793	221 143	60885	221 135	60965	221 115				

Bi Modal & Electric Multiple Units

Class 313 (Dual)

313 201	BI	62529	71213	62593		313 211	BI	62539	71223	62603
313 202	BI	62530	71214	62594		313 212	BI	62540	71224	62604
313 203	BI	62531	71215	62595		313 213	BI	62541	71225	62605
313 204	BI	62532	71216	62596		313 214	BI	62542	71226	62606
313 205	BI	62533	71217	62597		313 215	BI	62543	71227	62607
313 206	BI	62534	71218	62598		313 216	BI	62544	71228	62608
313 207	BI	62535	71219	62599		313 217	BI	62545	71229	62609
313 208	BI	62536	71220	62600		313 219	BI	62547	71231	62611
313 209	BI	62537	71221	62601		313 220	BI	62548	71232	62612
313 210	BI	62538	71222	62602						

Class 315 (OH)

315 819	IL	64497	71299	71407	64498	315 847	IL	64553	71327	71435	64554
315 820	IL	64499	71300	71408	64500	315 848	IL	64539	71328	71436	64556
315 837	IL	64533	71317	71425	64534	315 853	IL	64565	71333	71441	64566
315 838	IL	64535	71318	71426	64536	315 854	IL	64567	71334	71442	64568
315 839	IL	64537	71319	71427	64538	315 856	IL	64571	71336	71444	64572
315 844	IL	64547	71324	71432	64548	315 857	IL	64573	71337	71445	64574

Class 317 (OH)

317 337	IL	77036	62697	71613	77084	317 511	IL	77014	62674	71591	77062
317 338	IL	77037	62698	71614	77085	317 512	IL	77015	62675	71592	77050
317 339	IL	77038	62699	71615	77086	317 513	IL	77016	62677	71593	77064
317 340	IL	77039	62700	71616	77087	317 515	IL	77019	62680	71596	77067
317 341	IL	77040	62701	71617	77088	317 708	EY(s)	77007	62668	71584	77055
317 342	IL	77041	62702	71618	77089	317 709	EY(s)	77008	62669	71585	77056
317 343	IL	77042	62703	71619	77090	317 710	EY(s)	77009	62670	71586	77057
317 344	IL	77029	62690	71620	77091	317 714	EY(s)	77013	62673	71590	77061
317 345	EY(s)	77044	62705			317 719	EY(s)	77018	62679	71595	77066
317 347	IL	77046	62707	71623	77094	317 723	EY(s)	77022	62683	71599	77070
317 348	IL	77047	62708	71624	77095	317 729	EY(s)	77028	62689	71605	77076
317 501	IL	77024	62661	71577	77048	317 732	EY(s)	77031	62692	71608	77079
317 502	IL	77001	62662	71578	77049	317 881	IL	77020	62681	71597	77068
317 504	IL	77003	62664	71580	77051	317 882	IL	77023	62684	71600	77071
317 506	IL	77005	62666	71582	77053	317 883	IL	77000	62685	71601	77072
317 507	IL	77006	62667	71583	77054	317 884	IL	77025	62686	71602	77073
317 508	IL	77010	62697	71587	77058	317 885	IL	77026	62687	71603	77074
317 509	EY(s)	77011	62671	71588	77059	317 886	IL	77027	62688	71604	77075
317 510	IL	77012	62672	71589	77060	317 892	EY(s)	77035	62696	71612	77083

Named Units

317 348	Richard A Jenner	317 507	University of Cambridge 800 Years 1209-2009

Class 318 (OH)

318 250	GW	77260	62866	77240	318 261	GW	77271	62877	77251
318 251	GW	77261	62867	77241	318 262	GW	77272	62878	77252
318 252	GW	77262	62868	77242	318 263	GW	77273	62879	77253
318 253	GW	77263	62869	77243	318 264	GW	77274	62880	77254
318 254	GW	77264	62870	77244	318 265	GW	77275	62881	77255
318 255	GW	77265	62871	77245	318 266	GW	77276	62882	77256
318 256	GW	77266	62872	77246	318 267	GW	77277	62883	77257
318 257	GW	77267	62873	77247	318 268	GW	77278	62884	77258
318 258	GW	77268	62874	77248	318 269	GW	77279	62885	77259
318 259	GW	77269	62875	77249	318 270	GW	77289	62890	77288
318 260	GW	77270	62876	77250					

Class 319 (Dual)

319 005	NN	77299	62895	71776	77298	319 371	LM(s)	77479	63053	71939	77478
319 011	ZG(s)	77311	62901	71782	77310	319 372	AN	77481	63054	71940	77480
319 012	NN	77313	62902	71783	77312	319 373	HQ	77483	63055	71941	77482
319 013	NN	77315	62903	71784	77314	319 374	LM(s)	77485	63056	71942	77484
319 214	NN	77317	62904	71785	77316	319 375	AN	77487	63057	71943	77486
319 215	NN	77319	62905	71786	77318	319 376	LM(s)	77489	63058	71944	77488
319 216	NN	77321	62906	71787	77320	319 377	ZG(s)	77491	63059	71945	77490
319 217	NN	77323	62907	71788	77322	319 378	AN	77493	63060	71946	77492
319 218	NN	77325	62908	71789	77324	319 379	AN	77495	63061	71947	77494
319 219	NN	77327	62909	71790	77326	319 380	ZG(s)	77497	63062	71948	77496
319 220	NN	77329	62910	71791	77328	319 381	AN	77973	63093	71979	77974
319 361	AN	77459	63043	71929	77458	319 383	AN	77977	63095	71981	77978
319 362	LM(s)	77461	63044	71930	77460	319 384	AN	77979	63096	71982	77980
319 363	LM(s)	77463	63045	71931	77462	319 385	AN	77981	63097	71983	77982
319 364	HQ(s)	77465	63046	71932	77464	319 386	AN	77983	63098	71984	77984
319 365	LM(s)	77467	63047	71933	77466	319 429	NN	77347	62919	71800	77346
319 366	AN	77469	63048	71934	77468	319 433	NN	77355	62923	71804	77354
319 367	AN	77471	63049	71935	77470	319 441	HQ(s)	77371	62931	71812	77370
319 368	AN	77473	63050	71936	77472	319 454	LM(s)	77445	62968	71873	77444
319 369	AN	77475	63051	71937	77474	319 457	NN	77451	62971	71876	77450
319 370	AN	77477	63052	71938	77476	319 460	NN	77457	62974	71879	77456

Class 320 (OH)

320 301	GW	77899	63021	77921	320 318	GW	77916	63038	77938
320 302	GW	77900	63022	77922	320 319	GW	77917	63039	77939
320 303	GW	77901	63023	77923	320 320	GW	77918	63040	77940
320 304	GW	77902	63024	77924	320 321	GW	77919	63041	77941
320 305	GW	77903	63025	77925	320 322	GW	77920	63042	77942
320 306	GW	77904	63026	77926	320 401	GW	78095	63063	77943
320 307	GW	77905	63027	77927	320 403	GW	78097	63065	77945
320 308	GW	77906	63028	77928	320 404	GW	78098	63066	77946
320 309	GW	77907	63029	77929	320 411	GW	78105	63073	77953
320 310	GW	77908	63030	77930	320 412	GW	78106	63074	77954
320 311	GW	77909	63031	77931	320 413	GW	78107	63075	77955
320 312	GW	77910	63032	77932	320 414	GW	78108	63076	77956
320 313	GW	77911	63033	77933	320 415	GW	78109	63077	77957
320 314	GW	77912	63034	77934	320 416	GW	78110	63078	77958
320 315	GW	77913	63035	77935	320 417	GW	78111	63079	77959
320 316	GW	77914	63036	77936	320 418	GW	78112	63080	77960
320 317	GW	77915	63037	77937	320 420	GW	78114	63082	77962

Class 321 (OH)

321 301	IL	78049	62975	71880	77853	321 339	IL	78087	63013	71918	77891
321 302	IL	78050	62976	71881	77854	321 340	IL	78088	63014	71919	77892
321 303	IL	78051	62977	71882	77855	321 341	IL	78089	63015	71920	77893
321 304	IL	78052	62978	71883	77856	321 342	IL	78090	63016	71921	77894
321 305	IL	78053	62979	71884	77857	321 343	IL	78091	63017	71922	77895
321 306	IL	78054	62980	71885	77858	321 365	ZB(s)	78149	63123	72009	78298
321 307	IL	78055	62981	71886	77859	321 402	HQ(s)	78096	63064	71950	77944
321 308	IL	78056	62982	71887	77860	321 405	HQ(s)	78099	63067	71953	77947
321 309	IL	78057	62983	71888	77861	321 406	IL	78100	63068	71954	77948
321 310	IL	78058	62984	71889	77862	321 407	ZN(s)	78101	63069	71955	77949
321 311	IL	78059	62985	71890	77863	321 408	HQ(s)	78102	63070	71956	77950
321 312	IL	78060	62986	71891	77864	321 409	IL	78103	63071	71957	77951
321 313	IL	78061	62987	71892	77865	321 410	IL	78104	63072	71958	77952
321 314	IL	78062	62988	71893	77866	321 419	ZN(s)	78113	63081	71967	77961
321 315	IL	78063	62989	71894	77867	321 421	IL	78115	63083	71969	77963
321 316	IL	78064	62990	71895	77868	321 423	IL	78117	63085	71971	77965
321 317	IL	78065	62991	71896	77869	321 424	IL	78118	63086	71972	77966
321 318	IL	78066	62992	71897	77870	321 426	IL	78120	63088	71974	77968
321 319	IL	78067	62993	71898	77871	321 427	IL	78121	63089	71975	77969
321 320	IL	78068	62994	71899	77872	321 428	ZN(s)	78122	63090	71976	77970
321 321	IL	78069	62995	71900	77873	321 429	ZN(s)	78123	63091	71977	77971
321 322	IL	78070	62996	71901	77874	321 430	HQ(s)	78124	63092	71978	77972
321 323	IL	78071	62997	71902	77875	321 431	HQ(s)	78151	63125	72011	78300
321 324	IL	78072	62998	71903	77876	321 432	WP(s)	78152	63126	72012	78301
321 325	IL	78073	62999	71904	77877	321 433	IL	78153	63127	72013	78302
321 326	IL	78074	63000	71905	77878	321 434	IL	78154	63128	72014	78303
321 327	IL	78075	63001	71906	77879	321 436	IL	78156	63130	72016	78305
321 328	IL	78076	63002	71907	77880	321 439	HQ(s)	78159	63133	72019	78308
321 329	IL	78077	63003	71908	77881	321 440	IL	78160	63134	72020	78309
321 330	IL	78078	63004	71909	77882	321 441	IL	78161	63135	72021	78310
321 331	IL	78079	63005	71910	77883	321 443	HQ(s)	78125	63099	71985	78274
321 332	WP(s)	78080	63006	71911	77884	321 444	HQ(s)	78126	63100	71986	78275
321 333	IL	78081	63007	71912	77885	321 445	HQ(s)	78127	63101	71987	78276
321 334	HQ	78082	63008	71913	77886	321 447	IL	78129	63103	71989	78278
321 335	IL	78083	63009	71914	77887	321 901	IL	77990	63153	72128	77993
321 336	IL	78084	63010	71915	77888	321 902	IL	77991	63154	72129	77994
321 337	IL	78085	63011	71916	77889	321 903	IL	77992	63155	72130	77995
321 338	IL	78086	63012	71917	77890						

Named Units		
321 336	Geoffrey Freeman Allen	
321 342	R. Barnes	
321 343	RSA - Railway Study Association	
321 428	The Essex Commuter	
321 444	Essex Lifeboats	

Class 322 (OH)

322 481	IL	77985	72023	63137	78163	322 484	IL	77988	72026	63140	78166
322 482	IL	77986	72024	63138	78164	322 485	IL	77989	72027	63141	78167
322 483	IL	77987	72025	63139	78165						

Class 323 (OH)

323 201	SI	64001	72201	65001		323 223	AN		64023	72223	65023
323 202	SI	64002	72202	65002		323 224	AN		64024	72224	65024
323 203	SI	64003	72203	65003		323 225	AN		64025	72225	65025
323 204	SI	64004	72204	65004		323 226	AN		64026	72226	65026
323 205	SI	64005	72205	65005		323 227	AN		64027	72227	65027
323 206	SI	64006	72206	65006		323 228	AN		64028	72228	65028
323 207	SI	64007	72207	65007		323 229	AN		64029	72229	65029
323 208	SI	64008	72208	65008		323 230	AN		64030	72230	65030
323 209	SI	64009	72209	65009		323 231	AN		64031	72231	65031
323 210	SI	64010	72210	65010		323 232	AN		64032	72232	65032
323 211	SI	64011	72211	65011		323 233	AN		64033	72233	65033
323 212	SI	64012	72212	65012		323 234	AN		64034	72234	65034
323 213	SI	64013	72213	65013		323 235	AN		64035	72235	65035
323 214	SI	64014	72214	65014		323 236	AN		64036	72236	65036
323 215	SI	64015	72215	65015		323 237	AN		64037	72237	65037
323 216	SI	64016	72216	65016		323 238	AN		64038	72238	65038
323 217	SI	64017	72217	65017		323 239	AN		64039	72239	65039
323 218	SI	64018	72218	65018		323 240	SI		64040	72340	65040
323 219	SI	64019	72219	65019		323 241	SI		64041	72341	65041
323 220	SI	64020	72220	65020		323 242	SI		64042	72342	65042
323 221	SI	64021	72221	65021		323 243	SI		64043	72343	65043
323 222	SI	64022	72222	65022							

Named Unit

323 241   Dave Pomroy 323 Fleet Engineer 40 Years Service

Class 325 (OH)

325 001	CE	68300	68340	68360	68301	325 009	CE	68316	68349	68368	68317
325 002	CE	68302	68341	68361	68303	325 011	CE	68320	68350	68370	68321
325 003	CE	68304	68342	68362	68305	325 012	CE	68322	68351	68371	68323
325 004	CE	68306	68343	68363	68307	325 013	CE	68324	68352	68372	68325
325 005	CE	68308	68344	68364	68309	325 014	CE	68326	68353	68373	68327
325 006	CE	68310	68345	68365	68311	325 015	CE	68328	68354	68374	68329
325 007	CE	68312	68346	68366	68313	325 016	CE	68330	68355	68375	68331
325 008	CE	68314	68347	68367	68315						

Named Unit

325 008   Peter Howarth CBE

Class 326 (Orion Rail conversion from class 319)

326 001	326 003	326 005	326 007	326 009
326 002	326 004	326 006	326 008	326 010

Class 331 (OH) — Northern

Unit	Op					Unit	Op				
331 001	AN	463001	464001		466001	331 023	AN	463023	464023		466023
331 002	AN	463002	464002		466002	331 024	AN	463024	464024		466024
331 003	AN	463003	464003		466003	331 025	AN	463025	464025		466025
331 004	AN	463004	464004		466004	331 026	AN	463026	464026		466026
331 005	AN	463005	464005		466005	331 027	AN	463027	464027		466027
331 006	AN	463006	464006		466006	331 028	AN	463028	464028		466028
331 007	AN	463007	464007		466007	331 029	AN	463029	464029		466029
331 008	AN	463008	464008		466008	331 030	AN	463030	464030		466030
331 009	AN	463009	464009		466009	331 031	AN	463031	464031		466031
331 010	AN	463010	464010		466010	331 101	NL	463101	464101	465101	466101
331 011	AN	463011	464011		466011	331 102	NL	463102	464102	465102	466102
331 012	AN	463012	464012		466012	331 103	NL	463103	464103	465103	466103
331 013	AN	463013	464013		466013	331 104	NL	463104	464104	465104	466104
331 014	AN	463014	464014		466014	331 105	NL	463105	464105	465105	466105
331 015	AN	463015	464015		466015	331 106	NL	463106	464106	465106	466106
331 016	AN	463016	464016		466016	331 107	NL	463107	464107	465107	466107
331 017	AN	463017	464017		466017	331 108	NL	463108	464108	465108	466108
331 018	AN	463018	464018		466018	331 109	NL	463109	464109	465109	466109
331 019	AN	463019	464019		466019	331 110	NL	463110	464110	465110	466110
331 020	AN	463020	464020		466020	331 111	NL	463111	464111	465111	466111
331 021	AN	463021	464021		466021	331 112	NL	463112	464112	465112	466112
331 022	AN	463022	464022		466022						

Named Units

331 106	Proud to be Northern		331 110	Proud to be Northern

Class 333 (OH)

Unit	Op					Unit	Op				
333 001	NL	78451	74461	74477	78452	333 009	NL	78467	74469	74485	78468
333 002	NL	78453	74462	74478	78454	333 010	NL	78469	74470	74486	78470
333 003	NL	78455	74463	74479	78456	333 011	NL	78471	74471	74487	78472
333 004	NL	78457	74464	74480	78458	333 012	NL	78473	74472	74488	78474
333 005	NL	78459	74465	74481	78460	333 013	NL	78475	74473	74489	78476
333 006	NL	78461	74466	74482	78462	333 014	NL	78477	74474	74490	78478
333 007	NL	78463	74467	74483	78464	333 015	NL	78479	74475	74491	78480
333 008	NL	78465	74468	74484	78466	333 016	NL	78481	74476	74492	78482

Class 334 (OH) — Juniper

Unit	Op				Unit	Op			
334 001	GW	64101	74301	65101	334 021	GW	64121	74321	65121
334 002	GW	64102	74302	65102	334 022	GW	64122	74322	65122
334 003	GW	64103	74303	65103	334 023	GW	64123	74323	65123
334 004	GW	64104	74304	65104	334 024	GW	64124	74324	65124
334 005	GW	64105	74305	65105	334 025	GW	64125	74325	65125
334 006	GW	64106	74306	65106	334 026	GW	64126	74326	65126
334 007	GW	64107	74307	65107	334 027	GW	64127	74327	65127
334 008	GW	64108	74308	65108	334 028	GW	64128	74328	65128
334 009	GW	64109	74309	65109	334 029	GW	64129	74329	65129
334 010	GW	64110	74310	65110	334 030	GW	64130	74330	65130
334 011	GW	64111	74311	65111	334 031	GW	64131	74331	65131
334 012	GW	64112	74312	65112	334 032	GW	64132	74332	65132
334 013	GW	64113	74313	65113	334 033	GW	64133	74333	65133
334 014	GW	64114	74314	65114	334 034	GW	64134	74334	65134
334 015	GW	64115	74315	65115	334 035	GW	64135	74335	65135
334 016	GW	64116	74316	65116	334 036	GW	64136	74336	65136
334 017	GW	64117	74317	65117	334 037	GW	64137	74337	65137
334 018	GW	64118	74318	65118	334 038	GW	64138	74338	65138
334 019	GW	64119	74319	65119	334 039	GW	64139	74339	65139
334 020	GW	64120	74320	65120	334 040	GW	64140	74340	65140

Class 345(OH)		Aventra				*on test		

Note: + Individual coaches stored

345 001	OC	340101	340201	340301	340401	340501 340601	340701	340801	340901
345 002	OC	340102	340202	340302	340402	340502 340602	340702	340802	340902
345 003	IL	340103	340203	340303		340503	340703	340803	340903
345 004	OC	340104	340204	340304	340404	340504 340604	340704	340804	340904
345 005	IL	340105	340205	340305		340505	340705	340805	340905
345 006	IL	340106	340206	340306		340506	340706	340806	340906
345 007	IL	340107	340207	340307		340507	340707	340807	340907
345 008	IL	340108	340208	340308	340408	340508 340608	340708	340808	340908
345 009	IL	340109	340209	340309		340509	340709	340809	340909
345 010	OC	340110	340210	340310	340410	340510 340610	340710	340810	340910
345 011	IL	340111	340211	340311		340511	340711	340811	340911
345 012	IL	340112	340212	340312		340512	340712	340812	340912
345 013	IL	340113	340213	340313		340513	340713	340813	340913
345 014	IL	340114	340214	340314		340514	340714	340814	340914
345 015	IL	340115	340215	340315		340515	340715	340815	340915
345 016	IL	340116	340216	340316		340516	340716	340816	340916
345 017	IL	340117	340217	340317		340517	340717	340817	340917
345 018*		340118	340218	340318	340418	340518 340618	340718	340818	340918
345 019*		340119	340219	340319	340419	340519 340619	340719	340819	340919
345 020	OC	340120	340220	340320	340420	340520 340620	340720	340820	340920
345 021	OC	340121	340221	340321	340421	340521 340621	340721	340821	340921
345 022	IL	340122	340222	340322		340522	340722	340822	340922
345 023	OC	340123	340223	340323	340423	340523 340623	340723	340823	340923
345 024	OC	340124	340224	340324	340424	340524 340624	340724	340824	340924
345 025	OC	340125	340225	340325	340425	340525 340625	340725	340825	340925
345 026	OC	340126	340226	340326	340426	340526 340626	340726	340826	340926
345 027	OC	340127	340227	340327	340427	340527 340627	340727	340827	340927
345 028	OC	340128	340228	340328	340428	340528 340628	340728	340828	340928
345 029	OC	340129	340229	340329	340429	340529 340629	340729	340829	340929
345 030	OC	340130	340230	340330	340430	340530 340630	340730	340830	340930
345 031	OC	340131	340231	340331	340431	340531 340631	340731	340831	340931
345 032*		340132	340232	340332	340432	340532 340632	340732	340832	340932
345 033	OC	340133	340233	340333	340433	340533 340633	340733	340833	340933
345 034	OC	340134	340234	340334	340434	340534 340634	340734	340834	340934
345 035	OC	340135	340235	340335	340435	340535 340635	340735	340835	340935
345 036	OC	340136	340236	340336	340436	340536 340636	340736	340836	340936
345 037	OC	340137	340237	340337	340437	340537 340637	340737	340837	340937
345 038	IL	340138	340238	340338	340438+	340538 340638+	340738	340838	340938
345 039	OC	340139	340239	340339	340439	340539 340639	340739	340839	340939
345 040	OC	340140	340240	340340	340440	340540 340640	340740	340840	340940
345 041*		340141	340241	340341	340441	340541 340641	340741	340841	340941
345 042	IL	340142	340242	340342	340442+	340542 340642+	340742	340842	340942
345 043	OC	340143	340243	340343	340443	340543 340643	340743	340843	340943
345 044	OC	340144	340244	340344	340444	340544 340644	340744	340844	340944
345 045	OC	340145	340245	340345	340445	340545 340645	340745	340845	340945
345 046	OC	340146	340246	340346	340446	340546 340646	340746	340846	340946
345 047	OC	340147	340247	340347	340447	340547 340647	340747	340847	340947
345 048	OC	340148	340248	340348	340448	340548 340648	340748	340848	340948
345 049	OC	340149	340249	340349	340449	340549 340649	340749	340849	340949
345 050*		340150	340250	340350	340450	340550 340650	340750	340850	340950
345 051	OC	340151	340251	340351	340451	340551 340651	340751	340851	340951
345 052	OC	340152	340252	340352	340452	340552 340652	340752	340852	340952
345 053	OC	340153	340253	340353	340453	340553 340653	340753	340853	340953
345 054	OC	340154	340254	340354	340454	340554 340654	340754	340854	340954
345 055	OC	340155	340255	340355	340455	340555 340655	340755	340855	340955

Class 345(OH) — Aventra

345 056	IL	340156	340256	340356	340456+	340556	340656+	340756	340856	340956
345 057	OC	340157	340257	340357	340457	340557	340657	340757	340857	340957
345 058	OC	340158	340258	340358	340458	340558	340658	340758	340858	340958
345 059	OC	340159	340259	340359	340459	340559	340659	340759	340859	340959
345 060	OC	340160	340260	340360	340460	340560	340660	340760	340860	340960
345 061	OC	340161	340261	340361	340461	340561	340661	340761	340861	340961
345 062	OC	340162	340262	340362	340462	340562	340662	340762	340862	340962
345 063	OC	340163	340263	340363	340463	340563	340663	340763	340863	340963
345 064	IL	340164	340264	340364	340464+	340564	340664+	340764	340864	340964
345 065	OC	340165	340265	340365	340465	340565	340665	340765	340865	340965
345 066	OC	340166	340266	340366	340466	340566	340666	340766	340866	340966
345 067*		340167	340267	340367	340467	340567	340667	340767	340867	340967
345 068	OC	340168	340268	340368	340468	340568	340668	340768	340868	340968
345 069*		340169	340269	340369	340469	340569	340669	340769	340869	340969
345 070	OC	340170	340270	340370	340470	340570	340670	340770	340870	340970

Class 350 (OH) — Desiro

350 101	NN	63711	66861	66811	63761
350 102	NN	63712	66862	66812	63762
350 103	NN	63713	66863	66813	63765
350 104	NN	63714	66864	66814	63764
350 105	NN	63715	66868	66815	63763
350 106	NN	63716	66866	66816	63766
350 107	NN	63717	66867	66817	63767
350 108	NN	63718	66865	66818	63768
350 109	NN	63719	66869	66819	63769
350 110	NN	63720	66870	66820	63770
350 111	NN	63721	66871	66821	63771
350 112	NN	63722	66872	66822	63772
350 113	NN	63723	66873	66823	63773
350 114	NN	63724	66874	66824	63774
350 115	NN	63725	66875	66825	63775
350 116	NN	63726	66876	66826	63776
350 117	NN	63727	66877	66827	63777
350 118	NN	63728	66878	66828	63778
350 119	NN	63729	66879	66829	63779
350 120	NN	63730	66880	66830	63780
350 121	NN	63731	66881	66831	63781
350 122	NN	63732	66882	66832	63782
350 123	NN	63733	66883	66833	63783
350 124	NN	63734	66884	66834	63784
350 125	NN	63735	66885	66835	63785
350 126	NN	63736	66886	66836	63786
350 127	NN	63737	66887	66837	63787
350 128	NN	63738	66888	66838	63788
350 129	NN	63739	66889	66839	63789
350 130	NN	63740	66890	66840	63790
350 231	NN	61431	65231	67531	61531
350 232	NN	61432	65232	67532	61532
350 233	NN	61433	65233	67533	61546
350 234	NN	61434	65234	67534	61534
350 235	NN	61435	65235	67535	61535
350 236	NN	61436	65236	67536	61536
350 237	NN	61437	65237	67537	61537
350 238	NN	61438	65238	67538	61538
350 239	NN	61439	65239	67539	61539
350 240	NN	61440	65240	67540	61540
350 241	NN	61441	65241	67541	61541
350 242	NN	61442	65242	67542	61542
350 243	NN	61443	65243	67543	61543
350 244	NN	61444	65244	67544	61544
350 245	NN	61445	65245	67545	61545
350 246	NN	61446	65246	67546	61564
350 247	NN	61447	65247	67547	61547
350 248	NN	61448	65248	67548	61548
350 249	NN	61449	65249	67549	61549
350 250	NN	61450	65250	67550	61550
350 251	NN	61451	65251	67551	61551
350 252	NN	61452	65252	67552	61552
350 253	NN	61453	65253	67553	61553
350 254	NN	61454	65254	67554	61554
350 255	NN	61455	65255	67555	61555
350 256	NN	61456	65256	67556	61556
350 257	NN	61457	65257	67557	61557
350 258	NN	61458	65258	67558	61558
350 259	NN	61459	65259	67559	61559
350 260	NN	61460	65260	67560	61560
350 261	NN	61461	65261	67561	61561
350 262	NN	61462	65262	67562	61562
350 263	NN	61463	65263	67563	61563
350 264	NN	61464	65264	67564	61533
350 265	NN	61465	65265	67565	61565
350 266	NN	61466	65266	67566	61566
350 267	NN	61467	65267	67567	61567
350 368	NN	60141	60511	60651	60151
350 369	NN	60142	60512	60652	60152
350 370	NN	60143	60513	60653	60153
350 371	NN	60144	60514	60654	60154
350 372	NN	60145	60515	60655	60155
350 373	NN	60146	60516	60656	60156
350 374	NN	60147	60517	60657	60157
350 375	NN	60148	60518	60658	60158
350 376	NN	60149	60519	60659	60159
350 377	NN	60150	60520	60660	60160
350 401	NN	60691	60901	60941	60671

Class 350 (cont)

350 402	NN	60692	60902	60942	60672	350 407	NN	60697	60907	60947	60677
350 403	NN	60693	60903	60943	60673	350 408	NN	60698	60908	60948	60678
350 404	NN	60694	60904	60944	60674	350 409	NN	60699	60909	60949	60679
350 405	NN	60695	60905	60945	60675	350 410	NN	60700	60910	60950	60680
350 406	NN	60696	60906	60946	60676						

Named Units

350 375	Vic Hall	350 377	Graeme Taylor O.B.E

Class 357 (OH) Electrostar

357 001	EM	67651	74151	74051	67751	357 038	EM	67688	74188	74088	67788
357 002	EM	67652	74152	74052	67752	357 039	EM	67689	74189	74089	67789
357 003	EM	67653	74153	74053	67753	357 040	EM	67690	74190	74090	67790
357 004	EM	67654	74154	74054	67754	357 041	EM	67691	74191	74091	67791
357 005	EM	67655	74155	74055	67755	357 042	EM	67692	74192	74092	67792
357 006	EM	67656	74156	74056	67756	357 043	EM	67693	74193	74093	67793
357 007	EM	67657	74157	74057	67757	357 044	EM	67694	74194	74094	67794
357 008	EM	67658	74158	74058	67758	357 045	EM	67695	74195	74095	67795
357 009	EM	67659	74159	74059	67759	357 046	EM	67696	74196	74096	67796
357 010	EM	67660	74160	74060	67760	357 201	EM	68601	74601	74701	68701
357 011	EM	67661	74161	74061	67761	357 202	EM	68602	74602	74702	68702
357 012	EM	67662	74162	74062	67762	357 203	EM	68603	74603	74703	68703
357 013	EM	67663	74163	74063	67763	357 204	EM	68604	74604	74704	68704
357 014	EM	67664	74164	74064	67764	357 205	EM	68605	74605	74705	68705
357 015	EM	67665	74165	74065	67765	357 206	EM	68606	74606	74706	68706
357 016	EM	67666	74166	74066	67766	357 207	EM	68607	74607	74707	68707
357 017	EM	67667	74167	74067	67767	357 208	EM	68608	74608	74708	68708
357 018	EM	67668	74168	74068	67768	357 209	EM	68609	74609	74709	68709
357 019	EM	67669	74169	74069	67769	357 210	EM	68610	74610	74710	68710
357 020	EM	67670	74170	74070	67770	357 211	EM	68611	74611	74711	68711
357 021	EM	67671	74171	74071	67771	357 312	EM	68612	74612	74712	68712
357 022	EM	67672	74172	74072	67772	357 313	EM	68613	74613	74713	68713
357 023	EM	67673	74173	74073	67773	357 314	EM	68614	74614	74714	68714
357 024	EM	67674	74174	74074	67774	357 315	EM	68615	74615	74715	68715
357 025	EM	67675	74175	74075	67775	357 316	EM	68616	74616	74716	68716
357 026	EM	67676	74176	74076	67776	357 317	EM	68617	74617	74717	68717
357 027	EM	67677	74177	74077	67777	357 318	EM	68618	74618	74718	68718
357 028	EM	67678	74178	74078	67778	357 319	EM	68619	74619	74719	68719
357 029	EM	67679	74179	74079	67779	357 320	EM	68620	74620	74720	68720
357 030	EM	67680	74180	74080	67780	357 321	EM	68621	74621	74721	68721
357 031	EM	67681	74181	74081	67781	357 322	EM	68622	74622	74722	68722
357 032	EM	67682	74182	74082	67782	357 323	EM	68623	74623	74723	68723
357 033	EM	67683	74183	74083	67783	357 324	EM	68624	74624	74724	68724
357 034	EM	67684	74184	74084	67784	357 325	EM	68625	74625	74725	68725
357 035	EM	67685	74185	74085	67785	357 326	EM	68626	74626	74726	68726
357 036	EM	67686	74186	74086	67786	357 327	EM	68627	74627	74727	68727
357 037	EM	67687	74187	74087	67787	357 328	EM	68628	74628	74728	68728

Named Units

357 001	Barry Flaxman	357 011	John Lowing
357 002	Arthur Lewis Stride 1841-1922	357 028	London, Tilbury & Southend Railway
357 003	Southend City on Sea		1854 - 2004
357 004	Tony Amos	357 029	Thomas Whitelegg 1840 - 1922
357 005	Southend 2017 Alternative	357 030	Robert Harben Whitelegg 1871 - 1957
	City of Culture	357 201	Ken Bird
357 006	Diamond Jubilee 1952 - 2012	357 202	Kenny Mitchell
357 007	Sir Andrew Foster	357 203	Henry Pumfrett

Named Units (cont)		
357 204	Derek Fowers	
357 205	John D'Silva	
357 206	Martin Aungier	
357 207	John Page	
357 208	Dave Davis	
357 209	James Snelling	
357 313	Upminster IECC	
357 317	Alan Burnell	
357 327	Southend United	

Class 360/1 (OH)   Desiro

360 101	BF	65551	72551	74551	68551
360 102	BF	65552	72552	74552	68552
360 103	BF	65553	72553	74553	68553
360 104	BF	65554	72554	74554	68554
360 105	BF	65555	72555	74555	68555
360 106	BF	65556	72556	74556	68556
360 107	BF	65557	72557	74557	68557
360 108	BF	65558	72558	74558	68558
360 109	BF	65559	72559	74559	68559
360 110	BF	65560	72560	74560	68560
360 111	BF	65561	72561	74561	68561
360 112	BF	65562	72562	74562	68562
360 113	BF	65563	72563	74563	68563
360 114	BF	65564	72564	74564	68564
360 115	BF	65565	72565	74565	68565
360 116	BF	65566	72566	74566	68566
360 117	BF	65567	72567	74567	68567
360 118	BF	65568	72568	74568	68568
360 119	BF	65569	72569	74569	68569
360 120	BF	65570	72570	74570	68570
360 121	BF	65571	72571	74571	68571

Class 360/2 (OH)   Desiro

360 201	BC(s)	78431	63421	72431	72421	78441
360 202	BC(s)	78432	63422	72432	72422	78442
360 203	BC(s)	78433	63423	72433	72423	78443
360 204	BC(s)	78434	63424	72434	72424	78444
360 205	BC(s)	78435	63425	72435	72425	78445

Class 365 (OH)   Networker Express

365 502	HQ(s)	65895	72243	72242	65936
365 504	HQ(s)	65897	72247	72246	65938
365 506	HQ(s)	65899	72251	72250	65940
365 507	CP(s)	65900	72253	72252	65941
365 508	HQ(s)	65901	72255	72254	65942
365 509	CP(s)	65902	72257	72256	65943
365 510	HQ(s)	65903	72259	72258	65944
365 512	HQ(s)	65905	72263	72262	65946
365 514	HQ(s)	65907	72267	72266	65948
365 515	HQ(s)	65908	72269	72268	65949
365 516	HQ(s)	65909	72271	72270	65950
365 518	HQ(s)	65911	72275	72274	65952
365 519	CP(s)	65912	72277	72276	65953
365 520	HQ(s)	65913	72279	72278	65954
365 521	CP(s)	65914	72281	72280	65955
365 522	HQ(s)	65915	72283	72282	65956
365 523	CP(s)	65916	72285	72284	65957
365 524	HQ(s)	65917	72287	72286	65958
365 525	BC(s)	65918	72289	72288	65959
365 528	HQ(s)	65921	72295	72294	65962
365 529	CP(s)	65922	72297	72296	65963
365 530	HQ(s)	65923	72299	72298	65964
365 532	HQ(s)	65925	72303	72302	65966
365 533	CP(s)	65926	72305	72304	65967
365 534	HQ(s)	65927	72307	72306	65968
365 535	CP(s)	65928	72309	72308	65969
365 536	HQ(s)	65929	72311	72310	65970
365 538	HQ(s)	65931	72315	72314	65972
365 539	CP(s)	65932	72317	72316	65973
365 540	HQ(s)	65933	72319	72318	65974
365 541	CP(s)	65934	72321	72320	65975

Class 373 (Dual) — Eurostar

3007	TI	3209	LY	3215	TI(s)	3220	LY	3229	LY	3309	AM(s)
3008	TI	3210	LY	3216	TI(s)	3221	LY	3230	LY	3310	AM(s)
3015	TI	3211	LY	3217	TI(s)	3222	LY	3302	AM(s)	3311	AM(s)
3016	TI	3212	LY	3218	TI(s)	3223	LY(s)	3305	AM(s)	3312	AM(s)
3205	LY	3213	LY	3219	LY	3224	LY	3306	AM(s)	3999	TI
3206	LY	3214	LY(s)								

Named Units

3007	Waterloo Sunset	3008	Waterloo Sunset

Class 374 (E320) — Siemens Eurostar Velaro

4001	TI	4007	TI	4013	TI	4019	TI	4025	TI	4030	TI
4002	TI	4008	TI	4014	TI	4020	TI	4026	TI	4031	TI
4003	TI	4009	TI	4015	TI	4021	TI	4027	TI	4032	TI
4004	TI	4010	TI	4016	TI	4022	TI	4028	TI	4033	TI
4005	TI	4011	TI	4017	TI	4023	TI	4029	TI	4034	TI
4006	TI	4012	TI	4018	TI	4024	TI				

Class 375 (3rd / Dual*) — Electrostar

Unit						Unit					
375 301	RM	67921	74351		67931	375 628	RM*	67828	74278	74228	67878
375 302	RM	67922	74352		67932	375 629	RM*	67829	74279	74229	67879
375 303	RM	67923	74353		67933	375 630	RM*	67830	74280	74230	67880
375 304	RM	67924	74354		67934	375 701	RM	67831	74281	74231	67881
375 305	RM	67925	74355		67935	375 702	RM	67832	74282	74232	67882
375 306	RM	67926	74356		67936	375 703	RM	67833	74283	74233	67883
375 307	RM	67927	74357		67937	375 704	RM	67834	74284	74234	67884
375 308	RM	67928	74358		67938	375 705	RM	67835	74285	74235	67885
375 309	RM	67929	74359		67939	375 706	RM	67836	74286	74236	67886
375 310	RM	67930	74360		67940	375 707	RM	67837	74287	74237	67887
375 601	RM*	67801	74251	74201	67851	375 708	RM	67838	74288	74238	67888
375 602	RM*	67802	74252	74202	67852	375 709	RM	67839	74289	74239	67889
375 603	RM*	67803	74253	74203	67853	375 710	RM	67840	74290	74240	67890
375 604	RM*	67804	74254	74204	67854	375 711	RM	67841	74291	74241	67891
375 605	RM*	67805	74255	74205	67855	375 712	RM	67842	74292	74242	67892
375 606	RM*	67806	74256	74206	67856	375 713	RM	67843	74293	74243	67893
375 607	RM*	67807	74257	74207	67857	375 714	RM	67844	74294	74244	67894
375 608	RM*	67808	74258	74208	67858	375 715	RM	67845	74295	74245	67895
375 609	RM*	67809	74259	74209	67859	375 801	RM	73301	79001	78201	73701
375 610	RM*	67810	74260	74210	67860	375 802	RM	73302	79002	78202	73702
375 611	RM*	67811	74261	74211	67861	375 803	RM	73303	79003	78203	73703
375 612	RM*	67812	74262	74212	67862	375 804	RM	73304	79004	78204	73704
375 613	RM*	67813	74263	74213	67863	375 805	RM	73305	79005	78205	73705
375 614	RM*	67814	74264	74214	67864	375 806	RM	73306	79006	78206	73706
375 615	RM*	67815	74265	74215	67865	375 807	RM	73307	79007	78207	73707
375 616	RM*	67816	74266	74216	67866	375 808	RM	73308	79008	78208	73708
375 617	RM*	67817	74267	74217	67867	375 809	RM	73309	79009	78209	73709
375 618	RM*	67818	74268	74218	67868	375 810	RM	73310	79010	78210	73710
375 619	RM*	67819	74269	74219	67869	375 811	RM	73311	79011	78211	73711
375 620	RM*	67820	74270	74220	67870	375 812	RM	73312	79012	78212	73712
375 621	RM*	67821	74271	74221	67871	375 813	RM	73313	79013	78213	73713
375 622	RM*	67822	74272	74222	67872	375 814	RM	73314	79014	78214	73714
375 623	RM*	67823	74273	74223	67873	375 815	RM	73315	79015	78215	73715
375 624	RM*	67824	74274	74224	67874	375 816	RM	73316	79016	78216	73716
375 625	RM*	67825	74275	74225	67875	375 817	RM	73317	79017	78217	73717
375 626	RM*	67826	74276	74226	67876	375 818	RM	73318	79018	78218	73718
375 627	RM*	67827	74277	74227	67877	375 819	RM	73319	79019	78219	73719

Class 375 (3rd) — Electrostar

375 820	RM	73320	79020	78220	73720	375 909	RM	73339	79039	79069	73739
375 821	RM	73321	79021	78221	73721	375 910	RM	73340	79040	79070	73740
375 822	RM	73322	79022	78222	73722	375 911	RM	73341	79041	79071	73741
375 823	RM	73323	79023	78223	73723	375 912	RM	73342	79042	79072	73742
375 824	RM	73324	79024	78224	73724	375 913	RM	73343	79043	79073	73743
375 825	RM	73325	79025	78225	73725	375 914	RM	73344	79044	79074	73744
375 826	RM	73326	79026	78226	73726	375 915	RM	73345	79045	79075	73745
375 827	RM	73327	79027	78227	73727	375 916	RM	73346	79046	79076	73746
375 828	RM	73328	79028	78228	73728	375 917	RM	73347	79047	79077	73747
375 829	RM	73329	79029	78229	73729	375 918	RM	73348	79048	79078	73748
375 830	RM	73330	79030	78230	73730	375 919	RM	73349	79049	79079	73749
375 901	RM	73331	79031	79061	73731	375 920	RM	73350	79050	79080	73750
375 902	RM	73332	79032	79062	73732	375 921	RM	73351	79051	79081	73751
375 903	RM	73333	79033	79063	73733	375 922	RM	73352	79052	79082	73752
375 904	RM	73334	79034	79064	73734	375 923	RM	73353	79053	79083	73753
375 905	RM	73335	79035	79065	73735	375 924	RM	73354	79054	79084	73754
375 906	RM	73336	79036	79066	73736	375 925	RM	73355	79055	79085	73755
375 907	RM	73337	79037	79067	73737	375 926	RM	73356	79056	79086	73756
375 908	RM	73338	79038	79068	73738	375 927	RM	73357	79057	79087	73757

Named Units

375 619	Driver John Neve
375 710	Rochester Castle
375 714	Rochester Cathedral
375 823	Ashford proudly served by rail for 175 years

Class 376 (3rd) — Suburban Electrostar

376 001	SG	61101	63301	64301	63501	61601	376 019	SG	61119	63319	64319	63519	61619
376 002	SG	61102	63302	64302	63502	61602	376 020	SG	61120	63320	64320	63520	61620
376 003	SG	61103	63303	64303	63503	61603	376 021	SG	61121	63321	64321	63521	61621
376 004	SG	61104	63304	64304	63504	61604	376 022	SG	61122	63322	64322	63522	61622
376 005	SG	61105	63305	64305	63505	61605	376 023	SG	61123	63323	64323	63523	61623
376 006	SG	61106	63306	64306	63506	61606	376 024	SG	61124	63324	64324	63524	61624
376 007	SG	61107	63307	64307	63507	61607	376 025	SG	61125	63325	64325	63525	61625
376 008	SG	61108	63308	64308	63508	61608	376 026	SG	61126	63326	64326	63526	61626
376 009	SG	61109	63309	64309	63509	61609	376 027	SG	61127	63327	64327	63527	61627
376 010	SG	61110	63310	64310	63510	61610	376 028	SG	61128	63328	64328	63528	61628
376 011	SG	61111	63311	64311	63511	61611	376 029	SG	61129	63329	64329	63529	61629
376 012	SG	61112	63312	64312	63512	61612	376 030	SG	61130	63330	64330	63530	61630
376 013	SG	61113	63313	64313	63513	61613	376 031	SG	61131	63331	64331	63531	61631
376 014	SG	61114	63314	64314	63514	61614	376 032	SG	61132	63332	64332	63532	61632
376 015	SG	61115	63315	64315	63515	61615	376 033	SG	61133	63333	64333	63533	61633
376 016	SG	61116	63316	64316	63516	61616	376 034	SG	61134	63334	64334	63534	61634
376 017	SG	61117	63317	64317	63517	61617	376 035	SG	61135	63335	64335	63535	61635
376 018	SG	61118	63318	64318	63518	61618	376 036	SG	61136	63336	64336	63536	61636

Named Unit

376 001	Allan Doggett

Class 377 (3rd/Dual*)   Electrostar

377 101	BI	78501	78901	77101	78701	377 157	BI	78557	78957	77157	78757
377 102	BI	78502	78902	77102	78702	377 158	BI	78558	78958	77158	78758
377 103	BI	78503	78903	77103	78703	377 159	BI	78559	78959	77159	78759
377 104	BI	78504	78904	77104	78704	377 160	BI	78560	78960	77160	78760
377 105	BI	78505	78905	77105	78705	377 161	BI	78561	78961	77161	78761
377 106	BI	78506	78906	77106	78706	377 162	BI	78562	78962	77162	78762
377 107	BI	78507	78907	77107	78707	377 163	SU	78563	78963	77163	78763
377 108	BI	78508	78908	77108	78708	377 164	SU	78564	78964	77164	78764
377 109	BI	78509	78909	77109	78709	377 201*	SU	78571	77171	78971	78771
377 110	BI	78510	78910	77110	78710	377 202*	SU	78572	77172	78972	78772
377 111	BI	78511	78911	77111	78711	377 203*	SU	78573	77173	78973	78773
377 112	BI	78512	78912	77112	78712	377 204*	SU	78574	77174	78974	78774
377 113	BI	78513	78913	77113	78713	377 205*	SU	78575	77175	78975	78775
377 114	BI	78514	78914	77114	78714	377 206*	SU	78576	77176	78976	78776
377 115	BI	78515	78915	77115	78715	377 207*	SU	78577	77177	78977	78777
377 116	BI	78516	78916	77116	78716	377 208*	SU	78578	77178	78978	78778
377 117	BI	78517	78917	77117	78717	377 209*	SU	78579	77179	78979	78779
377 118	BI	78518	78918	77118	78718	377 210*	SU	78580	77180	78980	78780
377 119	BI	78519	78919	77119	78719	377 211*	SU	78581	77181	78981	78781
377 120	BI	78520	78920	77120	78720	377 212*	SU	78582	77182	78982	78782
377 121	BI	78521	78921	77121	78721	377 213*	SU	78583	77183	78983	78783
377 122	BI	78522	78922	77122	78722	377 214*	SU	78584	77184	78984	78784
377 123	BI	78523	78923	77123	78723	377 215*	SU	78585	77185	78985	78785
377 124	BI	78524	78924	77124	78724	377 301	SU	68201	74801	68401	
377 125	BI	78525	78925	77125	78725	377 302	SU	68202	74802	68402	
377 126	BI	78526	78926	77126	78726	377 303	SU	68203	74803	68403	
377 127	BI	78527	78927	77127	78727	377 304	SU	68204	74804	68404	
377 128	BI	78528	78928	77128	78728	377 305	SU	68205	74805	68405	
377 129	BI	78529	78929	77129	78729	377 306	SU	68206	74806	68406	
377 130	BI	78530	78930	77130	78730	377 307	SU	68207	74807	68407	
377 131	BI	78531	78931	77131	78731	377 308	SU	68208	74808	68408	
377 132	BI	78532	78932	77132	78732	377 309	SU	68209	74809	68409	
377 133	BI	78533	78933	77133	78733	377 310	SU	68210	74810	68410	
377 134	BI	78534	78934	77134	78734	377 311	SU	68211	74811	68411	
377 135	BI	78535	78935	77135	78735	377 312	SU	68212	74812	68412	
377 136	BI	78536	78936	77136	78736	377 313	SU	68213	74813	68413	
377 137	BI	78537	78937	77137	78737	377 314	SU	68214	74814	68414	
377 138	BI	78538	78938	77138	78738	377 315	SU	68215	74815	68415	
377 139	BI	78539	78939	77139	78739	377 316	SU	68216	74816	68416	
377 140	BI	78540	78940	77140	78740	377 317	SU	68217	74817	68417	
377 141	BI	78541	78941	77141	78741	377 318	SU	68218	74818	68418	
377 142	BI	78542	78942	77142	78742	377 319	SU	68219	74819	68419	
377 143	BI	78543	78943	77143	78743	377 320	SU	68220	74820	68420	
377 144	BI	78544	78944	77144	78744	377 321	SU	68221	74821	68421	
377 145	BI	78545	78945	77145	78745	377 322	SU	68222	74822	68422	
377 146	BI	78546	78946	77146	78746	377 323	SU	68223	74823	68423	
377 147	BI	78547	78947	77147	78747	377 324	SU	68224	74824	68424	
377 148	BI	78548	78948	77148	78748	377 325	SU	68225	74825	68425	
377 149	BI	78549	78949	77149	78749	377 326	SU	68226	74826	68426	
377 150	BI	78550	78950	77150	78750	377 327	SU	68227	74827	68427	
377 151	BI	78551	78951	77151	78751	377 328	SU	68228	74828	68428	
377 152	BI	78552	78952	77152	78752	377 401	BI	73401	78801	78601	73801
377 153	BI	78553	78953	77153	78753	377 402	BI	73402	78802	78602	73802
377 154	BI	78554	78954	77154	78754	377 403	BI	73403	78803	78603	73803
377 155	BI	78555	78955	77155	78755	377 404	BI	73404	78804	78604	73804
377 156	BI	78556	78956	77156	78756	377 405	BI	73405	78805	78605	73805

Class 377 (3rd/Dual*)　　　　Electrostar

377 406	BI	73406	78806	78606	73806
377 407	BI	73407	78807	78607	73807
377 408	BI	73408	78808	78608	73808
377 409	BI	73409	78809	78609	73809
377 410	BI	73410	78810	78610	73810
377 411	BI	73411	78811	78611	73811
377 412	BI	73412	78812	78612	73812
377 413	BI	73413	78813	78613	73813
377 414	BI	73414	78814	78614	73814
377 415	BI	73415	78815	78615	73815
377 416	BI	73416	78816	78616	73816
377 417	BI	73417	78817	78617	73817
377 418	BI	73418	78818	78618	73818
377 419	BI	73419	78819	78619	73819
377 420	BI	73420	78820	78620	73820
377 421	BI	73421	78821	78621	73821
377 422	BI	73422	78822	78622	73822
377 423	BI	73423	78823	78623	73823
377 424	BI	73424	78824	78624	73824
377 425	BI	73425	78825	78625	73825
377 426	BI	73426	78826	78626	73826
377 427	BI	73427	78827	78627	73827
377 428	BI	73428	78828	78628	73828
377 429	BI	73429	78829	78629	73829
377 430	BI	73430	78830	78630	73830
377 431	BI	73431	78831	78631	73831
377 432	BI	73432	78832	78632	73832
377 433	BI	73433	78833	78633	73833
377 434	BI	73434	78834	78634	73834
377 435	BI	73435	78835	78635	73835
377 436	BI	73436	78836	78636	73836
377 437	BI	73437	78837	78637	73837
377 438	BI	73438	78838	78638	73838
377 439	BI	73439	78839	78639	73839
377 440	BI	73440	78840	78640	73840
377 441	BI	73441	78841	78641	73841
377 442	BI	73442	78842	78642	73842
377 443	BI	73443	78843	78643	73843
377 444	BI	73444	78844	78644	73844
377 445	BI	73445	78845	78645	73845
377 446	BI	73446	78846	78646	73846
377 447	BI	73447	78847	78647	73847
377 448	BI	73448	78848	78648	73848
377 449	BI	73449	78849	78649	73849
377 450	BI	73450	78850	78650	73850
377 451	BI	73451	78851	78651	73851
377 452	BI	73452	78852	78652	73852
377 453	BI	73453	78853	78653	73853
377 454	BI	73454	78854	78654	73854
377 455	BI	73455	78855	78655	73855
377 456	BI	73456	78856	78656	73856
377 457	BI	73457	78857	78657	73857
377 458	BI	73458	78858	78658	73858
377 459	BI	73459	78859	78659	73859
377 460	BI	73460	78860	78660	73860
377 461	BI	73461	78861	78661	73861
377 462	BI	73462	78862	78662	73862
377 463	BI	73463	78863	78663	73863
377 464	BI	73464	78864	78664	73864
377 465	BI	73465	78865	78665	73865
377 466	BI	73466	78866	78666	73866
377 467	BI	73467	78867	78667	73867
377 468	BI	73468	78868	78668	73868
377 469	BI	73469	78869	78669	73869
377 470	BI	73470	78870	78670	73870
377 471	BI	73471	78871	78671	73871
377 472	BI	73472	78872	78672	73872
377 473	BI	73473	78873	78673	73873
377 474	BI	73474	78874	78674	73874
377 475	BI	73475	78875	78675	73875
377 501	SU*	73501	75901	74901	73601
377 502	SU*	73502	75902	74902	73602
377 503	SU*	73503	75903	74903	73603
377 504	SU*	73504	75904	74904	73604
377 505	SU*	73505	75905	74905	73605
377 506	SU*	73506	75906	74906	73606
377 507	SU*	73507	75907	74907	73607
377 508	SU*	73508	75908	74908	73608
377 509	SU*	73509	75909	74909	73609
377 510	SU*	73510	75910	74910	73610
377 511	SU*	73511	75911	74911	73611
377 512	SU*	73512	75912	74912	73612
377 513	SU*	73513	75913	74913	73613
377 514	SU*	73514	75914	74914	73614
377 515	SU*	73515	75915	74915	73615
377 516	SU*	73516	75916	74916	73616
377 517	SU*	73517	75917	74917	73617
377 518	SU*	73518	75918	74918	73618
377 519	SU*	73519	75919	74919	73619
377 520	SU*	73520	75920	74920	73620
377 521	SU*	73521	75921	74921	73621
377 522	SU*	73522	75922	74922	73622
377 523	SU*	73523	75923	74923	73623

Class 377 (3rd/*Dual)   Electrostar

377 601	SU	70101	70201	70301	70401	70501
377 602	SU	70102	70202	70302	70402	70502
377 603	SU	70103	70203	70303	70403	70503
377 604	SU	70104	70204	70304	70404	70504
377 605	SU	70105	70205	70305	70405	70505
377 606	SU	70106	70206	70306	70406	70506
377 607	SU	70107	70207	70307	70407	70507
377 608	SU	70108	70208	70308	70408	70508
377 609	SU	70109	70209	70309	70409	70509
377 610	SU	70110	70210	70310	70410	70510
377 611	SU	70111	70211	70311	70411	70511
377 612	SU	70112	70212	70312	70412	70512
377 613	SU	70113	70213	70313	70413	70513
377 614	SU	70114	70214	70314	70414	70514
377 615	SU	70115	70215	70315	70415	70515
377 616	SU	70116	70216	70316	70416	70516
377 617	SU	70117	70217	70317	70417	70517
377 618	SU	70118	70218	70318	70418	70518
377 619	SU	70119	70219	70319	70419	70519
377 620	SU	70120	70220	70320	70420	70520
377 621	SU	70121	70221	70321	70421	70521
377 622	SU	70122	70222	70322	70422	70522
377 623	SU	70123	70223	70323	70423	70523
377 624	SU	70124	70224	70324	70424	70524
377 625	SU	70125	70225	70325	70425	70525
377 626	SU	70126	70226	70326	70426	70526
377 701	SU*	65201	70601	65601	70701	65401
377 702	SU*	65202	70602	65602	70702	65402
377 703	SU*	65203	70603	65603	70703	65403
377 704	SU*	65204	70604	65604	70704	65404
377 705	SU*	65205	70605	65605	70705	65405
377 706	SU*	65206	70606	65606	70706	65406
377 707	SU*	65207	70607	65607	70707	65407
377 708	SU*	65208	70608	65608	70708	65408

Class 378 (3rd/*Dual)   Capitalstar

378 135	NG	38035	38235	38335	38435	38135	Daks Hamilton
378 136	NG	38036	38236	38336	38436	38136	
378 137	NG	38037	38237	38337	38437	38137	
378 138	NG	38038	38238	38338	38438	38138	
378 139	NG	38039	38239	38339	38439	38139	
378 140	NG	38040	38240	38340	38440	38140	
378 141	NG	38041	38241	38341	38441	38141	
378 142	NG	38042	38242	38342	38442	38142	
378 143	NG	38043	38243	38343	38443	38143	
378 144	NG	38044	38244	38344	38444	38144	
378 145	NG	38045	38245	38345	38445	38145	
378 146	NG	38046	38246	38346	38446	38146	
378 147	NG	38047	38247	38347	38447	38147	
378 148	NG	38048	38248	38348	38448	38148	
378 149	NG	38049	38249	38349	38449	38149	
378 150	NG	38050	38250	38350	38450	38150	
378 151	NG	38051	38251	38351	38451	38151	
378 152	NG	38052	38252	38352	38452	38152	
378 153	NG	38053	38253	38353	38453	38153	
378 154	NG	38054	38254	38354	38454	38154	
378 201*	WN	38001	38201	38301	38401	38101	

Class 378 (3rd/*Dual) — Capitalstar

Unit	Depot						Name
378 202*	WN	38002	38202	38302	38402	38102	
378 203*	WN	38003	38203	38303	38403	38103	
378 204*	WN	38004	38204	38304	38404	38104	Professor Sir Peter Hall
378 205*	WN	38005	38205	38305	38405	38105	
378 206*	WN	38006	38206	38306	38406	38106	
378 207*	WN	38007	38207	38307	38407	38107	
378 208*	WN	38008	38208	38308	38408	38108	
378 209*	WN	38009	38209	38309	38409	38109	
378 210*	WN	38010	38210	38310	38410	38110	
378 211*	WN	38011	38211	38311	38411	38111	Gary Hunter
378 212*	WN	38012	38212	38312	38412	38112	
378 213*	WN	38013	38213	38313	38413	38113	
378 214*	WN	38014	38214	38314	38414	38114	
378 215*	WN	38015	38215	38315	38415	38115	
378 216*	WN	38016	38216	38316	38416	38116	
378 217*	WN	38017	38217	38317	38417	38117	
378 218*	WN	38018	38218	38318	38418	38118	
378 219*	WN	38019	38219	38319	38419	38119	
378 220*	WN	38020	38220	38320	38420	38120	
378 221*	WN	38021	38221	38321	38421	38121	
378 222*	WN	38022	38222	38322	38422	38122	
378 223*	WN	38023	38223	38323	38423	38123	
378 224*	WN	38024	38224	38324	38424	38124	
378 225*	WN	38025	38225	38325	38425	38125	
378 226*	WN	38026	38226	38326	38426	38126	
378 227*	WN	38027	38227	38327	38427	38127	
378 228*	WN	38028	38228	38328	38428	38128	
378 229*	WN	38029	38229	38329	38429	38129	
378 230*	WN	38030	38230	38330	38430	38130	
378 231*	WN	38031	38231	38331	38431	38131	
378 232*	WN	38032	38232	38332	38432	38132	
378 233*	NG	38033	38233	38333	38433	38133	Ian Brown CBE
378 234*	NG	38034	38234	38334	38434	38134	
378 255*	NG	38055	38255	38355	38435	38155	
378 256*	NG	38056	38256	38356	38436	38156	
378 257*	NG	38057	38257	38357	38437	38157	

Class 379 (OH) — Electrostar

Unit	Depot					Unit	Depot				
379 001	IL	61201	61701	61901	62101	379 016	IL	61216	61716	61916	62116
379 002	IL	61202	61702	61902	62102	379 017	IL	61217	61717	61917	62117
379 003	IL	61203	61703	61903	62103	379 018	IL	61218	61718	61918	62118
379 004	IL	61204	61704	61904	62104	379 019	IL	61219	61719	61919	62119
379 005	IL	61205	61705	61905	62105	379 020	IL	61220	61720	61920	62120
379 006	IL	61206	61706	61906	62106	379 021	IL	61221	61721	61921	62121
379 007	IL	61207	61707	61907	62107	379 022	IL	61222	61722	61922	62122
379 008	IL	61208	61708	61908	62108	379 023	IL	61223	61723	61923	62123
379 009	IL	61209	61709	61909	62109	379 024	IL	61224	61724	61924	62124
379 010	IL	61210	61710	61910	62110	379 025	IL	61225	61725	61925	62125
379 011	IL	61211	61711	61911	62111	379 026	IL	61226	61726	61926	62126
379 012	IL	61212	61712	61912	62112	379 027	IL	61227	61727	61927	62127
379 013	IL	61213	61713	61913	62113	379 028	IL	61228	61728	61928	62128
379 014	IL	61214	61714	61914	62114	379 029	IL	61229	61729	61929	62129
379 015	IL	61215	61715	61915	62115	379 030	IL	61230	61730	61930	62130

Named Units

379 005 Stanstead Express	379 012 The West Anglian	379 025 Go Discover
379 011 Ely Cathedral	379 015 City of Cambridge	

Class 380 (OH) — Desiro

380 001	GW	38501	38601	38701
380 002	GW	38502	38602	38702
380 003	GW	38503	38603	38703
380 004	GW	38504	38604	38704
380 005	GW	38505	38605	38705
380 006	GW	38506	38606	38706
380 007	GW	38507	38607	38707
380 008	GW	38508	38608	38708
380 009	GW	38509	38609	38709
380 010	GW	38510	38610	38710
380 011	GW	38511	38611	38711
380 012	GW	38512	38612	38712
380 013	GW	38513	38613	38713
380 014	GW	38514	38614	38714
380 015	GW	38515	38615	38715
380 016	GW	38516	38616	38716
380 017	GW	38517	38617	38717
380 018	GW	38518	38618	38718
380 019	GW	38519	38619	38719

380 020	GW	38520	38620		38720
380 021	GW	38521	38621		38721
380 022	GW	38522	38622		38722
380 101	GW	38551	38651	38851	38751
380 102	GW	38552	38652	38852	38752
380 103	GW	38553	38653	38853	38753
380 104	GW	38554	38654	38854	38754
380 105	GW	38555	38655	38855	38755
380 106	GW	38556	38656	38856	38756
380 107	GW	38557	38657	38857	38757
380 108	GW	38558	38658	38858	38758
380 109	GW	38559	38659	38859	38759
380 110	GW	38560	38660	38860	38760
380 111	GW	38561	38661	38861	38761
380 112	GW	38562	38662	38862	38762
380 113	GW	38563	38663	38863	38763
380 114	GW	38564	38664	38864	38764
380 115	GW	38565	38665	38865	38765
380 116	GW	38566	38666	38866	38766

Class 385 (OH) — Scotrail

385 001	EC	441001	442001	443001	
385 002	EC	441002	442002	443002	
385 003	EC	441003	442003	443003	
385 004	EC	441004	442004	443004	
385 005	EC	441005	442005	443005	
385 006	EC	441006	442006	443006	
385 007	EC	441007	442007	443007	
385 008	EC	441008	442008	443008	
385 009	EC	441009	442009	443009	
385 010	EC	441010	442010	443010	
385 011	EC	441011	442011	443011	
385 012	EC	441012	442012	443012	
385 013	EC	441013	442013	443013	
385 014	EC	441014	442014	443014	
385 015	EC	441015	442015	443015	
385 016	EC	441016	442016	443016	
385 017	EC	441017	442017	443017	
385 018	EC	441018	442018	443018	
385 019	EC	441019	442019	443019	
385 020	EC	441020	442020	443020	
385 021	EC	441021	442021	443021	
385 022	EC	441022	442022	443022	
385 023	EC	441023	442023	443023	
385 024	EC	441024	442024	443024	
385 025	EC	441025	442025	443025	
385 026	EC	441026	442026	443026	
385 027	EC	441027	442027	443027	
385 028	EC	441028	442028	443028	
385 029	EC	441029	442029	443029	
385 030	EC	441030	442030	443030	
385 031	EC	441031	442031	443031	
385 032	EC	441032	442032	443032	
385 033	EC	441033	442033	443033	
385 034	EC	441034	442034	443034	
385 035	EC	441035	442035	443035	
385 036	EC	441036	442036	443036	
385 037	EC	441037	442037	443037	
385 038	EC	441038	442038	443038	
385 039	EC	441039	442039	443039	
385 040	EC	441040	442040	443040	
385 041	EC	441041	442041	443041	
385 042	EC	441042	442042	443042	
385 043	EC	441043	442043	443043	
385 044	EC	441044	442044	443044	
385 045	EC	441045	442045	443045	
385 046	EC	441046	442046	443046	
385 101	EC	441101	442101	443101	444101
385 102	EC	441102	442102	443102	444102
385 103	EC	441103	442103	443103	444103
385 104	EC	441104	442104	443104	444104
385 105	EC	441105	442105	443105	444105
385 106	EC	441106	442106	443106	444106
385 107	EC	441107	442107	443107	444107
385 108	EC	441108	442108	443108	444108
385 109	EC	441109	442109	443109	444109
385 110	EC	441110	442110	443110	444110
385 111	EC	441111	442111	443111	444111
385 112	EC	441112	442112	443112	444112
385 113	EC	441113	442113	443113	444113
385 114	EC	441114	442114	443114	444114
385 115	EC	441115	442115	443115	444115
385 116	EC	441116	442116	443116	444116
385 117	EC	441117	442117	443117	444117
385 118	EC	441118	442118	443118	444118
385 119	EC	441119	442119	443119	444119
385 120	EC	441120	442120	443120	444120
385 121	EC	441121	442121	443121	444121
385 122	EC	441122	442122	443122	444122
385 123	EC	441123	442123	443123	444123
385 124	EC	441124	442124	443124	444124

Class 387 (Dual)

387 101	HE	421101	422101	423101	424101	387 155	RG	421155	422155	423155	424155
387 102	HE	421102	422102	423102	424102	387 156	RG	421156	422156	423156	424156
387 103	HE	421103	422103	423103	424103	387 157	RG	421157	422157	423157	424157
387 104	HE	421104	422104	423104	424104	387 158	RG	421158	422158	423158	424158
387 105	HE	421105	422105	423105	424105	387 159	RG	421159	422159	423159	424159
387 106	HE	421106	422106	423106	424106	387 160	RG	421160	422160	423160	424160
387 107	HE	421107	422107	423107	424107	387 161	RG	421161	422161	423161	424161
387 108	HE	421108	422108	423108	424108	387 162	RG	421162	422162	423162	424162
387 109	HE	421109	422109	423109	424109	387 163	RG	421163	422163	423163	424163
387 110	HE	421110	422110	423110	424110	387 164	RG	421164	422164	423164	424164
387 111	HE	421111	422111	423111	424111	387 165	RG	421165	422165	423165	424165
387 112	HE	421112	422112	423112	424112	387 166	RG	421166	422166	423166	424166
387 113	HE	421113	422113	423113	424113	387 167	RG	421167	422167	423167	424167
387 114	HE	421114	422114	423114	424114	387 168	RG	421168	422168	423168	424168
387 115	HE	421115	422115	423115	424115	387 169	RG	421169	422169	423169	424169
387 116	HE	421116	422116	423116	424116	387 170	RG	421170	422170	423170	424170
387 117	HE	421117	422117	423117	424117	387 171	RG	421171	422171	423171	424171
387 118	HE	421118	422118	423118	424118	387 172	RG	421172	422172	423172	424172
387 119	HE	421119	422119	423119	424119	387 173	RG	421173	422173	423173	424173
387 120	HE	421120	422120	423120	424120	387 174	RG	421174	422174	423174	424174
387 121	HE	421121	422121	423121	424121	387 201	RG	421201	422201	423201	424201
387 122	HE	421122	422122	423122	424122	387 202	RG	421202	422202	423202	424202
387 123	HE	421123	422123	423123	424123	387 203	RG	421203	422203	423203	424203
387 124	HE	421124	422124	423124	424124	387 204	RG	421204	422204	423204	424204
387 125	HE	421125	422125	423125	424125	387 205	RG	421205	422205	423205	424205
387 126	HE	421126	422126	423126	424126	387 206	RG	421206	422206	423206	424206
387 127	HE	421127	422127	423127	424127	387 207	HE	421207	422207	423207	424207
387 128	HE	421128	422128	423128	424128	387 208	HE	421208	422208	423208	424208
387 129	HE	421129	422129	423129	424129	387 209	HE	421209	422209	423209	424209
387 130	RG	421130	422130	423130	424130	387 210	SL	421210	422210	423210	424210
387 131	RG	421131	422131	423131	424131	387 211	SL	421211	422211	423211	424211
387 132	RG	421132	422132	423132	424132	387 212	SL	421212	422212	423212	424212
387 133	RG	421133	422133	423133	424133	387 213	SL	421213	422213	423213	424213
387 134	RG	421134	422134	423134	424134	387 214	SL	421214	422214	423214	424214
387 135	RG	421135	422135	423135	424135	387 215	SL	421215	422215	423215	424215
387 136	RG	421136	422136	423136	424136	387 216	SL	421216	422216	423216	424216
387 137	RG	421137	422137	423137	424137	387 217	SL	421217	422217	423217	424217
387 138	RG	421138	422138	423138	424138	387 218	SL	421218	422218	423218	424218
387 139	RG	421139	422139	423139	424139	387 219	SL	421219	422219	423219	424219
387 140	RG	421140	422140	423140	424140	387 220	SL	421220	422220	423220	424220
387 141	RG	421141	422141	423141	424141	387 221	SL	421221	422221	423221	424221
387 142	RG	421142	422142	423142	424142	387 222	SL	421222	422222	423222	424222
387 143	RG	421143	422143	423143	424143	387 223	SL	421223	422223	423223	424223
387 144	RG	421144	422144	423144	424144	387 224	SL	421224	422224	423224	424224
387 145	RG	421145	422145	423145	424145	387 225	SL	421225	422225	423225	424225
387 146	RG	421146	422146	423146	424146	387 226	SL	421226	422226	423226	424226
387 147	RG	421147	422147	423147	424147	387 227	SL	421227	422227	423227	424227
387 148	RG	421148	422148	423148	424148	387 301	RG	421301	422301	423301	424301
387 149	RG	421149	422149	423149	424149	387 302	RG	421302	422302	423302	424302
387 150	RG	421150	422150	423150	424150	387 303	EM	421303	422303	423303	424303
387 151	RG	421151	422151	423151	424151	387 304	EM	421304	422304	423304	424304
387 152	RG	421152	422152	423152	424152	387 305	EM	421305	422305	423305	424305
387 153	RG	421153	422153	423153	424153	387 306	RG	421306	422306	423306	424306
387 154	RG	421154	422154	423154	424154						

Named Unit

387 124 Paul McCann

Class 390(OH) Pendolino

Unit											
390 001	LG	69101	69401	69501	69601	68801	69701	69801	69901	69201	
390 002	LG	69102	69402	69502	69602	68802	69702	69802	69902	69202	
390 103	LG	69103	69403	69503	69603	65303	68903	68803	69703	69803	69903 69203
390 104	LG	69104	69404	69504	69604	65304	68904	68804	69704	69804	69904 69204
390 005	LG	69105	69405	69505	69605	68805	69705	69805	69905	69205	
390 006	LG	69106	69406	69506	69606	68806	69706	69806	69906	69206	
390 107	LG	69107	69407	69507	69607	65307	68907	68807	69707	69807	69907 69207
390 008	LG	69108	69408	69508	69608	68808	69708	69808	69908	69208	
390 009	LG	69109	69409	69509	69609	68809	69709	69809	69909	69209	
390 010	LG	69110	69410	69510	69610	68810	69710	69810	69910	69210	
390 011	LG	69111	69411	69511	69611	68811	69711	69811	69911	69211	
390 112	LG	69112	69412	69512	69612	65312	68912	68812	69712	69812	69912 69212
390 013	LG	69113	69413	69513	69613	68813	69713	69813	69913	69213	
390 114	LG	69114	69414	69514	69614	65314	68914	68814	69714	69814	69914 69214
390 115	LG	69115	69415	69515	69615	65315	68915	68815	69715	69815	69915 69215
390 016	LG	69116	69416	69516	69616	68816	69716	69816	69916	69216	
390 117	LG	69117	69417	69517	69617	65317	68917	68817	69717	69817	69917 69217
390 118	LG	69118	69418	69518	69618	65318	68918	68818	69718	69818	69918 69218
390 119	LG	69119	69419	69519	69619	65319	68919	68819	69719	69819	69919 69219
390 020	LG	69120	69420	69520	69620	68820	69720	69820	69920	69220	
390 121	LG	69121	69421	69521	69621	65321	68921	68821	69721	69821	69921 69221
390 122	LG	69122	69422	69522	69622	65322	68922	68822	69722	69822	69922 69222
390 123	LG	69123	69423	69523	69623	65323	68923	68823	69723	69823	69923 69223
390 124	LG	69124	69424	69524	69624	65324	68924	68824	69724	69824	69924 69224
390 125	LG	69125	69425	69525	69625	65325	68925	68825	69725	69825	69925 69225
390 126	LG	69126	69426	69526	69626	65326	68926	68826	69726	69826	69926 69226
390 127	LG	69127	69427	69527	69627	65327	68927	68827	69727	69827	69927 69227
390 128	LG	69128	69428	69528	69628	65328	68928	68828	69728	69828	69928 69228
390 129	LG	69129	69429	69529	69629	65329	68929	68829	69729	69829	69929 69229
390 130	LG	69130	69430	69530	69630	65330	68930	68830	69730	69830	69930 69230
390 131	LG	69131	69431	69531	69631	65331	68931	68831	69731	69831	69931 69231
390 132	LG	69132	69432	69532	69632	65332	68932	68832	69732	69832	69932 69232
390 134	LG	69134	69434	69534	69634	65334	68934	68834	69734	69834	69934 69234
390 135	LG	69135	69435	69535	69635	65335	68935	68835	69735	69835	69935 69235
390 136	LG	69136	69436	69536	69636	65336	68936	68836	69736	69836	69936 69236
390 137	LG	69137	69437	69537	69637	65337	68937	68837	69737	69837	69937 69237
390 138	LG	69138	69438	69538	69638	65338	68938	68838	69738	69838	69938 69238
390 039	LG	69139	69439	69539	69639	68839	69739	69839	69939	69239	
390 040	LG	69140	69440	69540	69640	68840	69740	69840	69940	69240	
390 141	LG	69141	69441	69541	69641	65341	68941	68841	69741	69841	69941 69241
390 042	LG	69142	69442	69542	69642	68842	69742	69842	69942	69242	
390 043	LG	69143	69443	69543	69643	68843	69743	69843	69943	69243	
390 044	LG	69144	69444	69544	69644	68844	69744	69844	69944	69244	
390 045	LG	69145	69445	69545	69645	68845	69745	69845	69945	69245	
390 046	LG	69146	69446	69546	69646	68846	69746	69846	69946	69246	
390 047	LG	69147	69447	69547	69647	68847	69747	69847	69947	69247	
390 148	LG	69148	69448	69548	69648	65348	68948	68848	69748	69848	69948 69248
390 049	LG	69149	69449	69549	69649	68849	69749	69849	69949	69249	
390 050	LG	69150	69450	69550	69650	68850	69750	69850	69950	69250	
390 151	LG	69151	69451	69551	69651	65351	68951	68851	69751	69851	69951 69251
390 152	LG	69152	69452	69552	69652	65352	68952	68852	69752	69852	69952 69252
390 153	LG	69153	69453	69553	69653	63353	68953	68853	69753	69853	69953 69253
390 154	LG	69154	69454	69554	69654	65354	68954	68854	69754	69854	69954 69254
390 155	LG	69155	69455	69555	69655	65355	68955	68855	69755	69855	69955 69255
390 156	LG	69156	69456	69556	69656	65356	68956	68856	69756	69856	69956 69256
390 157	LG	69157	69457	69557	69657	65357	68957	68857	69757	69857	69957 69257

Pendolino Names

390 001 Bee Together	390 114 City of Manchester	390 134 City of Carlisle
390 002 Stephen Sutton	390 115 Crewe - All Change	390 135 City of Lancaster
390 104 Alstom Pendolino	390 117 Blue Peter	390 136 City of Coventry
390 005 City of Wolverhampton	390 119 Progress	390 138 City of London
390 006 Rethink Mental Illness	390 122 Penny the Pendolino	390 039 Lady Godiva
390 008 Charles Rennie	390 128 City of Preston	390 044 Royal Scot
Mackintosh	390 129 City of Stoke on Trent	390 148 Flying Scouseman
390 009 Treaty of Union	390 130 City of Edinburgh	390 151 Unknown Soldier
390 010 The Cumbrian Spirit	390 131 City of Liverpool	390 155 Railway Benefit Fund
390 011 City of Lichfield	390 132 City of Birmingham	390 157 Chad Varah
390 013 Blackpool Belle		

Class 395 (Dual) — Javelin

395 001	AD	39011	39012	39013	39014	39015	39016	Dame Kelly Holmes
395 002	AD	39021	39022	39023	39024	39025	39026	Sebastian Coe
395 003	AD	39031	39032	39033	39034	39035	39036	Sir Steve Redgrave
395 004	AD	39041	39042	39043	39044	39045	39046	Sir Chris Hoy
395 005	AD	39051	39052	39053	39054	39055	39056	Dame Tanni Grey Thompson
395 006	AD	39061	39062	39063	39064	39065	39066	Daley Thompson
395 007	AD	39071	39072	39073	39074	39075	39076	Steve Backley
395 008	AD	39081	39082	39083	39084	39085	39086	Ben Ainslie
395 009	AD	39091	39092	39093	39094	39095	39096	Rebecca Adlington
395 010	AD	39101	39102	39103	39104	39105	39106	Duncan Goodhew
395 011	AD	39111	39112	39113	39114	39115	39116	Katherine Grainger
395 012	AD	39121	39122	39123	39124	39125	39126	#Trainbow @ SE_Railway
395 013	AD	39131	39132	39133	39134	39135	39136	Hornby Visitor Centre
395 014	AD	39141	39142	39143	39144	39145	39146	Dina Asher-Smith
395 015	AD	39151	39152	39153	39154	39155	39156	Live On
395 016	AD	39161	39162	39163	39164	39165	39166	
395 017	AD	39171	39172	39173	39174	39175	39176	
395 018	AD	39181	39182	39183	39184	39185	39186	The Victory
395 019	AD	39191	39192	39193	39194	39195	39196	Jessica Ennis
395 020	AD	39201	39202	39203	39204	39205	39206	Jason Kenny
395 021	AD	39211	39212	39213	39214	39215	39216	Ed Clancy MBE
395 022	AD	39221	39222	39223	39224	39225	39226	Alistair Brownlee
395 023	AD	39231	39232	39233	39234	39235	39236	Ellie Simmonds
395 024	AD	39241	39242	39243	39244	39245	39246	Jonnie Peacock
395 025	AD	39251	39252	39253	39254	39255	39256	Victoria Pendleton
395 026	AD	39261	39262	39263	39264	39265	39266	Marc Woods
395 027	AD	39271	39272	39273	39274	39275	39276	Hannah Cockroft
395 028	AD	39281	39282	39283	39284	39285	39286	Laura Trott
395 029	AD	39291	39292	39293	39294	39295	39296	David Weir

Class 397 (OH) — Trans Pennine

397 001	LG	471001	472001	473001	474001	475001
397 002	LG	471002	472002	473002	474002	475002
397 003	LG	471003	472003	473003	474003	475003
397 004	LG	471004	472004	473004	474004	475004
397 005	LG	471005	472005	473005	474005	475005
397 006	LG	471006	472006	473006	474006	475006
397 007	LG	471007	472007	473007	474007	475007
397 008	LG	471008	472008	473008	474008	475008
397 009	LG	471009	472009	473009	474009	475009
397 010	LG	471010	472010	473010	474010	475010
397 011	LG	471011	472011	473011	474011	475011
397 012	LG	471012	472012	473012	474012	475012

Class 398 — Transport for Wales 3 car units on order

398 001	398 006	398 011	398 016	398 021	398 025	398 029	398 033
398 002	398 007	398 012	398 017	398 022	398 026	398 030	398 034
398 003	398 008	398 013	398 018	398 023	398 027	398 031	398 035
398 004	398 009	398 014	398 019	398 024	398 028	398 032	398 036
398 005	398 010	398 015	398 020				

Class 444 (3rd) — Desiro

444 001	NT	63801	67101	67151	67201	63851	444 024	NT	63824	67124	67174	67224	63874
444 002	NT	63802	67102	67152	67202	63852	444 025	NT	63825	67125	67175	67225	63875
444 003	NT	63803	67103	67153	67203	63853	444 026	NT	63826	67126	67176	67226	63876
444 004	NT	63804	67104	67154	67204	63854	444 027	NT	63827	67127	67177	67227	63877
444 005	NT	63805	67105	67155	67205	63855	444 028	NT	63828	67128	67178	67228	63878
444 006	NT	63806	67106	67156	67206	63856	444 029	NT	63829	67129	67179	67229	63879
444 007	NT	63807	67107	67157	67207	63857	444 030	NT	63830	67130	67180	67230	63880
444 008	NT	63808	67108	67158	67208	63858	444 031	NT	63831	67131	67181	67231	63881
444 009	NT	63809	67109	67159	67209	63859	444 032	NT	63832	67132	67182	67232	63882
444 010	NT	63810	67110	67160	67210	63860	444 033	NT	63833	67133	67183	67233	63883
444 011	NT	63811	67111	67161	67211	63861	444 034	NT	63834	67134	67184	67234	63884
444 012	NT	63812	67112	67162	67212	63862	444 035	NT	63835	67135	67185	67235	63885
444 013	NT	63813	67113	67163	67213	63863	444 036	NT	63836	67136	67186	67236	63886
444 014	NT	63814	67114	67164	67214	63864	444 037	NT	63837	67137	67187	67237	63887
444 015	NT	63815	67115	67165	67215	63865	444 038	NT	63838	67138	67188	67238	63888
444 016	NT	63816	67116	67166	67216	63866	444 039	NT	63839	67139	67189	67239	63889
444 017	NT	63817	67117	67167	67217	63867	444 040	NT	63840	67140	67190	67240	63890
444 018	NT	63818	67118	67168	67218	63868	444 041	NT	63841	67141	67191	67241	63891
444 019	NT	63819	67119	67169	67219	63869	444 042	NT	63842	67142	67192	67242	63892
444 020	NT	63820	67120	67170	67220	63870	444 043	NT	63843	67143	67193	67243	63893
444 021	NT	63821	67121	67171	67221	63871	444 044	NT	63844	67144	67194	67244	63894
444 022	NT	63822	67122	67172	67222	63872	444 045	NT	63845	67145	67195	67245	63895
444 023	NT	63823	67123	67173	67223	63873							

Named Units

444 001	Naomi House	444 038	South Western Railway
444 012	Destination Weymouth	444 040	The D Day Story Portsmouth
444 018	The Fab 444		

Class 450/0 (3rd)					Desiro				
450 001 NT	63201	64201	68101	63601	450 057 NT	63257	64257	68157	63657
450 002 NT	63202	64202	68102	63602	450 058 NT	63258	64258	68158	63658
450 003 NT	63203	64203	68103	63603	450 059 NT	63259	64259	68159	63659
450 004 NT	63204	64204	68104	63604	450 060 NT	63260	64260	68160	63660
450 005 NT	63205	64205	68105	63605	450 061 NT	63261	64261	68161	63661
450 006 NT	63206	64206	68106	63606	450 062 NT	63262	64262	68162	63662
450 007 NT	63207	64207	68107	63607	450 063 NT	63263	64263	68163	63663
450 008 NT	63208	64208	68108	63608	450 064 NT	63264	64264	68164	63664
450 009 NT	63209	64209	68109	63609	450 065 NT	63265	64265	68165	63665
450 010 NT	63210	64210	68110	63610	450 066 NT	63266	64266	68166	63666
450 011 NT	63211	64211	68111	63611	450 067 NT	63267	64267	68167	63667
450 012 NT	63212	64212	68112	63612	450 068 NT	63268	64268	68168	63668
450 013 NT	63213	64213	68113	63613	450 069 NT	63269	64269	68169	63669
450 014 NT	63214	64214	68114	63614	450 070 NT	63270	64270	68170	63670
450 015 NT	63215	64215	68115	63615	450 071 NT	63271	64271	68171	63671
450 016 NT	63216	64216	68116	63616	450 072 NT	63272	64272	68172	63672
450 017 NT	63217	64217	68117	63617	450 073 NT	63273	64273	68173	63673
450 018 NT	63218	64218	68118	63618	450 074 NT	63274	64274	68174	63674
450 019 NT	63219	64219	68119	63619	450 075 NT	63275	64275	68175	63675
450 020 NT	63220	64220	68120	63620	450 076 NT	63276	64276	68176	63676
450 021 NT	63221	64221	68121	63621	450 077 NT	63277	64277	68177	63677
450 022 NT	63222	64222	68122	63622	450 078 NT	63278	64278	68178	63678
450 023 NT	63223	64223	68123	63623	450 079 NT	63279	64279	68179	63679
450 024 NT	63224	64224	68124	63624	450 080 NT	63280	64280	68180	63680
450 025 NT	63225	64225	68125	63625	450 081 NT	63281	64281	68181	63681
450 026 NT	63226	64226	68126	63626	450 082 NT	63282	64282	68182	63682
450 027 NT	63227	64227	68127	63627	450 083 NT	63283	64283	68183	63683
450 028 NT	63228	64228	68128	63628	450 084 NT	63284	64284	68184	63684
450 029 NT	63229	64229	68129	63629	450 085 NT	63285	64285	68185	63685
450 030 NT	63230	64230	68130	63630	450 086 NT	63286	64286	68186	63686
450 031 NT	63231	64231	68131	63631	450 087 NT	63287	64287	68187	63687
450 032 NT	63232	64232	68132	63632	450 088 NT	63288	64288	68188	63688
450 033 NT	63233	64233	68133	63633	450 089 NT	63289	64289	68189	63689
450 034 NT	63234	64234	68134	63634	450 090 NT	63290	64290	68190	63690
450 035 NT	63235	64235	68135	63635	450 091 NT	63291	64291	68191	63691
450 036 NT	63236	64236	68136	63636	450 092 NT	63292	64292	68192	63692
450 037 NT	63237	64237	68137	63637	450 093 NT	63293	64293	68193	63693
450 038 NT	63238	64238	68138	63638	450 094 NT	63294	64294	68194	63694
450 039 NT	63239	64239	68139	63639	450 095 NT	63295	64295	68195	63695
450 040 NT	63240	64240	68140	63640	450 096 NT	63296	64296	68196	63696
450 041 NT	63241	64241	68141	63641	450 097 NT	63297	64297	68197	63697
450 042 NT	63242	64242	68142	63642	450 098 NT	63298	64298	68198	63698
450 043 NT	63243	64243	68143	63643	450 099 NT	63299	64299	68199	63699
450 044 NT	63244	64244	68144	63644	450 100 NT	63300	64300	68200	63700
450 045 NT	63245	64245	68145	63645	450 101 NT	63701	66801	66851	63751
450 046 NT	63246	64246	68146	63646	450 102 NT	63702	66802	66852	63752
450 047 NT	63247	64247	68147	63647	450 103 NT	63703	66803	66853	63753
450 048 NT	63248	64248	68148	63648	450 104 NT	63704	66804	66854	63754
450 049 NT	63249	64249	68149	63649	450 105 NT	63705	66805	66855	63755
450 050 NT	63250	64250	68150	63650	450 106 NT	63706	66806	66856	63756
450 051 NT	63251	64251	68151	63651	450 107 NT	63707	66807	66857	63757
450 052 NT	63252	64252	68152	63652	450 108 NT	63708	66808	66858	63758
450 053 NT	63253	64253	68153	63653	450 109 NT	63709	66809	66859	63759
450 054 NT	63254	64254	68154	63654	450 110 NT	63710	66810	66860	63760
450 055 NT	63255	64255	68155	63655	450 111 NT	63901	66921	66901	63921
450 056 NT	63256	64256	68156	63656	450 112 NT	63902	66922	66902	63922

Class 450 (3rd) Desiro

450 113	NT	63903	66923	66903	63923	450 121	NT	63911	66931	66911	63931
450 114	NT	63904	66924	66904	63924	450 122	NT	63912	66932	66912	63932
450 115	NT	63905	66925	66905	63925	450 123	NT	63913	66933	66913	63933
450 116	NT	63906	66926	66906	63926	450 124	NT	63914	66934	66914	63934
450 117	NT	63907	66927	66907	63927	450 125	NT	63915	66935	66915	63935
450 118	NT	63908	66928	66908	63928	450 126	NT	63916	66936	66916	63936
450 119	NT	63909	66929	66909	63929	450 127	NT	63917	66937	66917	63937
450 120	NT	63910	66930	66910	63930						

Named Units

450 015	Desiro	450 114	Fairbridge - Investing in the Future
450 042	Treleor College	450 127	Dave Gunson

Class 455 (3rd)

5701	WD	77727	62783	71545	77728	5750	WD	77811	62825	71538	77812
5702	WD	77729	62784	71547	77730	455 801	SU	77627	62709	71657	77580
5703	WD	77731	62785	71540	77732	455 802	SU	77581	62710	71664	77582
5704	WD	77733	62786	71548	77734	455 803	SU	77583	62711	71639	77584
5705	WD	77735	62787	71565	77736	455 804	SU	77585	62712	71640	77586
5706	WD	77737	62788	71534	77738	455 805	SU	77587	62713	71641	77588
5707	WD	77739	62789	71536	77740	455 806	SU	77589	62714	71642	77590
5708	WD	77741	62790	71560	77742	455 807	SU	77591	62715	71643	77592
5709	WD	77743	62791	71532	77744	455 808	SU	77637	62716	71644	77594
5710	WD	77745	62792	71566	77746	455 809	SU	77623	62717	71645	77602
5711	WD	77747	62793	71542	77748	455 810	SU	77597	62718	71646	77598
5712	WD	77749	62794	71546	77750	455 811	SU	77599	62719	71647	77600
5713	WD	77751	62795	71567	77752	455 812	SU	77595	62720	71648	77626
5714	WD	77753	62796	71559	77754	455 813	SU	77603	62721	71649	77604
5715	WD	77755	62797	71535	77756	455 814	SU	77605	62722	71650	77606
5716	WD	77757	62798	71564	77758	455 815	SU	77607	62723	71651	77608
5717	WD	77759	62799	71528	77760	455 816	SU	77609	62724	71652	77633
5718	WD	77761	62800	71557	77762	455 817	SU	77611	62725	71653	77612
5719	WD	77763	62801	71558	77764	455 818	SU	77613	62726	71654	77632
5720	WD	77765	62802	71568	77766	455 819	SU	77615	62727	71637	77616
5721	WD	77767	62803	71553	77768	455 820	SU	77617	62728	71656	77618
5722	WD	77769	62804	71533	77770	455 821	SU	77619	62729	71655	77620
5723	WD	77771	62805	71526	77772	455 822	SU	77621	62730	71658	77622
5724	WD	77773	62806	71561	77774	455 823	SU	77601	62731	71659	77596
5725	WD	77775	62807	71541	77776	455 824	SU	77593	62732	71660	77624
5726	WD	77777	62808	71556	77778	455 825	SU	77579	62733	71661	77628
5727	WD	77779	62809	71562	77780	455 826	SU	77630	62734	71662	77629
5728	WD	77781	62810	71527	77782	455 827	SU	77610	62735	71663	77614
5729	WD	77783	62811	71550	77784	455 828	SU	77631	62736	71638	77634
5730	WD	77785	62812	71551	77786	455 829	SU	77635	62737	71665	77636
5731	WD	77787	62813	71555	77788	455 830	SU	77625	62743	71666	77638
5732	WD	77789	62814	71552	77790	455 831	SU	77639	62739	71667	77640
5733	WD	77791	62815	71549	77792	455 832	SU	77641	62740	71668	77642
5734	WD	77793	62816	71531	77794	455 833	SU	77643	62741	71669	77644
5735	WD	77795	62817	71563	77796	455 834	SU	77645	62742	71670	77646
5736	WD	77797	62818	71554	77798	455 835	SU	77647	62738	71671	77648
5737	WD	77799	62819	71544	77800	455 836	SU	77649	62744	71672	77650
5738	WD	77801	62820	71529	77802	455 837	SU	77651	62745	71673	77652
5739	WD	77803	62821	71537	77804	455 838	SU	77653	62746	71674	77654
5740	WD	77805	62822	71530	77806	455 839	SU	77655	62747	71675	77656
5741	WD	77807	62823	71559	77808	455 840	SU	77657	62748	71676	77658
5742	WD	77809	62824	71543	77810	455 841	SU	77659	62749	71677	77660

Class 455 (3rd)

Unit	Depot					Unit	Depot				
455 842	SU	77661	62750	71678	77662	5869	WD	77715	62777	71705	77716
455 843	SU	77663	62751	71679	77664	5870	WD	77717	62778	71706	77718
455 844	SU	77665	62752	71680	77666	5871	WD	77719	62779	71707	77720
455 845	SU	77667	62753	71681	77668	5872	WD	77721	62780	71708	77722
455 846	SU	77669	62754	71682	77670	5873	WD	77723	62781	71709	77724
5847	WD	77671	62755	71683	77672	5874	WD	77725	62782	71710	77726
5848	WD	77673	62756	71684	77674	5901	WD	77813	62826	71714	77814
5849	WD	77675	62757	71685	77676	5902	WD	77815	62827	71715	77816
5850	WD	77677	62758	71686	77678	5903	WD	77817	62828	71716	77818
5851	WD	77679	62759	71687	77680	5904	WD	77819	62829	71717	77820
5852	WD	77681	62760	71688	77682	5905	WD	77821	62830	71725	77822
5853	WD	77683	62761	71689	77684	5906	WD	77823	62831	71719	77824
5854	WD	77685	62762	71690	77686	5907	WD	77825	62832	71720	77826
5855	WD	77687	62763	71691	77688	5908	WD	77827	62833	71721	77828
5856	WD	77689	62764	71692	77690	5909	WD	77829	62834	71722	77830
5857	WD	77691	62765	71693	77692	5910	WD	77831	62835	71723	77832
5858	WD	77693	62766	71694	77694	5911	WD	77833	62836	71724	77834
5859	WD	77695	62767	71695	77696	5912	WD	77835	62837	67400	77836
5860	WD	77697	62768	71696	77698	5913	WD	77837	67301	71726	77838
5861	WD	77699	62769	71697	77700	5914	WD	77839	62839	71727	77840
5862	WD	77701	62770	71698	77702	5915	WD	77841	62840	71728	77842
5863	WD	77703	62771	71699	77704	5916	WD	77843	62841	71729	77844
5864	WD	77705	62772	71700	77706	5917	WD	77845	62842	71730	77846
5865	WD	77707	62773	71701	77708	5918	WD	77847	62843	71732	77848
5866	WD	77709	62774	71702	77710	5919	WD	77849	62844	71718	77850
5867	WD	77711	62775	71703	77712	5920	WD	77851	62845	71733	77852
5868	WD	77713	62776	71704	77714						

Class 456 (3rd)

Unit	Depot			Unit	Depot		
456 001	WD	64735	78250	456 013	WD	64747	78262
456 002	WD	64736	78251	456 014	WD	64748	78263
456 003	WD	64737	78252	456 015	WD	64749	78264
456 004	WD	64738	78253	456 016	WD	64750	78265
456 005	WD	64739	78254	456 017	WD	64751	78266
456 006	WD	64740	78255	456 018	WD	64752	78267
456 007	WD	64741	78256	456 019	WD	64753	78268
456 008	WD	64742	78257	456 020	WD	64754	78269
456 009	WD	64743	78258	456 021	WD	64755	78270
456 010	WD	64744	78259	456 022	WD	64756	78271
456 011	WD	64745	78260	456 023	WD	64757	78272
456 012	WD	64746	78261	456 024	WD	64758	78273

Class 458 (3rd)   Juniper

458 501 WD	67601	74431	74001	74101	67701
458 502 WD	67602	74421	74002	74102	67702
458 503 WD	67603	74441	74003	74103	67703
458 504 WD	67604	74451	74004	74104	67704
458 505 WD	67605	74425	74005	74105	67705
458 506 WD	67606	74436	74006	74106	67706
458 507 WD	67607	74428	74007	74107	67707
458 508 WD	67608	74433	74008	74108	67708
458 509 WD	67609	74452	74009	74109	67709
458 510 WD	67610	74405	74010	74110	67710
458 511 WD	67611	74435	74011	74111	67711
458 512 WD	67612	74427	74012	74112	67712
458 513 WD	67613	74437	74013	74113	67713
458 514 WD	67614	74407	74014	74114	67714
458 515 WD	67615	74404	74015	74115	67715
458 516 WD	67616	74406	74016	74116	67716
458 517 WD	67617	74426	74017	74117	67717
458 518 WD	67618	74432	74018	74118	67718
458 519 WD	67619	74403	74019	74119	67719
458 520 WD	67620	74401	74020	74120	67720
458 521 WD	67621	74438	74021	74121	67721
458 522 WD	67622	74424	74022	74122	67722
458 523 WD	67623	74434	74023	74123	67723
458 524 WD	67624	74402	74024	74124	67724
458 525 WD	67625	74422	74025	74125	67725
458 526 WD	67626	74442	74026	74126	67726
458 527 WD	67627	74412	74027	74127	67727
458 528 WD	67628	74408	74028	74128	67728
458 529 WD	67629	74423	74029	74129	67729
458 530 WD	67630	74411	74030	74130	67730
458 531 WD	67913	74418	74446	74458	67912
458 532 WD	67904	74417	74447	74457	67905
458 533 WD	67917	74413	74443	74453	67916
458 534 WD	67914	74414	74444	74454	67918
458 535 WD	67915	74415	74445	74455	67911
458 536 WD	67906	74416	74448	74456	67902

Class 465 (3rd)   Networker

465 001 SG	64759	72028	72029	64809	465 019 SG	64777	72064	72065	64827
465 002 SG	64760	72030	72031	64810	465 020 SG	64778	72066	72067	64828
465 003 SG	64761	72032	72033	64811	465 021 SG	64779	72068	72069	64829
465 004 SG	64762	72034	72035	64812	465 022 SG	64780	72070	72071	64830
465 005 SG	64763	72036	72037	64813	465 023 SG	64781	72072	72073	64831
465 006 SG	64764	72038	72039	64814	465 024 SG	64782	72074	72075	64832
465 007 SG	64765	72040	72041	64815	465 025 SG	64783	72076	72077	64833
465 008 SG	64766	72042	72043	64816	465 026 SG	64784	72078	72079	64834
465 009 SG	64767	72044	72045	64817	465 027 SG	64785	72080	72081	64835
465 010 SG	64768	72046	72047	64818	465 028 SG	64786	72082	72083	64836
465 011 SG	64769	72048	72049	64819	465 029 SG	64787	72084	72085	64837
465 012 SG	64770	72050	72051	64820	465 030 SG	64788	72086	72087	64838
465 013 SG	64771	72052	72053	64821	465 031 SG	64789	72088	72089	64839
465 014 SG	64772	72054	72055	64822	465 032 SG	64790	72090	72091	64840
465 015 SG	64773	72056	72057	64823	465 033 SG	64791	72092	72093	64841
465 016 SG	64774	72058	72059	64824	465 034 SG	64792	72094	72095	64842
465 017 SG	64775	72060	72061	64825	465 035 SG	64793	72096	72097	64843
465 018 SG	64776	72062	72063	64826	465 036 SG	64794	72098	72099	64844

Class 465 (3rd)   Networker

Unit	Code					Unit	Code				
465 037	SG	64795	72100	72101	64845	465 193	SG	65842	72984	72985	65889
465 038	SG	64796	72102	72103	64846	465 194	SG	65843	72986	72987	65890
465 039	SG	64797	72104	72105	64847	465 195	SG	65844	72988	72989	65891
465 040	SG	64798	72106	72107	64848	465 196	SG	65845	72990	72991	65892
465 041	SG	64799	72108	72109	64849	465 197	SG	65846	72992	72993	65893
465 042	SG	64800	72110	72111	64850	465 235	WP(s)	65734	72787	72788	65784
465 043	SG	64801	72112	72113	64851	465 236	WP(s)	65735	72789	72790	65785
465 044	SG	64802	72114	72115	64852	465 237	WP(s)	65736	72791	72792	65786
465 045	SG	64803	72116	72117	64853	465 238	WP(s)	65737	72793	72794	65787
465 046	SG	64804	72118	72119	64854	465 239	WP(s)	65738	72795	72796	65788
465 047	SG	64805	72120	72121	64855	465 240	WP(s)	65739	72797	72798	65789
465 048	SG	64806	72122	72123	64856	465 241	WP(s)	65740	72799	72800	65790
465 049	SG	64807	72124	72125	64857	465 242	WP(s)	65741	72801	72802	65791
465 050	SG	64808	72126	72127	64858	465 243	WP(s)	65742	72803	72804	65792
465 151	SG	65800	72900	72901	65847	465 244	WP(s)	65743	72805	72806	65793
465 152	SG	65801	72902	72903	65848	465 245	WP(s)	65744	72807	72808	65794
465 153	SG	65802	72904	72905	65849	465 246	WP(s)	65745	72809	72810	65795
465 154	SG	65803	72906	72907	65850	465 247	WP(s)	65746	72811	72812	65796
465 155	SG	65804	72908	72909	65851	465 248	WP(s)	65747	72813	72814	65797
465 156	SG	65805	72910	72911	65852	465 249	WP(s)	65748	72815	72816	65798
465 157	SG	65806	72912	72913	65853	465 250	WP(s)	65749	72817	72818	65799
465 158	SG	65807	72914	72915	65854	465 901	SG	65700	72719	72720	65750
465 159	SG	65808	72916	72917	65855	465 902	SG	65701	72721	72722	65751
465 160	SG	65809	72918	72919	65856	465 903	SG	65702	72723	72724	65752
465 161	SG	65810	72920	72921	65857	465 904	SG	65703	72725	72726	65753
465 162	SG	65811	72922	72923	65858	465 905	SG	65704	72727	72728	65754
465 163	SG	65812	72924	72925	65859	465 906	SG	65705	72729	72730	65755
465 164	SG	65813	72926	72927	65860	465 907	SG	65706	72731	72732	65756
465 165	SG	65814	72928	72929	65861	465 908	SG	65707	72733	72734	65757
465 166	SG	65815	72930	72931	65862	465 909	SG	65708	72735	72736	65758
465 167	SG	65816	72932	72933	65863	465 910	SG	65709	72737	72738	65759
465 168	SG	65817	72934	72935	65864	465 911	SG	65710	72739	72740	65760
465 169	SG	65818	72936	72937	65865	465 912	SG	65711	72741	72742	65761
465 170	SG	65819	72938	72939	65866	465 913	SG	65712	72743	72744	65762
465 171	SG	65820	72940	72941	65867	465 914	SG	65713	72745	72746	65763
465 172	SG	65821	72942	72943	65868	465 915	SG	65714	72747	72748	65764
465 173	SG	65822	72944	72945	65869	465 916	SG	65715	72749	72750	65765
465 174	SG	65823	72946	72947	65870	465 917	SG	65716	72751	72752	65766
465 175	SG	65824	72948	72949	65871	465 918	SG	65717	72753	72754	65767
465 176	SG	65825	72950	72951	65872	465 919	SG	65718	72755	72756	65768
465 177	SG	65826	72952	72953	65873	465 920	SG	65719	72757	72758	65769
465 178	SG	65827	72954	72955	65874	465 921	SG	65720	72759	72760	65770
465 179	SG	65828	72956	72957	65875	465 922	SG	65721	72761	72762	65771
465 180	SG	65829	72958	72959	65876	465 923	SG	65722	72763	72764	65772
465 181	SG	65830	72960	72961	65877	465 924	SG	65723	72765	72766	65773
465 182	SG	65831	72962	72963	65878	465 925	SG	65724	72767	72768	65774
465 183	SG	65832	72964	72965	65879	465 926	SG	65725	72769	72770	65775
465 184	SG	65833	72966	72967	65880	465 927	SG	65726	72771	72772	65776
465 185	SG	65834	72968	72969	65881	465 928	SG	65727	72773	72774	65777
465 186	SG	65835	72970	72971	65882	465 929	SG	65728	72775	72776	65778
465 187	SG	65836	72972	72973	65883	465 930	SG	65729	72777	72778	65779
465 188	SG	65837	72974	72975	65884	465 931	SG	65730	72779	72780	65780
465 189	SG	65838	72976	72977	65885	465 932	SG	65731	72781	72782	65781
465 190	SG	65839	72978	72979	65886	465 933	SG	65732	72783	72784	65782
465 191	SG	65840	72980	72981	65887	465 934	SG	65733	72785	72786	65783
465 192	SG	65841	72982	72983	65888						

Class 466 (3rd) — Networker

Unit		1	2	Unit		1	2	Unit		1	2
466 001	SG	64860	78312	466 016	WP(s)	64875	78327	466 030	SG	64889	78341
466 002	SG	64861	78313	466 017	SG	64876	78328	466 031	SG	64890	78342
466 003	SG	64862	78314	466 018	SG	64877	78329	466 032	SG	64891	78343
466 004	WP(s)	64863	78315	466 019	SG	64878	78330	466 033	SG	64892	78344
466 005	SG	64864	78316	466 020	SG	64879	78331	466 034	SG	64893	78345
466 006	SG	64865	78317	466 021	SG	64880	78332	466 035	SG	64894	78346
466 007	SG	64866	78318	466 022	SG	64881	78333	466 036	SG	64895	78347
466 008	SG	64867	78319	466 023	WP(s)	64882	78334	466 037	SG	64896	78348
466 009	SG	64868	78320	466 024	SG	64883	78335	466 038	SG	64897	78349
466 010	WP(s)	64869	78321	466 025	SG	64884	78336	466 039	SG	64898	78350
466 011	SG	64870	78322	466 026	SG	64885	78337	466 040	SG	64899	78351
466 012	SG	64871	78323	466 027	SG	64886	78338	466 041	SG	64900	78352
466 013	SG	64872	78324	466 028	SG	64887	78339	466 042	SG	64901	78353
466 014	SG	64873	78325	466 029	SG	64888	78340	466 043	WP(s)	64902	78354
466 015	SG	64874	78326								

Class 484 (3rd) — Isle of Wight   *on test

Unit			Unit			Unit		
484 001*	131	231	484 003*	133	233	484 005*	135	235
484 002*	132	232	484 004*	134	234			

Class 507 (3rd) — Merseyrail

Unit					Unit				
507 001	BD	64367	71342	64405	507 018	BD	64384	71359	64422
507 002	BD	64368	71343	64406	507 019	BD	64385	71360	64423
507 003	BD	64369	71344	64407	507 020	BD	64386	71361	64424
507 004	BD	64388	71345	64408	507 021	BD	64387	71362	64425
507 005	BD	64371	71346	64409	507 023	BD	64389	71364	64427
507 007	BD	64373	71348	64411	507 024	BD	64390	71365	64428
507 008	BD	64374	71349	64412	507 025	BD	64391	71366	64429
507 009	BD	64375	71350	64413	507 026	BD	64392	71367	64430
507 010	BD	64376	71351	64414	507 027	BD	64393	71368	64431
507 011	BD	64377	71352	64415	507 028	BD	64394	71369	64432
507 012	BD	64378	71353	64416	507 029	BD	64395	71370	64433
507 013	BD	64379	71354	64417	507 030	BD	64396	71371	64434
507 014	BD	64380	71355	64418	507 031	BD	64397	71372	64435
507 015	BD	64381	71356	64419	507 032	BD	64398	71373	64436
507 016	BD	64382	71357	64420	507 033	BD	64399	71374	64437
507 017	BD	64383	71358	64421					

Named Units

Unit	Name	Unit	Name
507 004	Bob Paisley	507 020	John Peel
507 008	Harold Wilson	507 021	Red Rum
507 009	Dixie Dean	507 023	Operations Inspector Stuart Mason
507 016	Merseyrail - Celebrating the first ten years 2003 - 2013	507 026	Cllr George Howard
		507 033	Cllr Jack Spriggs

Class 508 (3rd) — Merseyrail

Unit					Unit				
508 103	BD	64651	71485	64694	508 123	BD	64671	71505	64714
508 104	BD	64652	71486	64695	508 124	BD	64672	71506	64715
508 108	BD	64656	71490	64699	508 125	BD	64673	71507	64716
508 111	BD	64659	71493	64702	508 126	BD	64674	71508	64717
508 112	BD	64660	71494	64703	508 127	BD	64675	71509	64718
508 114	BD	64662	71496	64705	508 128	BD	64676	71510	64719
508 115	BD	64663	71497	64706	508 130	BD	64678	71512	64721
508 117	BD	64665	71499	64708	508 131	BD	64679	71513	64722
508 120	BD	64668	71502	64711	508 136	BD	64684	71518	64727
508 122	BD	64670	71504	64713	508 137	BD	64685	71519	64728

Class 508 (cont)

508 138	BD	64686	71520	64729		508 141	BD	64689	71523	64732
508 139	BD	64687	71521	64730		508 143	BD	64691	71525	64734
508 140	BD	64688	71522	64731						

Named Units	
508 123 William Roscoe	508 136 Wilfred Owen MC

Class 600 — Hydrogen Multiple Unit

Note: This is in the process of conversion from 321448

600 001		78130	71990	78279

Class 614 (OH) — (Under Conversion to Hydrogen Power)

614 209	HQ(s)	64599	71458	64600

Class 700 (Dual) — Thameslink

700 001	TB	401001	402001	403001	406001	407001	410001	411001	412001
700 002	TB	401002	402002	403002	406002	407002	410002	411002	412002
700 003	TB	401003	402003	403003	406003	407003	410003	411003	412003
700 004	TB	401004	402004	403004	406004	407004	410004	411004	412004
700 005	TB	401005	402005	403005	406005	407005	410005	411005	412005
700 006	TB	401006	402006	403006	406006	407006	410006	411006	412006
700 007	TB	401007	402007	403007	406007	407007	410007	411007	412007
700 008	TB	401008	402008	403008	406008	407008	410008	411008	412008
700 009	TB	401009	402009	403009	406009	407009	410009	411009	412009
700 010	TB	401010	402010	403010	406010	407010	410010	411010	412010
700 011	TB	401011	402011	403011	406011	407011	410011	411011	412011
700 012	TB	401012	402012	403012	406012	407012	410012	411012	412012
700 013	TB	401013	402013	403013	406013	407013	410013	411013	412013
700 014	TB	401014	402014	403014	406014	407014	410014	411014	412014
700 015	TB	401015	402015	403015	406015	407015	410015	411015	412015
700 016	TB	401016	402016	403016	406016	407016	410016	411016	412016
700 017	TB	401017	402017	403017	406017	407017	410017	411017	412017
700 018	TB	401018	402018	403018	406018	407018	410018	411018	412018
700 019	TB	401019	402019	403019	406019	407019	410019	411019	412019
700 020	TB	401020	402020	403020	406020	407020	410020	411020	412020
700 021	TB	401021	402021	403021	406021	407021	410021	411021	412021
700 022	TB	401022	402022	403022	406022	407022	410022	411022	412022
700 023	TB	401023	402023	403023	406023	407023	410023	411023	412023
700 024	TB	401024	402024	403024	406024	407024	410024	411024	412024
700 025	TB	401025	402025	403025	406025	407025	410025	411025	412025
700 026	TB	401026	402026	403026	406026	407026	410026	411026	412026
700 027	TB	401027	402027	403027	406027	407027	410027	411027	412027
700 028	TB	401028	402028	403028	406028	407028	410028	411028	412028
700 029	TB	401029	402029	403029	406029	407029	410029	411029	412029
700 030	TB	401030	402030	403030	406030	407030	410030	411030	412030
700 031	TB	401031	402031	403031	406031	407031	410031	411031	412031
700 032	TB	401032	402032	403032	406032	407032	410032	411032	412032
700 033	TB	401033	402033	403033	406033	407033	410033	411033	412033
700 034	TB	401034	402034	403034	406034	407034	410034	411034	412034
700 035	TB	401035	402035	403035	406035	407035	410035	411035	412035
700 036	TB	401036	402036	403036	406036	407036	410036	411036	412036
700 037	TB	401037	402037	403037	406037	407037	410037	411037	412037
700 038	TB	401038	402038	403038	406038	407038	410038	411038	412038
700 039	TB	401039	402039	403039	406039	407039	410039	411039	412039
700 040	TB	401040	402040	403040	406040	407040	410040	411040	412040
700 041	TB	401041	402041	403041	406041	407041	410041	411041	412041

700 042	TB	401042	402042	403042	406042	407042	410042	411042 412042
700 043	TB	401043	402043	403043	406043	407043	410043	411043 412043
700 044	TB	401044	402044	403044	406044	407044	410044	411044 412044
700 045	TB	401045	402045	403045	406045	407045	410045	411045 412045
700 046	TB	401046	402046	403046	406046	407046	410046	411046 412046
700 047	TB	401047	402047	403047	406047	407047	410047	411047 412047
700 048	TB	401048	402048	403048	406048	407048	410048	411048 412048
700 049	TB	401049	402049	403049	406049	407049	410049	411049 412049
700 050	TB	401050	402050	403050	406050	407050	410050	411050 412050
700 051	TB	401051	402051	403051	406051	407051	410051	411051 412051
700 052	TB	401052	402052	403052	406052	407052	410052	411052 412052
700 053	TB	401053	402053	403053	406053	407053	410053	411053 412053
700 054	TB	401054	402054	403054	406054	407054	410054	411054 412054
700 055	TB	401055	402055	403055	406055	407055	410055	411055 412055
700 056	TB	401056	402056	403056	406056	407056	410056	411056 412056
700 057	TB	401057	402057	403057	406057	407057	410057	411057 412057
700 058	TB	401058	402058	403058	406058	407058	410058	411058 412058
700 059	TB	401059	402059	403059	406059	407059	410059	411059 412059
700 060	TB	401060	402060	403060	406060	407060	410060	411060 412060
700 101	TB	401101	402101	403101	404101	405101	406101	407101 408101
		409101	410101	411101	412101			
700 102	TB	401102	402102	403102	404102	405102	406102	407102 408102
		409102	410102	411102	412102			
700 103	TB	401103	402103	403103	404103	405103	406103	407103 408103
		409103	410103	411103	412103			
700 104	TB	401104	402104	403104	404104	405104	406104	407104 408104
		409104	410104	411104	412104			
700 105	TB	401105	402105	403105	404105	405105	406105	407105 408105
		409105	410105	411105	412105			
700 106	TB	401106	402106	403106	404106	405106	406106	407106 408106
		409106	410106	411106	412106			
700 107	TB	401107	402107	403107	404107	405107	406107	407107 408107
		409107	410107	411107	412107			
700 108	TB	401108	402108	403108	404108	405108	406108	407108 408108
		409108	410108	411108	412108			
700 109	TB	401109	402109	403109	404109	405109	406109	407109 408109
		409109	410109	411109	412109			
700 110	TB	401110	402110	403110	404110	405110	406110	407110 408110
		409110	410110	411110	412110			
700 111	TB	401111	402111	403111	404111	405111	406111	407111 408111
		409111	410111	411111	412111			
700 112	TB	401112	402112	403112	404112	405112	406112	407112 408112
		409112	410112	411112	412112			
700 113	TB	401113	402113	403113	404113	405113	406113	407113 408113
		409113	410113	411113	412113			
700 114	TB	401114	402114	403114	404114	405114	406114	407114 408114
		409114	410114	411114	412114			
700 115	TB	401115	402115	403115	404115	405115	406115	407115 408115
		409115	410115	411115	412115			
700 116	TB	401116	402116	403116	404116	405116	406116	407116 408116
		409116	410116	411116	412116			
700 117	TB	401117	402117	403117	404117	405117	406117	407117 408117
		409117	410117	411117	412117			
700 118	TB	401118	402118	403118	404118	405118	406118	407118 408118
		409118	410118	411118	412118			
700 119	TB	401119	402119	403119	404119	405119	406119	407119 408119
		409119	410119	411119	412119			

Class 700 (cont)

700 120	TB	401120	402120	403120	404120	405120	406120	407120	408120		
		409120	410120	411120	412120						
700 121	TB	401121	402121	403121	404121	405121	406121	407121	408121		
		409121	410121	411121	412121						
700 122	TB	401122	402122	403122	404122	405122	406122	407122	408122		
		409122	410122	411122	412122						
700 123	TB	401123	402123	403123	404123	405123	406123	407123	408123		
		409123	410123	411123	412123						
700 124	TB	401124	402124	403124	404124	405124	406124	407124	408124		
		409124	410124	411124	412124						
700 125	TB	401125	402125	403125	404125	405125	406125	407125	408125		
		409125	410125	411125	412125						
700 126	TB	401126	402126	403126	404126	405126	406126	407126	408126		
		409126	410126	411126	412126						
700 127	TB	401127	402127	403127	404127	405127	406127	407127	408127		
		409127	410127	411127	412127						
700 128	TB	401128	402128	403128	404128	405128	406128	407128	408128		
		409128	410128	411128	412128						
700 129	TB	401129	402129	403129	404129	405129	406129	407129	408129		
		409129	410129	411129	412129						
700 130	TB	401130	402130	403130	404130	405130	406130	407130	408130		
		409130	410130	411130	412130						
700 131	TB	401131	402131	403131	404131	405131	406131	407131	408131		
		409131	410131	411131	412131						
700 132	TB	401132	402132	403132	404132	405132	406132	407132	408132		
		409132	410132	411132	412132						
700 133	TB	401133	402133	403133	404133	405133	406133	407133	408133		
		409133	410133	411133	412133						
700 134	TB	401134	402134	403134	404134	405134	406134	407134	408134		
		409134	410134	411134	412134						
700 135	TB	401135	402135	403135	404135	405135	406135	407135	408135		
		409135	410135	411135	412135						
700 136	TB	401136	402136	403136	404136	405136	406136	407136	408136		
		409136	410136	411136	412136						
700 137	TB	401137	402137	403137	404137	405137	406137	407137	408137		
		409137	410137	411137	412137						
700 138	TB	401138	402138	403138	404138	405138	406138	407138	408138		
		409138	410138	411138	412138						
700 139	TB	401139	402139	403139	404139	405139	406139	407139	408139		
		409139	410139	411139	412139						
700 140	TB	401140	402140	403140	404140	405140	406140	407140	408140		
		409140	410140	411140	412140						
700 141	TB	401141	402141	403141	404141	405141	406141	407141	408141		
		409141	410141	411141	412141						
700 142	TB	401142	402142	403142	404142	405142	406142	407142	408142		
		409142	410142	411142	412142						
700 143	TB	401143	402143	403143	404143	405143	406143	407143	408143		
		409143	410143	411143	412143						
700 144	TB	401144	402144	403144	404144	405144	406144	407144	408144		
		409144	410144	411144	412144						
700 145	TB	401145	402145	403145	404145	405145	406145	407145	408145		
		409145	410145	411145	412145						
700 146	TB	401146	402146	403146	404146	405146	406146	407146	408146		
		409146	410146	411146	412146						
700 147	TB	401147	402147	403147	404147	405147	406147	407147	408147		
		409147	410147	411147	412147						

Class 700 (cont)

700 148	TB	401148 402148 403148 404148 405148 406148 407148 408148 409148 410148 411148 412148
700 149	TB	401149 402149 403149 404149 405149 406149 407149 408149 409149 410149 411149 412149
700 150	TB	401150 402150 403150 404150 405150 406150 407150 408150 409150 410150 411150 412150
700 151	TB	401151 402151 403151 404151 405151 406151 407151 408151 409151 410151 411151 412151
700 152	TB	401152 402152 403152 404152 405152 406152 407152 408152 409152 410152 411152 412152
700 153	TB	401153 402153 403153 404153 405153 406153 407153 408153 409153 410153 411153 412153
700 154	TB	401154 402154 403154 404154 405154 406154 407154 408154 409154 410154 411154 412154
700 155	TB	401155 402155 403155 404155 405155 406155 407155 408155 409155 410155 411155 412155

Class 701/0 (3rd)   South Western Railway   built / on test*

701 001*	480001 481001 482001 483001 484001 485001 486001 487001 488001 489001
701 002*	480002 481002 482002 483002 484002 485002 486002 487002 488002 489002
701 003*	480003 481003 482003 483003 484003 485003 486003 487003 488003 489003
701 004*	480004 481004 482004 483004 484004 485004 486004 487004 488004 489004
701 005*	480005 481005 482005 483005 484005 485005 486005 487005 488005 489005
701 006*	480006 481006 482006 483006 484006 485006 486006 487006 488006 489006
701 007*	480007 481007 482007 483007 484007 485007 486007 487007 488007 489007
701 008*	480008 481008 482008 483008 484008 485008 486008 487008 488008 489008
701 009*	480009 481009 482009 483009 484009 485009 486009 487009 488009 489009
701 010	480010 481010 482010 483010 484010 485010 486010 487010 488010 489010
701 011*	480011 481011 482011 483011 484011 485011 486011 487011 488011 489011
701 012*	480012 481012 482012 483012 484012 485012 486012 487012 488012 489012
701 013*	480013 481013 482013 483013 484013 485013 486013 487013 488013 489013
701 014*	480014 481014 482014 483014 484014 485014 486014 487014 488014 489014
701 015*	480015 481015 482015 483015 484015 485015 486015 487015 488015 489015
701 016*	480016 481016 482016 483016 484016 485016 486016 487016 488016 489016
701 017*	480017 481017 482017 483017 484017 485017 486017 487017 488017 489017
701 018*	480018 481018 482018 483018 484018 485018 486018 487018 488018 489018
701 019*	480019 481019 482019 483019 484019 485019 486019 487019 488019 489019
701 020*	480020 481020 482020 483020 484020 485020 486020 487020 488020 489020
701 021*	480021 481021 482021 483021 484021 485021 486021 487021 488021 489021
701 022*	480022 481022 482022 483022 484022 485022 486022 487022 488022 489022
701 023*	480023 481023 482023 483023 484023 485023 486023 487023 488023 489023
701 024	480024 481024 482024 483024 484024 485024 486024 487024 488024 489024
701 025*	480025 481025 482025 483025 484025 485025 486025 487025 488025 489025
701 026*	480026 481026 482026 483026 484026 485026 486026 487026 488026 489026
701 027*	480027 481027 482027 483027 484027 485027 486027 487027 488027 489027
701 028*	480028 481028 482028 483028 484028 485028 486028 487028 488028 489028
701 029*	480029 481029 482029 483029 484029 485029 486029 487029 488029 489029
701 030*	480030 481030 482030 483030 484030 485030 486030 487030 488030 489030
701 031*	480031 481031 482031 483031 484031 485031 486031 487031 488031 489031
701 032*	480032 481032 482032 483032 484032 485032 486032 487032 488032 489032
701 033*	480033 481033 482033 483033 484033 485033 486033 487033 488033 489033
701 034*	480034 481034 482034 483034 484034 485034 486034 487034 488034 489034
701 035*	480035 481035 482035 483035 484035 485035 486035 487035 488035 489035
701 036	480036 481036 482036 483036 484036 485036 486036 487036 488036 489036
701 037	480037 481037 482037 483037 484037 485037 486037 487037 488037 489037
701 038	480038 481038 482038 483038 484038 485038 486038 487038 488038 489038

Class 701/0 (3rd) South Western Railway

701 039	480039	481039	482039	483039	484039	485039	486039	487039	488039	489039
701 040	480040	481040	482040	483040	484040	485040	486040	487040	488040	489040
701 041	480041	481041	482041	483041	484041	485041	486041	487041	488041	489041
701 042	480042	481042	482042	483042	484042	485042	486042	487042	488042	489042
701 043	480043	481043	482043	483043	484043	485043	486043	487043	488043	489043
701 044	480044	481044	482044	483044	484044	485044	486044	487044	488044	489044
701 045	480045	481045	482045	483045	484045	485045	486045	487045	488045	489045
701 046	480046	481046	482046	483046	484046	485046	486046	487046	488046	489046
701 047	480047	481047	482047	483047	484047	485047	486047	487047	488047	489047
701 048	480048	481048	482048	483048	484048	485048	486048	487048	488048	489048
701 049	480049	481049	482049	483049	484049	485049	486049	487049	488049	489049
701 050	480050	481050	482050	483050	484050	485050	486050	487050	488050	489050
701 051	480051	481051	482051	483051	484051	485051	486051	487051	488051	489051
701 052	480052	481052	482052	483052	484052	485052	486052	487052	488052	489052
701 053	480053	481053	482053	483053	484053	485053	486053	487053	488053	489053
701 054	480054	481054	482054	483054	484054	485054	486054	487054	488054	489054
701 055	480055	481055	482055	483055	484055	485055	486055	487055	488055	489055
701 056	480056	481056	482056	483056	484056	485056	486056	487056	488056	489056
701 057	480057	481057	482057	483057	484057	485057	486057	487057	488057	489057
701 058	480058	481058	482058	483058	484058	485058	486058	487058	488058	489058
701 059	480059	481059	482059	483059	484059	485059	486059	487059	488059	489059
701 060	480060	481060	482060	483060	484060	485060	486060	487060	488060	489060

Class 701/5 (3rd) South Western Railway built / on test*

701 501*	480101	481101	482101	483101	484101
701 502*	480102	481102	482102	483102	484102
701 503*	480103	481103	482103	483103	484103
701 504*	480104	481104	482104	483104	484104
701 505*	480105	481105	482105	483105	484105
701 506*	480106	481106	482106	483106	484106
701 507*	480107	481107	482107	483107	484107
701 508*	480108	481108	482108	483108	484108
701 509	480109	481109	482109	483109	484109
701 510*	480110	481110	482110	483110	484110
701 511	480111	481111	482111	483111	484111
701 512	480112	481112	482112	483112	484112
701 513	480113	481113	482113	483113	484113
701 514	480114	481114	482114	483114	484114
701 515	480115	481115	482115	483115	484115
701 516	480116	481116	482116	483116	484116
701 517	480117	481117	482117	483117	484117
701 518	480118	481118	482118	483118	484118
701 519	480119	481119	482119	483119	484119
701 520	480120	481120	482120	483120	484120
701 521	480121	481121	482121	483121	484121
701 522	480122	481122	482122	483122	484122
701 523	480123	481123	482123	483123	484123
701 524	480124	481124	482124	483124	484124
701 525	480125	481125	482125	483125	484125
701 526	480126	481126	482126	483126	484126
701 527	480127	481127	482127	483127	484127
701 528	480128	481128	482128	483128	484128
701 529	480129	481129	482129	483129	484129
701 530	480130	481130	482130	483130	484130

Class 707 (Dual)   Siemens

707 001	WD	421001	422001	423001	424001	425001
707 002	WD	421002	422002	423002	424002	425002
707 003	SG	421003	422003	423003	424003	425003
707 004	SG	421004	422004	423004	424004	425004
707 005	SG	421005	422005	423005	424005	425005
707 006	SG	421006	422006	423006	424006	425006
707 007	SG	421007	422007	423007	424007	425007
707 008	SG	421008	422008	423008	424008	425008
707 009	SG	421009	422009	423009	424009	425009
707 010	SG	421010	422010	423010	424010	425010
707 011	SG	421011	422011	423011	424011	425011
707 012	SG	421012	422012	423012	424012	425012
707 013	WD	421013	422013	423013	424013	425013
707 014	WD	421014	422014	423014	424014	425014
707 015	WD	421015	422015	423015	424015	425015
707 016	WD	421016	422016	423016	424016	425016
707 017	WD	421017	422017	423017	424017	425017
707 018	WD	421018	422018	423018	424018	425018
707 019	WD	421019	422019	423019	424019	425019
707 020	WD	421020	422020	423020	424020	425020
707 021	WD	421021	422021	423021	424021	425021
707 022	WD	421022	422022	423022	424022	425022
707 023	WD	421023	422023	423023	424023	425023
707 024	WD	421024	422024	423024	424024	425024
707 025	SG	421025	422025	423025	424025	425025
707 026	SG	421026	422026	423026	424026	425026
707 027	SG	421027	422027	423027	424027	425027
707 028	SG	421028	422028	423028	424028	425028
707 029	WD	421029	422029	423029	424029	425029
707 030	WD	421030	422030	423030	424030	425030

Class 710 (Dual)   London Overground

710 101	WN	431101	431201	431301	431501
710 102	WN	431102	431202	431302	431502
710 103	WN	431103	431203	431303	431503
710 104	WN	431104	431204	431304	431504
710 105	WN	431105	431205	431305	431505
710 106	WN	431106	431206	431306	431506
710 107	WN	431107	431207	431307	431507
710 108	WN	431108	431208	431308	431508
710 109	WN	431109	431209	431309	431509
710 110	WN	431110	431210	431310	431510
710 111	WN	431111	431211	431311	431511
710 112	WN	431112	431212	431312	431512
710 113	WN	431113	431213	431313	431513
710 114	WN	431114	431214	431314	431514
710 115	WN	431115	431215	431315	431515
710 116	WN	431116	431216	431316	431516
710 117	WN	431117	431217	431317	431517
710 118	WN	431118	431218	431318	431518
710 119	WN	431119	431219	431319	431519
710 120	WN	431120	431220	431320	431520
710 121	WN	431121	431221	431321	431521
710 122	WN	431122	431222	431322	431522
710 123	WN	431123	431223	431323	431523
710 124	WN	431124	431224	431324	431524
710 125	WN	431125	431225	431325	431525

TATA Steel 921 photographed at Neath, 14th August 2021 (Andy Fletcher)

66519 heads along the chord from Searchlight Lane Junction approaching Heamies Farm with 4M81 08.01 Felixstowe North to Crewe Basford Hall Freightliner service. Friday 4th June 2021. (Chris Perkins)

Ex Anglia pair 90003 & 90009 pass Stableford with 4L97 06.15 Trafford Park to Felixstowe North Freightliner service, 4th June 2021 (Chris Perkins)

Euro Tunnel 9801 photographed at Cheriton, 12th July 2020 (Andy Fletcher)

Northern 150211 photographed at Hatfield & Stainforth 1st July 2021 (Andy Fletcher)

Southern 455838 photographed at East Croydon 20th May 2021 (Daniel Jones)

Central Line 91195 photographed at West Ruislip 20th May 2021 (Andy Fletcher)

Chiltern Railways mark 3 open 12618 at Birmingham Moor Street (Stephen Jones)

Class 710 (cont)

710 126	WN	431126	431226	431326	431526	
710 127	WN	431127	431227	431327	431527	
710 128	WN	431128	431228	431328	431528	
710 129	WN	431129	431229	431329	431529	
710 130	WN	431130	431230	431330	431530	
710 256*		432156	432256	432356	432556	
710 257	WN	432157	432257	432357	432557	
710 258	WN	432158	432258	432358	432558	
710 259	WN	432159	432259	432359	432559	
710 260	WN	432160	432260	432360	432560	
710 261	WN	432161	432261	432361	432561	
710 262	WN	432162	432262	432362	432562	
710 263	WN	432163	432263	432363	432563	
710 264	WN	432164	432264	432364	432564	
710 265	WN	432165	432265	432365	432565	
710 266	WN	432166	432266	432366	432566	
710 267	WN	432167	432267	432367	432567	
710 268	WN	432168	432268	432368	432568	
710 269	WN	432169	432269	432369	432569	
710 270*		432170	432270	432370	432570	
710 271	WN	432171	432271	432371	432571	
710 272	WN	432172	432272	432372	432572	
710 273	WN	432173	432273	432373	432573	
710 374*		432174	432274	432374	432474	432574
710 375*		432175	432275	432375	432475	432575
710 376	WN	432176	432276	432376	432476	432576
710 377	WN	432177	432277	432377	432477	432577
710 378	WN	432178	432278	432378	432478	432578
710 379*		432179	432279	432379	432479	432579

Class 717 (OH) Govia Thameslink

717 001	HE	451001	452001	453001	454001	455001	456001
717 002	HE	451002	452002	453002	454002	455002	456002
717 003	HE	451003	452003	453003	454003	455003	456003
717 004	HE	451004	452004	453004	454004	455004	456004
717 005	HE	451005	452005	453005	454005	455005	456005
717 006	HE	451006	452006	453006	454006	455006	456006
717 007	HE	451007	452007	453007	454007	455007	456007
717 008	HE	451008	452008	453008	454008	455008	456008
717 009	HE	451009	452009	453009	454009	455009	456009
717 010	HE	451010	452010	453010	454010	455010	456010
717 011	HE	451011	452011	453011	454011	455011	456011
717 012	HE	451012	452012	453012	454012	455012	456012
717 013	HE	451013	452013	453013	454013	455013	456013
717 014	HE	451014	452014	453014	454014	455014	456014
717 015	HE	451015	452015	453015	454015	455015	456015
717 016	HE	451016	452016	453016	454016	455016	456016
717 017	HE	451017	452017	453017	454017	455017	456017
717 018	HE	451018	452018	453018	454018	455018	456018
717 019	HE	451019	452019	453019	454019	455019	456019
717 020	HE	451020	452020	453020	454020	455020	456020
717 021	HE	451021	452021	453021	454021	455021	456021
717 022	HE	451022	452022	453022	454022	455022	456022
717 023	HE	451023	452023	453023	454023	455023	456023
717 024	HE	451024	452024	453024	454024	455024	456024
717 025	HE	451025	452025	453025	454025	455025	456025

Class 720 (OH)			Greater Anglia			built / on test*
720 101	450101	451101	452101	453101	459101	
720 102*	450102	451102	452102	453102	459102	
720 103	450103	451103	452103	453103	459103	
720 104	450104	451104	452104	453104	459104	
720 105	450105	451105	452105	453105	459105	
720 106	450106	451106	452106	453106	459106	
720 107	450107	451107	452107	453107	459107	
720 108	450108	451108	452108	453108	459108	
720 109	450109	451109	452109	453109	459109	
720 110	450110	451110	452110	453110	459110	
720 111	450111	451111	452111	453111	459111	
720 112	450112	451112	452112	453112	459112	
720 113	450113	451113	452113	453113	459113	
720 114	450114	451114	452114	453114	459114	
720 115	450115	451115	452115	453115	459115	
720 116	450116	451116	452116	453116	459116	
720 117	450117	451117	452117	453117	459117	
720 118	450118	451118	452118	453118	459118	
720 119	450119	451119	452119	453119	459119	
720 120	450120	451120	452120	453120	459120	
720 121	450121	451121	452121	453121	459121	
720 122	450122	451122	452122	453122	459122	
720 123	450123	451123	452123	453123	459123	
720 124	450124	451124	452124	453124	459124	
720 125	450125	451125	452125	453125	459125	
720 126	450126	451126	452126	453126	459126	
720 127	450127	451127	452127	453127	459127	
720 128	450128	451128	452128	453128	459128	
720 129	450129	451129	452129	453129	459129	
720 130	450130	451130	452130	453130	459130	
720 131	450131	451131	452131	453131	459131	
720 132	450132	451132	452132	453132	459132	
720 133	450133	451133	452133	453133	459133	
720 134	450134	451134	452134	453134	459134	
720 135	450135	451135	452135	453135	459135	
720 136	450136	451136	452136	453136	459136	
720 137	450137	451137	452137	453137	459137	
720 138	450138	451138	452138	453138	459138	
720 139	450139	451139	452139	453139	459139	
720 140	450140	451140	452140	453140	459140	
720 141	450141	451141	452141	453141	459141	
720 142	450142	451142	452142	453142	459142	
720 143	450143	451143	452143	453143	459143	
720 144	450144	451144	452144	453144	459144	

Class 720 (OH)			Greater Anglia			built / on test*
720 501*	450501	451501	452501	453501	459501	
720 502*	450502	451502	452502	453502	459502	
720 503*	450503	451503	452503	453503	459503	
720 504*	450504	451504	452504	453504	459504	
720 505*	450505	451505	452505	453505	459505	
720 506*	450506	451506	452506	453506	459506	
720 507*	450507	451507	452507	453507	459507	
720 508*	450508	451508	452508	453508	459508	
720 509*	450509	451509	452509	453509	459509	
720 510*	450510	451510	452510	453510	459510	

Class 720 (cont)					Greater Anglia on order
720 511	IL	450511	451511	452511	453511	459511
720 512*		450512	451512	452512	453512	459512
720 513*		450513	451513	452513	453513	459513
720 514*		450514	451514	452514	453514	459514
720 515	IL	450515	451515	452515	453515	459515
720 516*		450516	451516	452516	453516	459516
720 517	IL	450517	451517	452517	453517	459517
720 518*		450518	451518	452518	453518	459518
720 519*		450519	451519	452519	453519	459519
720 520*		450520	451520	452520	453520	459520
720 521*		450521	451521	452521	453521	459521
720 522	IL	450522	451522	452522	453522	459522
720 523*		450523	451523	452523	453523	459523
720 524*		450524	451524	452524	453524	459524
720 525*		450525	451525	452525	453525	459525
720 526*		450526	451526	452526	453526	459526
720 527*		450527	451527	452527	453527	459527
720 528*		450528	451528	452528	453528	459528
720 529*		450529	451529	452529	453529	459529
720 530*		450530	451530	452530	453530	459530
720 531*		450531	451531	452531	453531	459531
720 532*		450532	451532	452532	453532	459532
720 533*		450533	451533	452533	453533	459533
720 534*		450534	451534	452534	453534	459534
720 535*		450535	451535	452535	453535	459535
720 536	IL	450536	451536	452536	453536	459536
720 537	IL	450537	451537	452537	453537	459537
720 538	IL	450538	451538	452538	453538	459538
720 539	IL	450539	451539	452539	453539	459539
720 540	IL	450540	451540	452540	453540	459540
720 541*		450541	451541	452541	453541	459541
720 542	IL	450542	451542	452542	453542	459542
720 543	IL	450543	451543	452543	453543	459543
720 544*		450544	451544	452544	453544	459544
720 545	IL	450545	451545	452545	453545	459545
720 546*		450546	451546	452546	453546	459546
720 547	IL	450547	451547	452547	453547	459547
720 548	IL	450548	451548	452548	453548	459548
720 549	IL	450549	451549	452549	453549	459549
720 550	IL	450550	451550	452550	453550	459550
720 551	IL	450551	451551	452551	453551	459551
720 552	IL	450552	451552	452552	453552	459552
720 553	IL	450553	451553	452553	453553	459553
720 554	IL	450554	451554	452554	453554	459554
720 555*		450555	451555	452555	453555	459555
720 556	IL	450556	451556	452556	453556	459556
720 557	IL	450557	451557	452557	453557	459557
720 558	IL	450558	451558	452558	453558	459558
720 559	IL	450559	451559	452559	453559	459559
720 560	IL	450560	451560	452560	453560	459560
720 561	IL	450561	451561	452561	453561	459561
720 562	IL	450562	451562	452562	453562	459562
720 563	IL	450563	451563	452563	453563	459563
720 564	IL	450564	451564	452564	453564	459564
720 565*		450565	451565	452565	453565	459565
720 566	IL	450566	451566	452566	453566	459566

Class 720 (cont) — Greater Anglia — built / on test*

720 567*	450567	451567	452567	453567	459567
720 568 IL	450568	451568	452568	453568	459568
720 569 IL	450569	451569	452569	453569	459569
720 570*	450570	451570	452570	453570	459570
720 571 IL	450571	451571	452571	453571	459571
720 572*	450572	451572	452572	453572	459572
720 573 IL	450573	451573	452573	453573	459573
720 574*	450574	451574	452574	453574	459574
720 575*	450575	451575	452575	453575	459575
720 576	450576	451576	452576	453576	459576
720 577*	450577	451577	452577	453577	459577
720 578*	450578	451578	452578	453578	459578
720 579*	450579	451579	452579	453579	459579
720 580*	450580	451580	452580	453580	459580
720 581	450581	451581	452581	453581	459581
720 582	450582	451582	452582	453582	459582
720 583	450583	451583	452583	453583	459583
720 584	450584	451584	452584	453584	459584
720 585	450585	451585	452585	453585	459585
720 586	450586	451586	452586	453586	459586
720 587	450587	451587	452587	453587	459587
720 588	450588	451588	452588	453588	459588
720 589	450589	451589	452589	453589	459589

Class 720 — 12 x 5 Car Units on order for c2c

720 601	720 603	720 605	720 607	720 609	720 611
720 602	720 604	720 606	720 608	720 610	720 612

Class 730 (OH) — 3 car EMU for West Midlands — built / on test*

730 001*	490001	492001	494001	730 019	490019	492019	494019
730 002*	490002	492002	494002	730 020	490020	492020	494020
730 003*	490003	492003	494003	730 021	490021	492021	494021
730 004	490004	492004	494004	730 022	490022	492022	494022
730 005	490005	492005	494005	730 023	490023	492023	494023
730 006	490006	492006	494006	730 024	490024	492024	494024
730 007	490007	492007	494007	730 025	490025	492025	494025
730 008	490008	492008	494008	730 026	490026	492026	494026
730 009	490009	492009	494009	730 027	490027	492027	494027
730 010	490010	492010	494010	730 028	490028	492028	494028
730 011	490011	492011	494011	730 029	490029	492029	494029
730 012	490012	492012	494012	730 030	490030	492030	494030
730 013	490013	492013	494013	730 031	490031	492031	494031
730 014	490014	492014	494014	730 032	490032	492032	494032
730 015	490015	492015	494015	730 033	490033	492033	494033
730 016	490016	492016	494016	730 034	490034	492034	494034
730 017	490017	492017	494017	730 035	490035	492035	494035
730 018	490018	492018	494018	730 036	490036	492036	494036

Class 730 (OH)			5 car EMU for LNWR			built / on test*
730 101*	490101	491101	492101	493101	494101	
730 102*	490102	491102	492102	493102	494102	
730 103*	490103	491103	492103	493103	494103	
730 104	490104	491104	492104	493104	494104	
730 105	490105	491105	492105	493105	494105	
730 106	490106	491106	492106	493106	494106	
730 107	490107	491107	492107	493107	494107	
730 108	490108	491108	492108	493108	494108	
730 109	490109	491109	492109	493109	494109	
730 110	490110	491110	492110	493110	494110	
730 111	490111	491111	492111	493111	494111	
730 112	490112	491112	492112	493112	494112	
730 113	490113	491113	492113	493113	494113	
730 114	490114	491114	492114	493114	494114	
730 115	490115	491115	492115	493115	494115	
730 116	490116	491116	492116	493116	494116	
730 117	490117	491117	492117	493117	494117	
730 118	490118	491118	492118	493118	494118	
730 119	490119	491119	492119	493119	494119	
730 120	490120	491120	492120	493120	494120	
730 121	490121	491121	492121	493121	494121	
730 122	490122	491122	492122	493122	494122	
730 123	490123	491123	492123	493123	494123	
730 124	490124	491124	492124	493124	494124	
730 125	490125	491125	492125	493125	494125	
730 126	490126	491126	492126	493126	494126	
730 127	490127	491127	492127	493127	494127	
730 128	490128	491128	492128	493128	494128	
730 129	490129	491129	492129	493129	494129	
730 201	490201	491201	492201	493201	494201	
730 202	490202	491202	492202	493202	494202	
730 203	490203	491203	492203	493203	494203	
730 204	490204	491204	492204	493204	494204	
730 205	490205	491205	492205	493205	494205	
730 206	490206	491206	492206	493206	494206	
730 207	490207	491207	492207	493207	494207	
730 208	490208	491208	492208	493208	494208	
730 209	490209	491209	492209	493209	494209	
730 210	490210	491210	492210	493210	494210	
730 211	490211	491211	492211	493211	494211	
730 212	490212	491212	492212	493212	494212	
730 213	490213	491213	492213	493213	494213	
730 214	490214	491214	492214	493214	494214	
730 215	490215	491215	492215	493215	494215	
730 216	490216	491216	492216	493216	494216	

Class 745 (OH)　　　　　　Stadler

745 001	NC	313001	326001	332001	343001	341001	301001	302001	342001
		344001	346001	322001	312001				
745 002	NC	313002	326002	332002	343002	341002	301002	302002	342002
		344002	346002	322002	312002				
745 003	NC	313003	326003	332003	343003	341003	301003	302003	342003
		344003	346003	322003	312003				
745 004	NC	313004	326004	332004	343004	341004	301004	302004	342004
		344004	346004	322004	312004				
745 005	NC	313005	326005	332005	343005	341005	301005	302005	342005
		344005	346005	322005	312005				
745 006	NC	313006	326006	332006	343006	341006	301006	302006	342006
		344006	346006	322006	312006				
745 007	NC	313007	326007	332007	343007	341007	301007	302007	342007
		344007	346007	322007	312007				
745 008	NC	313008	326008	332008	343008	341008	301008	302008	342008
		344008	346008	322008	312008				
745 009	NC	313009	326009	332009	343009	341009	301009	302009	342009
		344009	346009	322009	312009				
745 010	NC	313010	326010	332010	343010	341010	301010	302010	342010
		344010	346010	322010	312010				
745 101	NC	313101	326101	332101	343101	341101	301101	302101	342101
		344101	346101	322101	312101				
745 102	NC	313102	326102	332102	343102	341102	301102	302102	342102
		344102	346102	322102	312102				
745 103	NC	313103	326103	332103	343103	341103	301103	302103	342103
		344103	346103	322103	312103				
745 104	NC	313104	326104	332104	343104	341104	301104	302104	342104
		344104	346104	322104	312104				
745 105	NC	313105	326105	332105	343105	341105	301105	302105	342105
		344105	346105	322105	312105				
745 106	NC	313106	326106	332106	343106	341106	301106	302106	342106
		344106	346106	322106	312106				
745 107	NC	313107	326107	332107	343107	341107	301107	302107	342107
		344107	346107	322107	312107				
745 108	NC	313108	326108	332108	343108	341108	301108	302108	342108
		344108	346108	322108	312108				
745 109	NC	313109	326109	332109	343109	341109	301109	302109	342109
		344109	346109	322109	312109				
745 110	NC	313110	326110	332110	343110	341110	301110	302110	342110
		344110	346110	322110	312110				

Class 755/3 (Bi-Mode)　　　　　　Stadler

755 325	NC	911325	971325	981325	912325
755 326	NC	911326	971326	981326	912326
755 327	NC	911327	971327	981327	912327
755 328	NC	911328	971328	981328	912328
755 329	NC	911329	971329	981329	912329
755 330	NC	911330	971330	981330	912330
755 331	NC	911331	971331	981331	912331
755 332	NC	911332	971332	981332	912332
755 333	NC	911333	971333	981333	912333
755 334	NC	911334	971334	981334	912334
755 335	NC	911335	971335	981335	912335
755 336	NC	911336	971336	981336	912336
755 337	NC	911337	971337	981337	912337
755 338	NC	911338	971338	981338	912338

Class 755/4 Stadler

755 401	NC	911401	961401	971401	981401	912401
755 402	NC	911402	961402	971402	981402	912402
755 403	NC	911403	961403	971403	981403	912403
755 404	NC	911404	961404	971404	981404	912404
755 405	NC	911405	961405	971405	981405	912405
755 406	NC	911406	961406	971406	981406	912406
755 407	NC	911407	961407	971407	981407	912407
755 408	NC	911408	961408	971408	981408	912408
755 409	NC	911409	961409	971409	981409	912409
755 410	NC	911410	961410	971410	981410	912410
755 411	NC	911411	961411	971411	981411	912411
755 412	NC	911412	961412	971412	981412	912412
755 413	NC	911413	961413	971413	981413	912413
755 414	NC	911414	961414	971414	981414	912414
755 415	NC	911415	961415	971415	981415	912415
755 416	NC	911416	961416	971416	981416	912416
755 417	NC	911417	961417	971417	981417	912417
755 418	NC	911418	961418	971418	981418	912418
755 419	NC	911419	961419	971419	981419	912419
755 420	NC	911420	961420	971420	981420	912420
755 421	NC	911421	961421	971421	981421	912421
755 422	NC	911422	961422	971422	981422	912422
755 423	NC	911423	961423	971423	981423	912423
755 424	NC	911424	961424	971424	981424	912424

Class 756 (Tri-Mode) Stadler 7 x 3 Car Units for Transport for Wales

756 001 756 002	756 003	756 004	756 005	756 006	756 007

Class 756 (Tri-Mode) Stadler 17 x 4 Car Units for Transport for Wales

756 101 756 102 756 103	756 104 756 105 756 106	756 107 756 108 756 109	756 110 756 111 756 112	756 113 756 114 756 115	756 116 756 117

Notes

Class 768 (Bi Mode/Orion Rail) Converted class 319   *on test

768 001*	HQ	(ex 319 010)	77309	62900	71781	77308
768 002*	HQ	(ex 319 009)	77307	62899	71780	77306
768 003						
768 004						
768 005						
768 006						
768 007						
768 008						
768 009						
768 010						

Class 769 (Bi Mode)   Converted class 319   *on test

769 002	CF	(ex 319 002)	77293	62892	71773	77292
769 003	CF	(ex 319 003)	77295	62893	71774	77294
769 006	CF	(ex 319 006)	77301	62896	71777	77300
769 007	CF	(ex 319 007)	77303	62897	71778	77302
769 008	CF	(ex 319 008)	77305	62898	71779	77304
769 421	CF	(ex 319 421)	77331	62911	71792	77330
769 424	AN	(ex 319 424)	77337	62914	71795	77336
769 426	LB(s)	(ex 319 426)	77341	62916	71797	77340
769 431	AN	(ex 319 431)	77351	62921	71802	77350
769 434	AN	(ex 319 434)	77357	62924	71805	77356
769 442	AN	(ex 319 442)	77373	62932	71813	77372
769 445	CF	(ex 319 445)	77379	62935	71816	77378
769 448	AN	(ex 319 448)	77433	62962	71867	77432
769 450	AN	(ex 319 450)	77437	62964	71869	77436
769 452	CF	(ex 319 452)	77441	62966	71871	77440
769 456	AN	(ex 319 456)	77449	62970	71875	77448
769 458	AN	(ex 319 458)	77453	62972	71877	77452
769 922	ZN(s)	(ex 319 422)	77333	62912	71793	77332
769 923	ZN(s)	(ex 319 423)	77335	62913	71794	77334
769 925	ZN(s)	(ex 319 425)	77339	62915	71796	77338
769 927	ZN(s)	(ex 319 427)	77343	62917	71798	77342
769 928*	RG	(ex 319 428)	77345	62918	71799	77344
769 930*	RG	(ex 319 430)	77349	62920	71801	77348
769 932	ZN(s)	(ex 319 432)	77353	62922	71803	77352
769 935	ZN(s)	(ex 319 435)	77359	62925	71806	77358
769 936	ZN(s)	(ex 319 436)	77361	62926	71807	77360
769 937*	RG	(ex 319 437)	77363	62927	71808	77362
769 938*	RG	(ex 319 438)	77365	62928	71809	77364
769 939	ZN(s)	(ex 319 439)	77367	62929	71810	77366
769 940	ZN(s)	(ex 319 440)	77369	62930	71811	77368
769 943*	RG	(ex 319 443)	77375	62933	71814	77374
769 944	BU(s)	(ex 319 444)	77377	62934	71815	77376
769 946*	RG	(ex 319 446)	77381	62936	71817	77380
769 947	BU(s)	(ex 319 447)	77431	62961	71866	77430
769 949	ZN(s)	(ex 319 449)	77435	62963	71868	77434
769 959*	RG	(ex 319 459)	77455	62973	71878	77454

Class 777 (3rd)   Stadler - Merseyrail Metro Units   built / on test*

777 001*	427001	428001	429001	430001	777 027	427027	428027	429027	430027
777 002*	427002	428002	429002	430002	777 028	427028	428028	429028	430028
777 003*	427003	428003	429003	430003	777 029	427029	428029	429029	430029
777 004*	427004	428004	429004	430004	777 030	427030	428030	429030	430030
777 005*	427005	428005	429005	430005	777 031	427031	428031	429031	430031
777 006*	427006	428006	429006	430006	777 032	427032	428032	429032	430032
777 007*	427007	428007	429007	430007	777 033	427033	428033	429033	430033
777 008*	427008	428008	429008	430008	777 034	427034	428034	429034	430034
777 009*	427009	428009	429009	430009	777 035	427035	428035	429035	430035
777 010*	427010	428010	429010	430010	777 036	427036	428036	429036	430036
777 011	427011	428011	429011	430011	777 037	427037	428037	429037	430037
777 012*	427012	428012	429012	430012	777 038	427038	428038	429038	430038
777 013	427013	428013	429013	430013	777 039	427039	428039	429039	430039
777 014*	427014	428014	429014	430014	777 040	427040	428040	429040	430040
777 015	427015	428015	429015	430015	777 041	427041	428041	429041	430041
777 016*	427016	428016	429016	430016	777 042	427042	428042	429042	430042
777 017	427017	428017	429017	430017	777 043	427043	428043	429043	430043
777 018*	427018	428018	429018	430018	777 044	427044	428044	429044	430044
777 019	427019	428019	429019	430019	777 045	427045	428045	429045	430045
777 020	427020	428020	429020	430020	777 046	427046	428046	429046	430046
777 021	427021	428021	429021	430021	777 047	427047	428047	429047	430047
777 022	427022	428022	429022	430022	777 048	427048	428048	429048	430048
777 023	427023	428023	429023	430023	777 049	427049	428049	429049	430049
777 024	427024	428024	429024	430024	777 050	427050	428050	429050	430050
777 025	427025	428025	429025	430025	777 051	427051	428051	429051	430051
777 026	427026	428026	429026	430026	777 052	427052	428052	429052	430052

Class 799 (Ex-Class 319)   Tri-Mode Hydro Flex

799 001	LM	[319 001]	77291	62891	71772	77290
799 201	LM	[319 382]	77975	63094	71980	77976

Great Western IEP Units

Class 800 (Bi-Mode)

800 001	NP	811001	812001	813001	814001	815001
800 002	NP	811002	812002	813002	814002	815002
800 003	NP	811003	812003	813003	814003	815003
800 004	NP	811004	812004	813004	814004	815004 Tulbahadur Pun
800 005	NP	811005	812005	813005	814005	815005
800 006	NP	811006	812006	813006	814006	815006
800 007	NP	811007	812007	813007	814007	815007
800 008	NP	811008	812008	813008	814008	815008
800 009	NP	811009	812009	813009	814009	815009 Sir Gareth Edwards / John Charles
800 010	NP	811010	812010	813010	814010	815010 Paddington Bear / Michael Bond
800 011	NP	811011	812011	813011	814011	815011
800 012	NP	811012	812012	813012	814012	815012
800 013	NP	811013	812013	813013	814013	815013
800 014	NP	811014	812014	813014	814014	815014 Megan Lloyd George / Edith New
800 015	NP	811015	812015	813015	814015	815015
800 016	NP	811016	812016	813016	814016	815016
800 017	NP	811017	812017	813017	814017	815017
800 018	NP	811018	812018	813018	814018	815018
800 019	NP	811019	812019	813019	814019	815019 Joy Lofthouse / Johnny Johnson M.B.E
800 020	NP	811020	812020	813020	814020	815020 Bob Woodward / Elizabeth Ralph
800 021	NP	811021	812021	813021	814021	815021
800 022	NP	811022	812022	813022	814022	815022
800 023	NP	811023	812023	813023	814023	815023 Kathryn Osmond / Fleur Lombard
800 024	NP	811024	812024	813024	814024	815024
800 025	NP	811025	812025	813025	814025	815025 Capt. Tom Moore
800 026	NP	811026	812026	813026	814026	815026 Don Cameron
800 027	NP	811027	812027	813027	814027	815027
800 028	NP	811028	812028	813028	814028	815028
800 029	NP	811029	812029	813029	814029	815029
800 030	NP	811030	812030	813030	814030	815030 Lincoln Callaghan / Henry Cleary
800 031	NP	811031	812031	813031	814031	815031 Mazem Salmou / Charlotte Marsland
800 032	NP	811032	812032	813032	814032	815032
800 033	NP	811033	812033	813033	814033	815033
800 034	NP	811034	812034	813034	814034	815034
800 035	NP	811035	812035	813035	814035	815035
800 036	NP	811036	812036	813036	814036	815036 DR Paul Stephenson OBE

800 301	NP	821001	822001	823001	824001	825001	826001 827001	828001	829001
800 302	NP	821002	822002	823002	824002	825002	826002 827002	828002	829002
800 303	NP	821003	822003	823003	824003	825003	826003 827003	828003	829003
800 304	NP	821004	822004	823004	824004	825004	826004 827004	828004	829004
800 305	NP	821005	822005	823005	824005	825005	826005 827005	828005	829005
800 306	NP	821006	822006	823006	824006	825006	826006 827006	828006	829006
800 307	NP	821007	822007	823007	824007	825007	826007 827007	828007	829007
800 308	NP	821008	822008	823008	824008	825008	826008 827008	828008	829008
800 309	NP	821009	822009	823009	824009	825009	826009 827009	828009	829009
800 310	NP	821010	822010	823010	824010	825010	826010 827010	828010	829010
800 311	NP	821011	822011	823011	824011	825011	826011 827011	828011	829011
800 312	NP	821012	822012	823012	824012	825012	826012 827012	828012	829012
800 313	NP	821013	822013	823013	824013	825013	826013 827013	828013	829013
800 314	NP	821014	822014	823014	824014	825014	826014 827014	828014	829014
800 315	NP	821015	822015	823015	824015	825015	826015 827015	828015	829015
800 316	NP	821016	822016	823016	824016	825016	826016 827016	828016	829016
800 317	NP	821017	822017	823017	824017	825017	826017 827017	828017	829017
800 318	NP	821018	822018	823018	824018	825018	826018 827018	828018	829018

Class 800 (Bi Mode) (cont)

800 319	NP	821019	822019	823019	824019	825019	826019	827019	828019	829019
800 320	NP	821020	822020	823020	824020	825020	826020	827020	828020	829020
800 321	NP	821021	822021	823021	824021	825021	826021	827021	828021	829021

Named Units

800 301	Paddington Bear		800 314	Odette Hallowes MBE 1945 - 2020
800 306	Allan Leonard Lewis / Harold Day		800 317	Freya Bevan
800 310	Wing Commander Ken Rees			

Class 802 (Bi Mode)

802 001	NP	831001	832001	833001	834001	835001					
802 002	NP	831002	832002	833002	834002	835002	Steve Whiteway				
802 003	NP	831003	832003	833003	834003	835003					
802 004	NP	831004	832004	833004	834004	835004					
802 005	NP	831005	832005	833005	834005	835005					
802 006	NP	831006	832006	833006	834006	835006	Harry Billinge MBE				
802 007	NP	831007	832007	833007	834007	835007					
802 008	NP	831008	832008	833008	834008	835008	Rick Rescoria / RNLB Solomon Browne				
802 009	NP	831009	832009	833009	834009	835009					
802 010	NP	831010	832010	833010	834010	835010					
802 011	NP	831011	832011	833011	834011	835011	Captain Robert Falcon Scott				
802 012	NP	831012	832012	833012	834012	835012					
802 013	NP	831013	832013	833013	834013	835013	Michael Eavis				
802 014	NP	831014	832014	833014	834014	835014					
802 015	NP	831015	832015	833015	834015	835015					
802 016	NP	831016	832016	833016	834016	835016					
802 017	NP	831017	832017	833017	834017	835017					
802 018	NP	831018	832018	833018	834018	835018					
802 019	NP	831019	832019	833019	834019	835019					
802 020	NP	831020	832020	833020	834020	835020					
802 021	NP	831021	832021	833021	834021	835021					
802 022	NP	831022	832022	833022	834022	835022					
802 101	NP	831101	832101	833101	834101	835101	836101	837101	838101	839101	
802 102	NP	831102	832102	833102	834102	835102	836102	837102	838102	839102	
802 103	NP	831103	832103	833103	834103	835103	836103	837103	838103	839103	
802 104	NP	831104	832104	833104	834104	835104	836104	837104	838104	839104	
802 105	NP	831105	832105	833105	834105	835105	836105	837105	838105	839105	
802 106	NP	831106	832106	833106	834106	835106	836106	837106	838106	839106	
802 107	NP	831107	832107	833107	834107	835107	836107	837107	838107	839107	
802 108	NP	831108	832108	833108	834108	835108	836108	837108	838108	839108	
802 109	NP	831109	832109	833109	834109	835109	836109	837109	838109	839109	
802 110	NP	831110	832110	833110	834110	835110	836110	837110	838110	839110	
802 111	NP	831111	832111	833111	834111	835111	836111	837111	838111	839111	
802 112	NP	831112	832112	833112	834112	835112	836112	837112	838112	839112	
802 113	NP	831113	832113	833113	834113	835113	836113	837113	838113	839113	
802 114	NP	831114	832114	833114	834114	835114	836114	837114	838114	839114	

Named Unit

802 101	Nancy Astor

LNER East Coast Azuma Units

Class 800 (Bi-Mode)

800 101	DR	811101	812101	813101	814101	815101	816101	817101	818101	819101
800 102	DR	811102	812102	813102	814102	815102	816102	817102	818102	819102
800 103	DR	811103	812103	813103	814103	815103	816103	817103	818103	819103
800 104	DR	811104	812104	813104	814104	815104	816104	817104	818104	819104
800 105	DR	811105	812105	813105	814105	815105	816105	817105	818105	819105
800 106	DR	811106	812106	813106	814106	815106	816106	817106	818106	819106
800 107	DR	811107	812107	813107	814107	815107	816107	817107	818107	819107
800 108	DR	811108	812108	813108	814108	815108	816108	817108	818108	819108
800 109	DR	811109	812109	813109	814109	815109	816109	817109	818109	819109
800 110	DR	811110	812110	813110	814110	815110	816110	817110	818110	819110
800 111	DR	811111	812111	813111	814111	815111	816111	817111	818111	819111
800 112	DR	811112	812112	813112	814112	815112	816112	817112	818112	819112
800 113	DR	811113	812113	813113	814113	815113	816113	817113	818113	819113
800 201	DR	811201	812201	813201	814201	815201				
800 202	DR	811202	812202	813202	814202	815202				
800 203	DR	811203	812203	813203	814203	815203				
800 204	DR	811204	812204	813204	814204	815204				
800 205	DR	811205	812205	813205	814205	815205				
800 206	DR	811206	812206	813206	814206	815206				
800 207	DR	811207	812207	813207	814207	815207				
800 208	DR	811208	812208	813208	814208	815208				
800 209	DR	811209	812209	813209	814209	815209				
800 210	DR	811210	812210	813210	814210	815210				

Class 801 (OH)

801 101	DR	821101	822101	823101	824101	825101				
801 102	DR	821102	822102	823102	824102	825102				
801 103	DR	821103	822103	823103	824103	825103				
801 104	DR	821104	822104	823104	824104	825104				
801 105	DR	821105	822105	823105	824105	825105				
801 106	DR	821106	822106	823106	824106	825106				
801 107	DR	821107	822107	823107	824107	825107				
801 108	DR	821108	822108	823108	824108	825108				
801 109	DR	821109	822109	823109	824109	825109				
801 110	DR	821110	822110	823110	824110	825110				
801 111	DR	821111	822111	823111	824111	825111				
801 112	DR	821112	822112	823112	824112	825112				
801 201	DR	821201	822201	823201	824201	825201	826201	827201	828201	829201
801 202	DR	821202	822202	823202	824202	825202	826202	827202	828202	829202
801 203	DR	821203	822203	823203	824203	825203	826203	827203	828203	829203
801 204	DR	821204	822204	823204	824204	825204	826204	827204	828204	829204
801 205	DR	821205	822205	823205	824205	825205	826205	827205	828205	829205
801 206	DR	821206	822206	823206	824206	825206	826206	827206	828206	829206
801 207	DR	821207	822207	823207	824207	825207	826207	827207	828207	829207
801 208	DR	821208	822208	823208	824208	825208	826208	827208	828208	829208
801 209	DR	821209	822209	823209	824209	825209	826209	827209	828209	829209
801 210	DR	821210	822210	823210	824210	825210	826210	827210	828210	829210
801 211	DR	821211	822211	823211	824211	825211	826211	827211	828211	829211
801 212	DR	821212	822212	823212	824212	825212	826212	827212	828212	829212
801 213	DR	821213	822213	823213	824213	825213	826213	827213	828213	829213
801 214	DR	821214	822214	823214	824214	825214	826214	827214	828214	829214
801 215	DR	821215	822215	823215	824215	825215	826215	827215	828215	829215
801 216	DR	821216	822216	823216	824216	825216	826216	827216	828216	829216
801 217	DR	821217	822217	823217	824217	825217	826217	827217	828217	829217

Class 801 (OH) (cont)										
801 218	DR	821218	822218	823218	824218	825218	826218	827218	828218	829218
801 219	DR	821219	822219	823219	824219	825219	826219	827219	828219	829219
801 220	DR	821220	822220	823220	824220	825220	826220	827220	828220	829220
801 221	DR	821221	822221	823221	824221	825221	826221	827221	828221	829221
801 222	DR	821222	822222	823222	824222	825222	826222	827222	828222	829222
801 223	DR	821223	822223	823223	824223	825223	826223	827223	828223	829223
801 224	DR	821224	822224	823224	824224	825224	826224	827224	828224	829224
801 225	DR	821225	822225	823225	824225	825225	826225	827225	828225	829225
801 226	DR	821226	822226	823226	824226	825226	826226	827226	828226	829226
801 227	DR	821227	822227	823227	824227	825227	826227	827227	828227	829227
801 228	DR	821228	822228	823228	824228	825228	826228	827228	828228	829228
801 229	DR	821229	822229	823229	824229	825229	826229	827229	828229	829229
801 230	DR	821230	822230	823230	824230	825230	826230	827230	828230	829230

Trans Pennine Express 5 car Units

Class 802 (Bi-Mode)						
802 201	DR	831201	832201	833201	834201	835201
802 202	DR	831202	832202	833202	834202	835202
802 203	DR	831203	832203	833203	834203	835203
802 204	DR	831204	832204	833204	834204	835204
802 205	DR	831205	832205	833205	834205	835205
802 206	DR	831206	832206	833206	834206	835206
802 207	DR	831207	832207	833207	834207	835207
802 208	DR	831208	832208	833208	834208	835208
802 209	DR	831209	832209	833209	834209	835209
802 210	DR	831210	832210	833210	834210	835210
802 211	DR	831211	832211	833211	834211	835211
802 212	DR	831212	832212	833212	834212	835212
802 213	DR	831213	832213	833213	834213	835213
802 214	DR	831214	832214	833214	834214	835214
802 215	DR	831215	832215	833215	834215	835215
802 216	DR	831216	832216	833216	834216	835216
802 217	DR	831217	832217	833217	834217	835217
802 218	DR	831218	832218	833218	834218	835218
802 219	DR	831219	832219	833219	834219	835219

Hull Trains 5 car Units

Class 802 (Bi-Mode)						
802 301	BN	831301	832301	833301	834301	835301
802 302	BN	831302	832302	833302	834302	835302
802 303	BN	831303	832303	833303	834303	835303
802 304	BN	831304	832304	833304	834304	835304
802 305	BN	831305	832305	833305	834305	835305

East Coast Trains 5 car Units (LUMO)

Class 803 (Bi-Mode)						
803 001	DR	840001	842001	843001	844001	845001
803 002	DR	840002	842002	843002	844002	845002
803 003	DR	840003	842003	843003	844003	845003
803 004	DR	840004	842004	843004	844004	845004
803 005	DR	840005	842005	843005	844005	845005

Avanti Trains 5 car Units on order

Class 805 (Bi-Mode)

805 001	861001	862001	863001	864001	865001
805 002	861002	862002	863002	864002	865002
805 003	861003	862003	863003	864003	865003
805 004	861004	862004	863004	864004	865004
805 005	861005	862005	863005	864005	865005
805 006	861006	862006	863006	864006	865006
805 007	861007	862007	863007	864007	865007
805 008	861008	862008	863008	864008	865008
805 009	861009	862009	863009	864009	865009
805 010	861010	862010	863010	864010	865010
805 011	861011	862011	863011	864011	865011
805 012	861012	862012	863012	864012	865012
805 013	861013	862013	863013	864013	865013

Avanti Trains 7 car Units on order

Class 807 (OH)

807 001	871001	872001	873001	874001	875001	876001	877001
807 002	871002	872002	873002	874002	875002	876002	877002
807 003	871003	872003	873003	874003	875003	876003	877003
807 004	871004	872004	873004	874004	875004	876004	877004
807 005	871005	872005	873005	874005	875005	876005	877005
807 006	871006	872006	873006	874006	875006	876006	877006
807 007	871007	872007	873007	874007	875007	876007	877007
807 008	871008	872008	873008	874008	875008	876008	877008
807 009	871009	872009	873009	874009	875009	876009	877009
807 010	871010	872010	873010	874010	875010	876010	877010

East Midlands Trains 5 car Units on order

Class 810 (Bi-Mode)

810 001	851001	852001	853001	854001	855001
810 002	851002	852002	853002	854002	855002
810 003	851003	852003	853003	854003	855003
810 004	851004	852004	853004	854004	855004
810 005	851005	852005	853005	854005	855005
810 006	851006	852006	853006	854006	855006
810 007	851007	852007	853007	854007	855007
810 008	851008	852008	853008	854008	855008
810 009	851009	852009	853009	854009	855009
810 010	851010	852010	853010	854010	855010
810 011	851011	852011	853011	854011	855011
810 012	851012	852012	853012	854012	855012
810 013	851013	852013	853013	854013	855013
810 014	851014	852014	853014	854014	855014
810 015	851015	852015	853015	854015	855015
810 016	851016	852016	853016	854016	855016
810 017	851017	852017	853017	854017	855017
810 018	851018	852018	853018	854018	855018
810 019	851019	852019	853019	854019	855019
810 020	851020	852020	853020	854020	855020
810 021	851021	852021	853021	854021	855021
810 022	851022	852022	853022	854022	855022
810 023	851023	852023	853023	854023	855023
810 024	851024	852024	853024	854024	855024

Class 810 (cont)

810 025	851025	852025	853025	854025	855025
810 026	851026	852026	853026	854026	855026
810 027	851027	852027	853027	854027	855027
810 028	851028	852028	853028	854028	855028
810 029	851029	852029	853029	854029	855029
810 030	851030	852030	853030	854030	855030
810 031	851031	852031	853031	854031	855031
810 032	851032	852032	853032	854032	855032
810 033	851033	852033	853033	854033	855033

Notes

Preserved Electric Multiple Units

3304	MAR	[Eurostar]	65451	ELR	[504451]
3308	NRM	[Eurostar]	65617	NRS	[017, 306 017]
10239	MAR	[4732]	68001	SO	[9001, 931091]
11161	EKR	[3135, 3142]	68002	SO	[9002, 931092]
11187	EKR	[3135, 3142]	68003	EVR	[9003, 931093]
11201	SRC	[3142]	68004	MNR	[9004, 931094]
12354	MAR	[4732]	68005	EVR	[9005, 931095]
12795	MAR	[4732]	68008	SO	[9008, 931098]
12796	MAR	[4732]	68009	SO	[9009, 931099]
14351	NIRT	[5176]	68010	EVR	[9010, 931090]
14352	NIRT	[5176]	68500	ECVR	[6071, 9101, 61269]
14573	SRC	[6307, 5661]	68503	SPA	[6079, 9104, 61277]
15354	NIRT	[5176]	68506	ECVR	[6094, 9107, 61292]
15396	NIRT	[5176]	68509	BAR	[6082, 9110, 61280]
16117	SRC	[6307, 5661]	69013	EOR	[7105, 1537, 2325]
28361	MTT		69302	AVDC	[7032, 2101, 2251]
28690	MAR		69304	NIRT	[7034, 2110, 2260]
29289	MAR		69306	SPA	[7036, 2104, 2002, 2254]
29720	MAR		69316	WRH	[7046, 2108, 2258]
29896	MTT		69318	MNR	[7048, 2109, 2004, 2259]
48103	CHC	[370003]	69332	SWR	[7051, 2203]
48106	CHC	[370006]	69333	LAV	[7055, 2112, 2001, 2260]
48404	CHC	[370004]	69335	EVR	[7057, 2209, 2101]
48602	CHC	[370002]	69337	SE	[7058, 2210, 1001]
48603	CHC	[370003]	69339	BU	[7053, 2205, 1393]
49002	CHC	[370002]	70229	EVR	[7105, 2315, 2305]
49006	CHC	[370006]	70235	EOR	[7105, 1537, 2325]
61183	BC	[DB977349]	70262	SE	[7113, 1524, 1001]
61229	SO	[7105, 1537, 2325]	70273	EKR	[7124, 1530, 1392]
61230	SO	[7105, 1537, 2325]	70284	NIRT	[7135, 1520]
61275	NRS	[6077, 4308]	70292	GS	[7143, 1554, 1398]
61287	PEA	[6089, 4311]	70296	NIRT	[7147, 1559]
61503	BT	[303 023]	70345	HDH	[7153, 1500, 1547]
61736	CPRR	[7175, 2304, 1198]	70354	EVR	[7011, 2315, 2305]
61737	CPRR	[7175, 2304, 1198]	70510	NIRT	[7161, 1597]
61798	EVR	[7016, 2315, 2305]	70527	WRS	[7178, 1589, 1393]
61799	EVR	[7016, 2315, 2305]	70531	GS	[7152, 1610, 1396]
61804	EVR	[7019, 2311, 2301]	70539	EVR	[7190, 2311, 2301, 1568]
61805	EVR	[7019, 2311, 2301]	70547	GA	[7198, 1569]
61928	LAV	[977966, 309624, 960102]	70549	ELR	[7200, 1567]
61937	TAVR	[977963, 309616, 960101]	70573	CPRR	[7175, 2304, 1198]
62043	BU	[7327, 1127, 1753]	70576	GCR	[7178, 1589]
62174	SHP	[977845, 311103]	70607	EVR	[7109, 2311, 2301]
62236	SH	[7775, 3075, 3417]	70721	BU	[7327, 1127, 1753]
62321	BH	[3918, 7799, 3099, 3532]	70797	SH	[7717, 3017, 3417]
62364	BH	[7376, 1276, 2251, 1374]	70823	ZG	[34970, 412, 8012]
62385	EKR	[7397, 1297, 2256, 1399]	70824	SWR	[34984, 413, 8013]
62402	SPA	[7414, 1214, 1883, 1497]	70826	SRHC	[34980, 417, 8017]
65217	NRS	[017, 306 017]	70855	SWR	[13018, 412, 8012]
65302	BC	[977874, 5703, 6203, 930204]	70859	OS	[13040, 412, 8012]
65304	BC	[977875, 5705, 6205, 930204]	70860	LSS	[13019, 417, 8017]
65321	BAT	[977505, 5791, 6291]	70904	EKR	[7753, 3053, 3463, 3905]
65373	SO	[5759, 6259]	71041	HSK	[7373, 1273, 1819, 1306]
65379	BC	[977925, 5765, 6265, 930206]	71085	OWG	[7417, 1217, 1884]
65382	BC	[977924, 5768, 6268, 930206]	71163	ZG	[13097, 430, 8030]
65417	NRS	[017, 306 017]	71205	CVR	[312112, 312792]

Preserved Electric Multiple Units

71621	LSS	[317345]	76301	HCB	[4375, 417, 8017]
71758	CS	[309615, 309623, 5058]	76302	HCB	[4382, 417, 8017]
75023	CVR	[307123]	76322	SWR	[3936, 427, 413, 8027]
75033	MRM	[302201]	76324	ZG	[4009, 428, 8028]
75186	BC	[WGP8809]	76397	EKR	[7753, 3053, 3463, 3905]
75250	MRM	[302 277]	76398	EKR	[7753, 3053, 3463, 3905]
75395	NRM	[6077, 4308]	76433	SHP	[977844, 311103]
75407	PEA	[6089, 4311]	76527	ALY	[3918, 7799, 3099, 3532]
75597	BT	[303032]	76528	ALY	[3918, 7799, 3099, 3532]
75632	BT	[303032]	76747	EKR	[7397, 1297, 2256, 1399]
75642	TAVR	[977962, 309616, 960101]	76762	BH	[7412, 1212, 1881]
75881	CVR	[308136]	76764	SPA	[7414, 1214, 1883, 1497]
75965	LAV	[977965, 309624, 960102]	76835	SPA	[7414, 1214, 1883, 1497]
75972	LAV	[977967, 309624, 960102]	76875	EKR	[7861, 3161, 3545]
75981	TAVR	[977964, 309616, 960101]	76887	MMR	[7867, 3167, 3568]
76048	BU	[7327, 1127, 1753]	77092	EAR	[317345]
76102	BU	[7327, 1127, 1753]	77112	BAT	[977508, 5793, 6293]
76262	SH	[7717, 3017, 3417]	77172	ELR	[504451]
76263	SH	[7717, 3017, 3417]	77382	ZG	[442401]
76275	SWR	[3582, 3169, 3929, 404, 8004]	77558	SO	[5759, 6259]
76277	DMR	[4005, 405, 8005, DB977335]	78037	CVR	[312112, 312792]
76297	ZG	[3938, 415, 8015]	79998	RDR	[DB975003]
76298	SWR	[4004, 415, 413, 8015]	79999	RDR	[DB975004]

Brighton Belle Project

Note:- This unit is currently being restored at Crewe LSL

279	Hazel	PEA	287	Clare	PEA	291	Mabel	
282	Doris		288	Beryl		62266	spares donor	
285	Gravetye Manor							

Notes

EMU/DEMU Car Index

131	484 001	38766	380 116	39075	395 007	39172	395 017	39265	395 026
132	484 002	38851	380 101	39076	395 007	39173	395 017	39266	395 026
133	484 003	38852	380 102	39081	395 008	39174	395 017	39271	395 027
134	484 004	38853	380 103	39082	395 008	39175	395 017	39272	395 027
135	484 005	38854	380 104	39083	395 008	39176	395 017	39273	395 027
231	484 001	38855	380 105	39084	395 008	39181	395 018	39274	395 027
232	484 002	38856	380 106	39085	395 008	39182	395 018	39275	395 027
233	484 003	38857	380 107	39086	395 008	39183	395 018	39276	395 027
234	484 004	38858	380 108	39091	395 009	39184	395 018	39281	395 028
235	484 005	38859	380 109	39092	395 009	39185	395 018	39282	395 028
38551	380 101	38860	380 110	39093	395 009	39186	395 018	39283	395 028
38552	380 102	38861	380 111	39094	395 009	39191	395 019	39284	395 028
38553	380 103	38862	380 112	39095	395 009	39192	395 019	39285	395 028
38554	380 104	38863	380 113	39096	395 009	39193	395 019	39286	395 028
38555	380 105	38864	380 114	39101	395 010	39194	395 019	39291	395 029
38556	380 106	38865	380 115	39102	395 010	39195	395 019	39292	395 029
38557	380 107	38866	380 116	39103	395 010	39196	395 019	39293	395 029
38558	380 108	39011	395 001	39104	395 010	39201	395 020	39294	395 029
38559	380 109	39012	395 001	39105	395 010	39202	395 020	39295	395 029
38560	380 110	39013	395 001	39106	395 010	39203	395 020	39296	395 029
38561	380 111	39014	395 001	39111	395 011	39204	395 020	60141	350 368
38562	380 112	39015	395 001	39112	395 011	39205	395 020	60142	350 369
38563	380 113	39016	395 001	39113	395 011	39206	395 020	60143	350 370
38564	380 114	39021	395 002	39114	395 011	39211	395 021	60144	350 371
38565	380 115	39022	395 002	39115	395 011	39212	395 021	60145	350 372
38566	380 116	39023	395 002	39116	395 011	39213	395 021	60146	350 373
38651	380 101	39024	395 002	39121	395 012	39214	395 021	60147	350 374
38652	380 102	39025	395 002	39122	395 012	39215	395 021	60148	350 375
38653	380 103	39026	395 002	39123	395 012	39216	395 021	60149	350 376
38654	380 104	39031	395 003	39124	395 012	39221	395 022	60150	350 377
38655	380 105	39032	395 003	39125	395 012	39222	395 022	60151	350 368
38656	380 106	39033	395 003	39126	395 012	39223	395 022	60152	350 369
38657	380 107	39034	395 003	39131	395 013	39224	395 022	60153	350 370
38658	380 108	39035	395 003	39132	395 013	39225	395 022	60154	350 371
38659	380 109	39036	395 003	39133	395 013	39226	395 022	60155	350 372
38660	380 110	39041	395 004	39134	395 013	39231	395 023	60156	350 373
38661	380 111	39042	395 004	39135	395 013	39232	395 023	60157	350 374
38662	380 112	39043	395 004	39136	395 013	39233	395 023	60158	350 375
38663	380 113	39044	395 004	39141	395 014	39234	395 023	60159	350 376
38664	380 114	39045	395 004	39142	395 014	39235	395 023	60160	350 377
38665	380 115	39046	395 004	39143	395 014	39236	395 023	60511	350 368
38666	380 116	39051	395 005	39144	395 014	39241	395 024	60512	350 369
38751	380 101	39052	395 005	39145	395 014	39242	395 024	60513	350 370
38752	380 102	39053	395 005	39146	395 014	39243	395 024	60514	350 371
38753	380 103	39054	395 005	39151	395 015	39244	395 024	60515	350 372
38754	380 104	39055	395 005	39152	395 015	39245	395 024	60516	350 373
38755	380 105	39056	395 005	39153	395 015	39246	395 024	60517	350 374
38756	380 106	39061	395 006	39154	395 015	39251	395 025	60518	350 375
38757	380 107	39062	395 006	39155	395 015	39252	395 025	60519	350 376
38758	380 108	39063	395 006	39156	395 015	39253	395 025	60520	350 377
38759	380 109	39064	395 006	39161	395 016	39254	395 025	60651	350 368
38760	380 110	39065	395 006	39162	395 016	39255	395 025	60652	350 369
38761	380 111	39066	395 006	39163	395 016	39256	395 025	60653	350 370
38762	380 112	39071	395 007	39164	395 016	39261	395 026	60654	350 371
38763	380 113	39072	395 007	39165	395 016	39262	395 026	60655	350 372
38764	380 114	39073	395 007	39166	395 016	39263	395 026	60656	350 373
38765	380 115	39074	395 007	39171	395 017	39264	395 026	60657	350 374

EMU/DEMU Car Index

60658	350 375	62541	313 213	62700	317 340	62760	5852	62818	5736
60659	350 376	62542	313 214	62701	317 341	62761	5853	62819	5737
60660	350 377	62543	313 215	62702	317 342	62762	5854	62820	5738
60671	350 401	62544	313 216	62703	317 343	62763	5855	62821	5739
60672	350 402	62545	313 217	62705	317 345	62764	5856	62822	5740
60673	350 403	62547	313 219	62707	317 347	62765	5857	62823	5741
60674	350 404	62548	313 220	62708	317 348	62766	5858	62824	5742
60675	350 405	62593	313 201	62709	455 801	62767	5859	62825	5750
60676	350 406	62594	313 202	62710	455 802	62768	5860	62826	5901
60677	350 407	62595	313 203	62711	455 803	62769	5861	62827	5902
60678	350 408	62596	313 204	62712	455 804	62770	5862	62828	5903
60679	350 409	62597	313 205	62713	455 805	62771	5863	62829	5904
60680	350 410	62598	313 206	62714	455 806	62772	5864	62830	5905
60691	350 401	62599	313 207	62715	455 807	62773	5865	62831	5906
60692	350 402	62600	313 208	62716	455 808	62774	5866	62832	5907
60693	350 403	62601	313 209	62717	455 809	62775	5867	62833	5908
60694	350 404	62602	313 210	62718	455 810	62776	5868	62834	5909
60695	350 405	62603	313 211	62719	455 811	62777	5869	62835	5910
60696	350 406	62604	313 212	62720	455 812	62778	5870	62836	5911
60697	350 407	62605	313 213	62721	455 813	62779	5871	62837	5912
60698	350 408	62606	313 214	62722	455 814	62780	5872	62839	5914
60699	350 409	62607	313 215	62723	455 815	62781	5873	62840	5915
60700	350 410	62608	313 216	62724	455 816	62782	5874	62841	5916
60901	350 401	62609	313 217	62725	455 817	62783	5701	62842	5917
60902	350 402	62611	313 219	62726	455 818	62784	5702	62843	5918
60903	350 403	62612	313 220	62727	455 819	62785	5703	62844	5919
60904	350 404	62661	317 501	62728	455 820	62786	5704	62845	5920
60905	350 405	62662	317 502	62729	455 821	62787	5705	62866	318 250
60906	350 406	62664	317 504	62730	455 822	62788	5706	62867	318 251
60907	350 407	62666	317 506	62731	455 823	62789	5707	62868	318 252
60908	350 408	62667	317 507	62732	455 824	62790	5708	62869	318 253
60909	350 409	62668	317 708	62733	455 825	62791	5709	62870	318 254
60910	350 410	62669	317 709	62734	455 826	62792	5710	62871	318 255
60941	350 401	62670	317 710	62735	455 827	62793	5711	62872	318 256
60942	350 402	62671	317 337	62736	455 828	62794	5712	62873	318 257
60943	350 403	62672	317 509	62737	455 829	62795	5713	62874	318 258
60944	350 404	62673	317 510	62738	455 835	62796	5714	62875	318 259
60945	350 405	62674	317 714	62739	455 831	62797	5715	62876	318 260
60946	350 406	62675	317 511	62740	455 832	62798	5716	62877	318 261
60947	350 407	62676	317 512	62741	455 833	62799	5717	62878	318 262
60948	350 408	62677	317 513	62742	455 834	62800	5718	62879	318 263
60949	350 409	62679	317 719	62743	455 830	62801	5719	62880	318 264
60950	350 410	62680	317 515	62744	455 836	62802	5720	62881	318 265
61533	350 264	62681	317 881	62745	455 837	62803	5721	62882	318 266
61546	350 233	62683	317 723	62746	455 838	62804	5722	62883	318 267
61564	350 246	62684	317 882	62747	455 839	62805	5723	62884	318 268
62529	313 201	62685	317 883	62748	455 840	62806	5724	62885	318 269
62530	313 202	62686	317 884	62749	455 841	62807	5725	62890	318 270
62531	313 203	62687	317 885	62750	455 842	62808	5726	62891	799 001
62532	313 204	62688	317 886	62751	455 843	62809	5727	62892	769 002
62533	313 205	62689	317 729	62752	455 844	62810	5728	62893	769 003
62534	313 206	62690	317 344	62753	455 845	62811	5729	62895	319 005
62535	313 207	62692	317 732	62754	455 846	62812	5730	62896	769 006
62536	313 208	62696	317 892	62755	5847	62813	5731	62897	769 007
62537	313 209	62697	317 337	62756	5848	62814	5732	62898	769 008
62538	313 210	62697	317 508	62757	5849	62815	5733	62899	768 001
62539	313 211	62698	317 338	62758	5850	62816	5734	62900	768 002
62540	313 212	62699	317 339	62759	5851	62817	5735	62901	319 011

Car	Unit	Car	Unit	Car	Unit	Car	Unit	Car	Unit
62902	319 012	62987	321 313	63048	319 366	63130	321 436	63762	350 102
62903	319 013	62988	321 314	63049	319 367	63133	321 439	63763	350 105
62904	319 214	62989	321 315	63050	319 368	63134	321 440	63764	350 104
62905	319 215	62990	321 316	63051	319 369	63135	321 441	63765	350 103
62906	319 216	62991	321 317	63052	319 370	63137	322 481	63766	350 106
62907	319 217	62992	321 318	63053	319 371	63138	322 482	63767	350 107
62908	319 218	62993	321 319	63054	319 372	63139	322 483	63768	350 108
62909	319 219	62994	321 320	63055	319 373	63140	322 484	63769	350 109
62910	319 220	62995	321 321	63056	319 374	63141	322 485	63770	350 110
62911	769 421	62996	321 322	63057	319 375	63153	321 901	63771	350 111
62912	769 922	62997	321 323	63058	319 376	63154	321 902	63772	350 112
62913	769 923	62998	321 324	63059	319 377	63155	321 903	63773	350 113
62914	769 424	62999	321 325	63060	319 378	63421	360 201	63774	350 114
62915	769 925	63000	321 326	63061	319 379	63422	360 202	63775	350 115
62916	769 426	63001	321 327	63062	319 380	63423	360 203	63776	350 116
62917	769 927	63002	321 328	63063	320 401	63424	360 204	63777	350 117
62918	769 928	63003	321 329	63064	321 402	63425	360 205	63778	350 118
62919	319 429	63004	321 330	63065	320 403	63711	350 101	63779	350 119
62920	769 930	63005	321 331	63066	320 404	63712	350 102	63780	350 120
62921	769 431	63006	321 332	63067	321 405	63713	350 103	63781	350 121
62922	769 932	63007	321 333	63068	321 406	63714	350 104	63782	350 122
62923	319 433	63008	321 334	63069	321 407	63715	350 105	63783	350 123
62924	769 434	63009	321 335	63070	321 408	63716	350 106	63784	350 124
62925	769 935	63010	321 336	63071	321 409	63717	350 107	63785	350 125
62926	769 936	63011	321 337	63072	321 410	63718	350 108	63786	350 126
62927	769 937	63012	321 338	63073	320 411	63719	350 109	63787	350 127
62928	769 938	63013	321 339	63074	320 412	63720	350 110	63788	350 128
62929	769 939	63014	321 340	63075	320 413	63721	350 111	63789	350 129
62930	769 440	63015	321 341	63076	320 414	63722	350 112	63790	350 130
62931	319 441	63016	321 342	63077	320 415	63723	350 113	63851	444 001
62932	769 442	63017	321 343	63078	320 416	63724	350 114	63852	444 002
62933	769 943	63021	320 301	63079	320 417	63725	350 115	63853	444 003
62934	769 944	63022	320 302	63080	320 418	63726	350 116	63854	444 004
62935	769 445	63023	320 303	63081	321 419	63727	350 117	63855	444 005
62936	769 446	63024	320 304	63082	320 420	63728	350 118	63856	444 006
62961	769 947	63025	320 305	63083	321 421	63729	350 119	63857	444 007
62962	769 448	63026	320 306	63085	321 423	63730	350 120	63858	444 008
62963	769 949	63027	320 307	63086	321 424	63731	350 121	63859	444 009
62964	769 450	63028	320 308	63088	321 426	63732	350 122	63860	444 010
62966	769 452	63029	320 309	63089	321 427	63733	350 123	63861	444 011
62968	319 454	63030	320 310	63090	321 428	63734	350 124	63862	444 012
62970	769 456	63031	320 311	63091	321 429	63735	350 125	63863	444 013
62971	319 457	63032	320 312	63092	321 430	63736	350 126	63864	444 014
62972	769 458	63033	320 313	63093	319 381	63737	350 127	63865	444 015
62973	769 959	63034	320 314	63094	799 201	63738	350 128	63866	444 016
62974	319 460	63035	320 315	63095	319 383	63739	350 129	63867	444 017
62975	321 301	63036	320 316	63096	319 384	63740	350 130	63868	444 018
62976	321 302	63037	320 317	63097	319 385	63751	450 101	63869	444 019
62977	321 303	63038	320 318	63098	319 386	63752	450 102	63870	444 020
62978	321 304	63039	320 319	63099	321 443	63753	450 103	63871	444 021
62979	321 305	63040	320 320	63100	321 444	63754	450 104	63872	444 022
62980	321 306	63041	320 321	63101	321 445	63755	450 105	63873	444 023
62981	321 307	63042	320 322	63103	321 447	63756	450 106	63874	444 024
62982	321 308	63043	319 361	63123	321 365	63757	450 107	63875	444 025
62983	321 309	63044	319 362	63125	321 431	63758	450 108	63876	444 026
62984	321 310	63045	319 363	63126	321 432	63759	450 109	63877	444 027
62985	321 311	63046	319 364	63127	321 433	63760	450 110	63878	444 028
62986	321 312	63047	319 365	63128	321 434	63761	350 101	63879	444 029

EMU/DEMU Car Index

63880	444 030	64377	507 011	64533	315 837	64716	508 125	64780	465 022
63881	444 031	64378	507 012	64534	315 837	64717	508 126	64781	465 023
63882	444 032	64379	507 013	64535	315 838	64718	508 127	64782	465 024
63883	444 033	64380	507 014	64536	315 838	64719	508 128	64783	465 025
63884	444 034	64381	507 015	64537	315 839	64721	508 130	64784	465 026
63885	444 035	64382	507 016	64538	315 839	64722	508 131	64785	465 027
63886	444 036	64383	507 017	64539	315 848	64727	508 136	64786	465 028
63887	444 037	64384	507 018	64547	315 844	64728	508 137	64787	465 029
63888	444 038	64385	507 019	64548	315 844	64729	508 138	64788	465 030
63889	444 039	64386	507 020	64553	315 847	64730	508 139	64789	465 031
63890	444 040	64387	507 021	64554	315 847	64731	508 140	64790	465 032
63891	444 041	64388	507 004	64565	315 853	64732	508 141	64791	465 033
63892	444 042	64389	507 023	64566	315 853	64734	508 143	64792	465 034
63893	444 043	64390	507 024	64567	315 854	64735	456 001	64793	465 035
63894	444 044	64391	507 025	64568	315 854	64736	456 002	64794	465 036
63895	444 045	64392	507 026	64571	315 856	64737	456 003	64795	465 037
63901	450 111	64393	507 027	64572	315 856	64738	456 004	64796	465 038
63902	450 112	64394	507 028	64573	315 857	64739	456 005	64797	465 039
63903	450 113	64395	507 029	64574	315 857	64740	456 006	64798	465 040
63904	450 114	64396	507 030	64599	614 209	64741	456 007	64799	465 041
63905	450 115	64397	507 031	64600	614 209	64742	456 008	64800	465 042
63906	450 116	64398	507 032	64651	508 103	64743	456 009	64801	465 043
63907	450 117	64399	507 033	64652	508 104	64744	456 010	64802	465 044
63908	450 118	64405	507 001	64656	508 108	64745	456 011	64803	465 045
63909	450 119	64406	507 002	64659	508 111	64746	456 012	64804	465 046
63910	450 120	64407	507 003	64660	508 112	64747	456 013	64805	465 047
63911	450 121	64408	507 004	64662	508 114	64748	456 014	64806	465 048
63912	450 122	64409	507 005	64663	508 115	64749	456 015	64807	465 049
63913	450 123	64411	507 007	64665	508 117	64750	456 016	64808	465 050
63914	450 124	64412	507 008	64668	508 120	64751	456 017	64809	465 001
63915	450 125	64413	507 009	64670	508 122	64752	456 018	64810	465 002
63916	450 126	64414	507 010	64671	508 123	64753	456 019	64811	465 003
63917	450 127	64415	507 011	64672	508 124	64754	456 020	64812	465 004
63921	450 111	64416	507 012	64673	508 125	64755	456 021	64813	465 005
63922	450 112	64417	507 013	64674	508 126	64756	456 022	64814	465 006
63923	450 113	64418	507 014	64675	508 127	64757	456 023	64815	465 007
63924	450 114	64419	507 015	64676	508 128	64758	456 024	64816	465 008
63925	450 115	64420	507 016	64678	508 130	64759	465 001	64817	465 009
63926	450 116	64421	507 017	64679	508 131	64760	465 002	64818	465 010
63927	450 117	64422	507 018	64684	508 136	64761	465 003	64819	465 011
63928	450 118	64423	507 019	64685	508 137	64762	465 004	64820	465 012
63929	450 119	64424	507 020	64686	508 138	64763	465 005	64821	465 013
63930	450 120	64425	507 021	64687	508 139	64764	465 006	64822	465 014
63931	450 121	64427	507 023	64688	508 140	64765	465 007	64823	465 015
63932	450 122	64428	507 024	64689	508 141	64766	465 008	64824	465 016
63933	450 123	64429	507 025	64691	508 143	64767	465 009	64825	465 017
63934	450 124	64430	507 026	64694	508 103	64768	465 010	64826	465 018
63935	450 125	64431	507 027	64695	508 104	64769	465 011	64827	465 019
63936	450 126	64432	507 028	64699	508 108	64770	465 012	64828	465 020
63937	450 127	64433	507 029	64702	508 111	64771	465 013	64829	465 021
64367	507 001	64434	507 030	64703	508 112	64772	465 014	64830	465 022
64368	507 002	64435	507 031	64705	508 114	64773	465 015	64831	465 023
64369	507 003	64436	507 032	64706	508 115	64774	465 016	64832	465 024
64371	507 005	64437	507 033	64708	508 117	64775	465 017	64833	465 025
64373	507 007	64497	315 819	64711	508 120	64776	465 018	64834	465 026
64374	507 008	64498	315 819	64713	508 122	64777	465 019	64835	465 027
64375	507 009	64499	315 820	64714	508 123	64778	465 020	64836	465 028
64376	507 010	64500	315 820	64715	508 124	64779	465 021	64837	465 029

EMU/DEMU Car Index

64838	465 030	64897	466 038	65707	465 908	65765	465 916	65823	465 174
64839	465 031	64898	466 039	65708	465 909	65766	465 917	65824	465 175
64840	465 032	64899	466 040	65709	465 910	65767	465 918	65825	465 176
64841	465 033	64900	466 041	65710	465 911	65768	465 919	65826	465 177
64842	465 034	64901	466 042	65711	465 912	65769	465 920	65827	465 178
64843	465 035	64902	466 043	65712	465 913	65770	465 921	65828	465 179
64844	465 036	65201	377 701	65713	465 914	65771	465 922	65829	465 180
64845	465 037	65202	377 702	65714	465 915	65772	465 923	65830	465 181
64846	465 038	65203	377 703	65715	465 916	65773	465 924	65831	465 182
64847	465 039	65204	377 704	65716	465 917	65774	465 925	65832	465 183
64848	465 040	65205	377 705	65717	465 918	65775	465 926	65833	465 184
64849	465 041	65206	377 706	65718	465 919	65776	465 927	65834	465 185
64850	465 042	65207	377 707	65719	465 920	65777	465 928	65835	465 186
64851	465 043	65208	377 708	65720	465 921	65778	465 929	65836	465 187
64852	465 044	65401	377 701	65721	465 922	65779	465 930	65837	465 188
64853	465 045	65402	377 702	65722	465 923	65780	465 931	65838	465 189
64854	465 046	65403	377 703	65723	465 924	65781	465 932	65839	465 190
64855	465 047	65404	377 704	65724	465 925	65782	465 933	65840	465 191
64856	465 048	65405	377 705	65725	465 926	65783	465 934	65841	465 192
64857	465 049	65406	377 706	65726	465 927	65784	465 235	65842	465 193
64858	465 050	65407	377 707	65727	465 928	65785	465 236	65843	465 194
64860	466 001	65408	377 708	65728	465 929	65786	465 237	65844	465 195
64861	466 002	65551	360 101	65729	465 930	65787	465 238	65845	465 196
64862	466 003	65552	360 102	65730	465 931	65788	465 239	65846	465 197
64863	466 004	65553	360 103	65731	465 932	65789	465 240	65847	465 151
64864	466 005	65554	360 104	65732	465 933	65790	465 241	65848	465 152
64865	466 006	65555	360 105	65733	465 934	65791	465 242	65849	465 153
64866	466 007	65556	360 106	65734	465 235	65792	465 243	65850	465 154
64867	466 008	65557	360 107	65735	465 236	65793	465 244	65851	465 155
64868	466 009	65558	360 108	65736	465 237	65794	465 245	65852	465 156
64869	466 010	65559	360 109	65737	465 238	65795	465 246	65853	465 157
64870	466 011	65560	360 110	65738	465 239	65796	465 247	65854	465 158
64871	466 012	65561	360 111	65739	465 240	65797	465 248	65855	465 159
64872	466 013	65562	360 112	65740	465 241	65798	465 249	65856	465 160
64873	466 014	65563	360 113	65741	465 242	65799	465 250	65857	465 161
64874	466 015	65564	360 114	65742	465 243	65800	465 151	65858	465 162
64875	466 016	65565	360 115	65743	465 244	65801	465 152	65859	465 163
64876	466 017	65566	360 116	65744	465 245	65802	465 153	65860	465 164
64877	466 018	65567	360 117	65745	465 246	65803	465 154	65861	465 165
64878	466 019	65568	360 118	65746	465 247	65804	465 155	65862	465 166
64879	466 020	65569	360 119	65747	465 248	65805	465 156	65863	465 167
64880	466 021	65570	360 120	65748	465 249	65806	465 157	65864	465 168
64881	466 022	65571	360 121	65749	465 250	65807	465 158	65865	465 169
64882	466 023	65601	377 701	65750	465 901	65808	465 159	65866	465 170
64883	466 024	65602	377 702	65751	465 902	65809	465 160	65867	465 171
64884	466 025	65603	377 703	65752	465 903	65810	465 161	65868	465 172
64885	466 026	65604	377 704	65753	465 904	65811	465 162	65869	465 173
64886	466 027	65605	377 705	65754	465 905	65812	465 163	65870	465 174
64887	466 028	65606	377 706	65755	465 906	65813	465 164	65871	465 175
64888	466 029	65607	377 707	65756	465 907	65814	465 165	65872	465 176
64889	466 030	65608	377 708	65757	465 908	65815	465 166	65873	465 177
64890	466 031	65700	465 901	65758	465 909	65816	465 167	65874	465 178
64891	466 032	65701	465 902	65759	465 910	65817	465 168	65875	465 179
64892	466 033	65702	465 903	65760	465 911	65818	465 169	65876	465 180
64893	466 034	65703	465 904	65761	465 912	65819	465 170	65877	465 181
64894	466 035	65704	465 905	65762	465 913	65820	465 171	65878	465 182
64895	466 036	65705	465 906	65763	465 914	65821	465 172	65879	465 183
64896	466 037	65706	465 907	65764	465 915	65822	465 173	65880	465 184

65881	465 185	65957	365 523	66864	350 104	66935	450 125	67659	357 009
65882	465 186	65958	365 524	66865	350 108	66936	450 126	67660	357 010
65883	465 187	65959	365 525	66866	350 106	66937	450 127	67661	357 011
65884	465 188	65962	365 528	66867	350 107	67151	444 001	67662	357 012
65885	465 189	65963	365 529	66868	350 105	67152	444 002	67663	357 013
65886	465 190	65964	365 530	66869	350 109	67153	444 003	67664	357 014
65887	465 191	65966	365 532	66870	350 110	67154	444 004	67665	357 015
65888	465 192	65967	365 533	66871	350 111	67155	444 005	67666	357 016
65889	465 193	65968	365 534	66872	350 112	67156	444 006	67667	357 017
65890	465 194	65969	365 535	66873	350 113	67157	444 007	67668	357 018
65891	465 195	65970	365 536	66874	350 114	67158	444 008	67669	357 019
65892	465 196	65972	365 538	66875	350 115	67159	444 009	67670	357 020
65893	465 197	65973	365 539	66876	350 116	67160	444 010	67671	357 021
65895	365 502	65974	365 540	66877	350 117	67161	444 011	67672	357 022
65897	365 504	65975	365 541	66878	350 118	67162	444 012	67673	357 023
65899	365 506	66811	350 101	66879	350 119	67163	444 013	67674	357 024
65900	365 507	66812	350 102	66880	350 120	67164	444 014	67675	357 025
65901	365 508	66813	350 103	66881	350 121	67165	444 015	67676	357 026
65902	365 509	66814	350 104	66882	350 122	67166	444 016	67677	357 027
65903	365 510	66815	350 105	66883	350 123	67167	444 017	67678	357 028
65905	365 512	66816	350 106	66884	350 124	67168	444 018	67679	357 029
65907	365 514	66817	350 107	66885	350 125	67169	444 019	67680	357 030
65908	365 515	66818	350 108	66886	350 126	67170	444 020	67681	357 031
65909	365 516	66819	350 109	66887	350 127	67171	444 021	67682	357 032
65911	365 518	66820	350 110	66888	350 128	67172	444 022	67683	357 033
65913	365 520	66821	350 111	66889	350 129	67173	444 023	67684	357 034
65914	365 521	66822	350 112	66890	350 130	67174	444 024	67685	357 035
65915	365 522	66823	350 113	66901	450 111	67175	444 025	67686	357 036
65916	365 523	66824	350 114	66902	450 112	67176	444 026	67687	357 037
65917	365 524	66825	350 115	66903	450 113	67177	444 027	67688	357 038
65918	365 525	66826	350 116	66904	450 114	67178	444 028	67689	357 039
65921	365 528	66827	350 117	66905	450 115	67179	444 029	67690	357 040
65922	365 529	66828	350 118	66906	450 116	67180	444 030	67691	357 041
65923	365 530	66829	350 119	66907	450 117	67181	444 031	67692	357 042
65925	365 532	66830	350 120	66908	450 118	67182	444 032	67693	357 043
65926	365 533	66831	350 121	66909	450 119	67183	444 033	67694	357 044
65927	365 534	66832	350 122	66910	450 120	67184	444 034	67695	357 045
65928	365 535	66833	350 123	66911	450 121	67185	444 035	67696	357 046
65929	365 536	66834	350 124	66912	450 122	67186	444 036	67751	357 001
65931	365 538	66835	350 125	66913	450 123	67187	444 037	67752	357 002
65932	365 539	66836	350 126	66914	450 124	67188	444 038	67753	357 003
65933	365 540	66837	350 127	66915	450 125	67189	444 039	67754	357 004
65934	365 541	66838	350 128	66916	450 126	67190	444 040	67755	357 005
65936	365 502	66839	350 129	66917	450 127	67191	444 041	67756	357 006
65938	365 504	66840	350 130	66921	450 111	67192	444 042	67757	357 007
65940	365 506	66851	450 101	66922	450 112	67193	444 043	67758	357 008
65941	365 507	66852	450 102	66923	450 113	67194	444 044	67759	357 009
65942	365 508	66853	450 103	66924	450 114	67195	444 045	67760	357 010
65943	365 509	66854	450 104	66925	450 115	67301	5913	67761	357 011
65944	365 510	66855	450 105	66926	450 116	67400	5912	67762	357 012
65946	365 512	66856	450 106	66927	450 117	67651	357 001	67763	357 013
65948	365 514	66857	450 107	66928	450 118	67652	357 002	67764	357 014
65949	365 515	66858	450 108	66929	450 119	67653	357 003	67765	357 015
65950	365 516	66859	450 109	66930	450 120	67654	357 004	67766	357 016
65952	365 518	66860	450 110	66931	450 121	67655	357 005	67767	357 017
65954	365 520	66861	350 101	66932	450 122	67656	357 006	67768	357 018
65955	365 521	66862	350 102	66933	450 123	67657	357 007	67769	357 019
65956	365 522	66863	350 103	66934	450 124	67658	357 008	67770	357 020

EMU/DEMU Car Index

67771	357 021	67833	375 703	67902	458 536	68227	377 327	68372	325 013
67772	357 022	67834	375 704	67904	458 532	68228	377 328	68373	325 014
67773	357 023	67835	375 705	67905	458 532	68300	325 001	68374	325 015
67774	357 024	67836	375 706	67906	458 536	68301	325 001	68375	325 016
67775	357 025	67837	375 707	67911	458 535	68302	325 002	68401	377 301
67776	357 026	67838	375 708	67912	458 531	68303	325 002	68402	377 302
67777	357 027	67839	375 709	67913	458 531	68304	325 003	68403	377 303
67778	357 028	67840	375 710	67914	458 534	68305	325 003	68404	377 304
67779	357 029	67841	375 711	67915	458 535	68306	325 004	68405	377 305
67780	357 030	67842	375 712	67916	458 533	68307	325 004	68406	377 306
67781	357 031	67843	375 713	67917	458 533	68308	325 005	68407	377 307
67782	357 032	67844	375 714	67918	458 534	68309	325 005	68408	377 308
67783	357 033	67845	375 715	67921	375 301	68310	325 006	68409	377 309
67784	357 034	67851	375 601	67922	375 302	68311	325 006	68410	377 310
67785	357 035	67852	375 602	67923	375 303	68312	325 007	68411	377 311
67786	357 036	67853	375 603	67924	375 304	68313	325 007	68412	377 312
67787	357 037	67854	375 604	67925	375 305	68314	325 008	68413	377 313
67788	357 038	67855	375 605	67926	375 306	68315	325 008	68414	377 314
67789	357 039	67856	375 606	67927	375 307	68316	325 009	68415	377 315
67790	357 040	67857	375 607	67928	375 308	68317	325 009	68416	377 316
67791	357 041	67858	375 608	67929	375 309	68320	325 011	68417	377 317
67792	357 042	67859	375 609	67930	375 310	68321	325 011	68418	377 318
67793	357 043	67860	375 610	67931	375 301	68322	325 012	68419	377 319
67794	357 044	67861	375 611	67932	375 302	68323	325 012	68420	377 320
67795	357 045	67862	375 612	67933	375 303	68324	325 013	68421	377 321
67796	357 046	67863	375 613	67934	375 304	68325	325 013	68422	377 322
67801	375 601	67864	375 614	67935	375 305	68326	325 014	68423	377 323
67802	375 602	67865	375 615	67936	375 306	68327	325 014	68424	377 324
67803	375 603	67866	375 616	67937	375 307	68328	325 015	68425	377 325
67804	375 604	67867	375 617	67938	375 308	68329	325 015	68426	377 326
67805	375 605	67868	375 618	67939	375 309	68330	325 016	68427	377 327
67806	375 606	67869	375 619	67940	375 310	68331	325 016	68428	377 328
67807	375 607	67870	375 620	68201	377 301	68340	325 001	68551	360 101
67808	375 608	67871	375 621	68202	377 302	68341	325 002	68552	360 102
67809	375 609	67872	375 622	68203	377 303	68342	325 003	68553	360 103
67810	375 610	67873	375 623	68204	377 304	68343	325 004	68554	360 104
67811	375 611	67874	375 624	68205	377 305	68344	325 005	68555	360 105
67812	375 612	67875	375 625	68206	377 306	68345	325 006	68556	360 106
67813	375 613	67876	375 626	68207	377 307	68346	325 007	68557	360 107
67814	375 614	67877	375 627	68208	377 308	68347	325 008	68558	360 108
67815	375 615	67878	375 628	68209	377 309	68349	325 009	68559	360 109
67816	375 616	67879	375 629	68210	377 310	68350	325 011	68560	360 110
67817	375 617	67880	375 630	68211	377 311	68351	325 012	68561	360 111
67818	375 618	67881	375 701	68212	377 312	68352	325 013	68562	360 112
67819	375 619	67882	375 702	68213	377 313	68353	325 014	68563	360 113
67820	375 620	67883	375 703	68214	377 314	68354	325 015	68564	360 114
67821	375 621	67884	375 704	68215	377 315	68355	325 016	68565	360 115
67822	375 622	67885	375 705	68216	377 316	68360	325 001	68566	360 116
67823	375 623	67886	375 706	68217	377 317	68361	325 002	68567	360 117
67824	375 624	67887	375 707	68218	377 318	68362	325 003	68568	360 118
67825	375 625	67888	375 708	68219	377 319	68363	325 004	68569	360 119
67826	375 626	67889	375 709	68220	377 320	68364	325 005	68570	360 120
67827	375 627	67890	375 710	68221	377 321	68365	325 006	68571	360 121
67828	375 628	67891	375 711	68222	377 322	68366	325 007	70101	377 601
67829	375 629	67892	375 712	68223	377 323	68367	325 008	70102	377 602
67830	375 630	67893	375 713	68224	377 324	68368	325 009	70103	377 603
67831	375 701	67894	375 714	68225	377 325	68370	325 011	70104	377 604
67832	375 702	67895	375 715	68226	377 326	68371	325 012	70105	377 605

EMU/DEMU Car Index

70106	377 606	70312	377 612	70518	377 618	71344	507 003	71512	508 130
70107	377 607	70313	377 613	70519	377 619	71345	507 004	71513	508 131
70108	377 608	70314	377 614	70520	377 620	71346	507 005	71518	508 136
70109	377 609	70315	377 615	70521	377 621	71348	507 007	71519	508 137
70110	377 610	70316	377 616	70522	377 622	71349	507 008	71520	508 138
70111	377 611	70317	377 617	70523	377 623	71350	507 009	71521	508 139
70112	377 612	70318	377 618	70524	377 624	71351	507 010	71522	508 140
70113	377 613	70319	377 619	70525	377 625	71352	507 011	71523	508 141
70114	377 614	70320	377 620	70526	377 626	71353	507 012	71525	508 143
70115	377 615	70321	377 621	70601	377 701	71354	507 013	71526	5723
70116	377 616	70322	377 622	70602	377 702	71355	507 014	71527	5728
70117	377 617	70323	377 623	70603	377 703	71356	507 015	71528	5717
70118	377 618	70324	377 624	70604	377 704	71357	507 016	71529	5738
70119	377 619	70325	377 625	70605	377 705	71358	507 017	71530	5740
70120	377 620	70326	377 626	70606	377 706	71359	507 018	71531	5734
70121	377 621	70401	377 601	70607	377 707	71360	507 019	71532	5709
70122	377 622	70402	377 602	70608	377 708	71361	507 020	71533	5722
70123	377 623	70403	377 603	70701	377 701	71362	507 021	71534	5706
70124	377 624	70404	377 604	70702	377 702	71364	507 023	71535	5715
70125	377 625	70405	377 605	70703	377 703	71365	507 024	71536	5707
70126	377 626	70406	377 606	70704	377 704	71366	507 025	71537	5739
70201	377 601	70407	377 607	70705	377 705	71367	507 026	71538	5750
70202	377 602	70408	377 608	70706	377 706	71368	507 027	71540	5703
70203	377 603	70409	377 609	70707	377 707	71369	507 028	71541	5725
70204	377 604	70410	377 610	70708	377 708	71370	507 029	71542	5711
70205	377 605	70411	377 611	71213	313 201	71371	507 030	71543	5742
70206	377 606	70412	377 612	71214	313 202	71372	507 031	71544	5737
70207	377 607	70413	377 613	71215	313 203	71373	507 032	71545	5701
70208	377 608	70414	377 614	71216	313 204	71374	507 033	71546	5712
70209	377 609	70415	377 615	71217	313 205	71407	315 819	71547	5702
70210	377 610	70416	377 616	71218	313 206	71408	315 820	71548	5704
70211	377 611	70417	377 617	71219	313 207	71425	315 837	71549	5733
70212	377 612	70418	377 618	71220	313 208	71426	315 838	71550	5729
70213	377 613	70419	377 619	71221	313 209	71427	315 839	71551	5730
70214	377 614	70420	377 620	71222	313 210	71432	315 844	71552	5732
70215	377 615	70421	377 621	71223	313 211	71435	315 847	71553	5721
70216	377 616	70422	377 622	71224	313 212	71436	315 848	71554	5736
70217	377 617	70423	377 623	71225	313 213	71441	315 853	71555	5731
70218	377 618	70424	377 624	71226	313 214	71442	315 854	71556	5726
70219	377 619	70425	377 625	71227	313 215	71444	315 856	71557	5718
70220	377 620	70426	377 626	71228	313 216	71445	315 857	71558	5719
70221	377 621	70501	377 601	71229	313 217	71458	614 209	71559	5714
70222	377 622	70502	377 602	71231	313 219	71485	508 103	71559	5741
70223	377 623	70503	377 603	71232	313 220	71486	508 104	71560	5708
70224	377 624	70504	377 604	71299	315 819	71490	508 108	71561	5724
70225	377 625	70505	377 605	71300	315 820	71493	508 111	71562	5727
70226	377 626	70506	377 606	71317	315 837	71494	508 112	71563	5735
70301	377 601	70507	377 607	71318	315 838	71496	508 114	71564	5716
70302	377 602	70508	377 608	71319	315 839	71497	508 115	71565	5705
70303	377 603	70509	377 609	71324	315 844	71499	508 117	71566	5710
70304	377 604	70510	377 610	71327	315 847	71502	508 120	71567	5713
70305	377 605	70511	377 611	71328	315 848	71504	508 122	71568	5720
70306	377 606	70512	377 612	71333	315 853	71505	508 123	71577	317 501
70307	377 607	70513	377 613	71334	315 854	71506	508 124	71578	317 502
70308	377 608	70514	377 614	71336	315 856	71507	508 125	71580	317 504
70309	377 609	70515	377 615	71337	315 857	71508	508 126	71582	317 506
70310	377 610	70516	377 616	71342	507 001	71509	508 127	71583	317 507
70311	377 611	70517	377 617	71343	507 002	71510	508 128	71584	317 708

EMU/DEMU Car Index

71585	317 709	71664	455 802	71725	5905	71873	319 454	71938	319 370
71586	317 710	71665	455 829	71726	5913	71875	769 456	71939	319 371
71587	317 508	71666	455 830	71727	5914	71876	319 457	71940	319 372
71588	317 509	71667	455 831	71728	5915	71877	769 458	71941	319 373
71589	317 510	71668	455 832	71729	5916	71878	769 959	71942	319 374
71590	317 714	71669	455 833	71730	5917	71879	319 460	71943	319 375
71591	317 511	71670	455 834	71732	5918	71880	321 301	71944	319 376
71592	317 512	71671	455 835	71733	5920	71881	321 302	71945	319 377
71593	317 513	71672	455 836	71772	799 001	71882	321 303	71946	319 378
71595	317 719	71673	455 837	71773	769 002	71883	321 304	71947	319 379
71596	317 515	71674	455 838	71774	769 003	71884	321 305	71948	319 380
71597	317 881	71675	455 839	71776	319 005	71885	321 306	71950	321 402
71599	317 723	71676	455 840	71777	769 006	71886	321 307	71953	321 405
71600	317 882	71677	455 841	71778	769 007	71887	321 308	71954	321 406
71601	317 883	71678	455 842	71779	769 008	71888	321 309	71955	321 407
71602	317 884	71679	455 843	71780	768 002	71889	321 310	71956	321 408
71603	317 885	71680	455 844	71781	768 001	71890	321 311	71957	321 409
71604	317 886	71681	455 845	71782	319 011	71891	321 312	71958	321 410
71605	317 729	71682	455 846	71783	319 012	71892	321 313	71967	321 419
71608	317 732	71683	5847	71784	319 013	71893	321 314	71969	321 421
71612	317 892	71684	5848	71785	319 214	71894	321 315	71971	321 423
71613	317 337	71685	5849	71786	319 215	71895	321 316	71972	321 424
71614	317 338	71686	5850	71787	319 216	71896	321 317	71974	321 426
71615	317 339	71687	5851	71788	319 217	71897	321 318	71975	321 427
71616	317 340	71688	5852	71789	319 218	71898	321 319	71976	321 428
71617	317 341	71689	5853	71790	319 219	71899	321 320	71977	321 429
71618	317 342	71690	5854	71791	319 220	71900	321 321	71978	321 430
71619	317 343	71691	5855	71792	769 421	71901	321 322	71979	319 381
71620	317 344	71692	5856	71793	769 922	71902	321 323	71980	799 201
71623	317 347	71693	5857	71794	769 923	71903	321 324	71981	319 383
71624	317 348	71694	5858	71795	769 424	71904	321 325	71982	319 384
71637	455 819	71695	5859	71796	769 925	71905	321 326	71983	319 385
71638	455 828	71696	5860	71797	769 426	71906	321 327	71984	319 386
71639	455 803	71697	5861	71798	769 927	71907	321 328	71985	321 443
71640	455 804	71698	5862	71799	769 928	71908	321 329	71986	321 444
71641	455 805	71699	5863	71800	319 429	71909	321 330	71987	321 445
71642	455 806	71700	5864	71801	769 930	71910	321 331	71989	321 447
71643	455 807	71701	5865	71802	769 431	71911	321 332	71990	600 001
71644	455 808	71702	5866	71803	769 932	71912	321 333	72009	321 365
71645	455 809	71703	5867	71804	319 433	71913	321 334	72011	321 431
71646	455 810	71704	5868	71805	769 434	71914	321 335	72012	321 432
71647	455 811	71705	5869	71806	769 935	71915	321 336	72013	321 433
71648	455 812	71706	5870	71807	769 936	71916	321 337	72014	321 434
71649	455 813	71707	5871	71808	769 937	71917	321 338	72016	321 436
71650	455 814	71708	5872	71809	769 938	71918	321 339	72019	321 439
71651	455 815	71709	5873	71810	769 939	71919	321 340	72020	321 440
71652	455 816	71710	5874	71811	769 440	71920	321 341	72021	321 441
71653	455 817	71714	5901	71812	319 441	71921	321 342	72023	322 481
71654	455 818	71715	5902	71813	769 442	71922	321 343	72024	322 482
71655	455 821	71716	5903	71814	769 943	71929	319 361	72025	322 483
71656	455 820	71717	5904	71815	769 944	71930	319 362	72026	322 484
71657	455 801	71718	5919	71816	769 445	71931	319 363	72027	322 485
71658	455 822	71719	5906	71817	769 446	71932	319 364	72028	465 001
71659	455 823	71720	5907	71866	769 947	71933	319 365	72029	465 001
71660	455 824	71721	5908	71867	769 448	71934	319 366	72030	465 002
71661	455 825	71722	5909	71868	769 949	71935	319 367	72031	465 002
71662	455 826	71723	5910	71869	769 450	71936	319 368	72032	465 003
71663	455 827	71724	5911	71871	769 452	71937	319 369	72033	465 003

EMU/DEMU Car Index

72034	465 004	72092	465 033	72269	365 515	72554	360 104	72759	465 921
72035	465 004	72093	465 033	72270	365 516	72555	360 105	72760	465 921
72036	465 005	72094	465 034	72271	365 516	72556	360 106	72761	465 922
72037	465 005	72095	465 034	72274	365 518	72557	360 107	72762	465 922
72038	465 006	72096	465 035	72275	365 518	72558	360 108	72763	465 923
72039	465 006	72097	465 035	72278	365 520	72559	360 109	72764	465 923
72040	465 007	72098	465 036	72279	365 520	72560	360 110	72765	465 924
72041	465 007	72099	465 036	72280	365 521	72561	360 111	72766	465 924
72042	465 008	72100	465 037	72281	365 521	72562	360 112	72767	465 925
72043	465 008	72101	465 037	72282	365 522	72563	360 113	72768	465 925
72044	465 009	72102	465 038	72283	365 522	72564	360 114	72769	465 926
72045	465 009	72103	465 038	72284	365 523	72565	360 115	72770	465 926
72046	465 010	72104	465 039	72285	365 523	72566	360 116	72771	465 927
72047	465 010	72105	465 039	72286	365 524	72567	360 117	72772	465 927
72048	465 011	72106	465 040	72287	365 524	72568	360 118	72773	465 928
72049	465 011	72107	465 040	72288	365 525	72569	360 119	72774	465 928
72050	465 012	72108	465 041	72289	365 525	72570	360 120	72775	465 929
72051	465 012	72109	465 041	72294	365 528	72571	360 121	72776	465 929
72052	465 013	72110	465 042	72295	365 528	72719	465 901	72777	465 930
72053	465 013	72111	465 042	72296	365 529	72720	465 901	72778	465 930
72054	465 014	72112	465 043	72297	365 529	72721	465 902	72779	465 931
72055	465 014	72113	465 043	72298	365 530	72722	465 902	72780	465 931
72056	465 015	72114	465 044	72299	365 530	72723	465 903	72781	465 932
72057	465 015	72115	465 044	72302	365 532	72724	465 903	72782	465 932
72058	465 016	72116	465 045	72303	365 532	72725	465 904	72783	465 933
72059	465 016	72117	465 045	72304	365 533	72726	465 904	72784	465 933
72060	465 017	72118	465 046	72305	365 533	72727	465 905	72785	465 934
72061	465 017	72119	465 046	72306	365 534	72728	465 905	72786	465 934
72062	465 018	72120	465 047	72307	365 534	72729	465 906	72787	465 235
72063	465 018	72121	465 047	72308	365 535	72730	465 906	72788	465 235
72064	465 019	72122	465 048	72309	365 535	72731	465 907	72789	465 236
72065	465 019	72123	465 048	72310	365 536	72732	465 907	72790	465 236
72066	465 020	72124	465 049	72311	365 536	72733	465 908	72791	465 237
72067	465 020	72125	465 049	72314	365 538	72734	465 908	72792	465 237
72068	465 021	72126	465 050	72315	365 538	72735	465 909	72793	465 238
72069	465 021	72127	465 050	72316	365 539	72736	465 909	72794	465 238
72070	465 022	72128	321 901	72317	365 539	72737	465 910	72795	465 239
72071	465 022	72129	321 902	72318	365 540	72738	465 910	72796	465 239
72072	465 023	72130	321 903	72319	365 540	72739	465 911	72797	465 240
72073	465 023	72242	365 502	72320	365 541	72740	465 911	72798	465 240
72074	465 024	72243	365 502	72321	365 541	72741	465 912	72799	465 241
72075	465 024	72246	365 504	72340	323 240	72742	465 912	72800	465 241
72076	465 025	72247	365 504	72341	323 241	72743	465 913	72801	465 242
72077	465 025	72250	365 506	72342	323 242	72744	465 913	72802	465 242
72078	465 026	72251	365 506	72343	323 243	72745	465 914	72803	465 243
72079	465 026	72252	365 507	72421	360 201	72746	465 914	72804	465 243
72080	465 027	72253	365 507	72422	360 202	72747	465 915	72805	465 244
72081	465 027	72254	365 508	72423	360 203	72748	465 915	72806	465 244
72082	465 028	72255	365 508	72424	360 204	72749	465 916	72807	465 245
72083	465 028	72256	365 509	72425	360 205	72750	465 916	72808	465 245
72084	465 029	72257	365 509	72431	360 201	72751	465 917	72809	465 246
72085	465 029	72258	365 510	72432	360 202	72752	465 917	72810	465 246
72086	465 030	72259	365 510	72433	360 203	72753	465 918	72811	465 247
72087	465 030	72262	365 512	72434	360 204	72754	465 918	72812	465 247
72088	465 031	72263	365 512	72435	360 205	72755	465 919	72813	465 248
72089	465 031	72266	365 514	72551	360 101	72756	465 919	72814	465 248
72090	465 032	72267	365 514	72552	360 102	72757	465 920	72815	465 249
72091	465 032	72268	365 515	72553	360 103	72758	465 920	72816	465 249

72817	465 250	72956	465 179	73321	375 821	73422	377 422	73505	377 505
72818	465 250	72957	465 179	73322	375 822	73423	377 423	73506	377 506
72900	465 151	72958	465 180	73323	375 823	73424	377 424	73507	377 507
72901	465 151	72959	465 180	73324	375 824	73425	377 425	73508	377 508
72902	465 152	72960	465 181	73325	375 825	73426	377 426	73509	377 509
72903	465 152	72961	465 181	73326	375 826	73427	377 427	73510	377 510
72904	465 153	72962	465 182	73327	375 827	73428	377 428	73511	377 511
72905	465 153	72963	465 182	73328	375 828	73429	377 429	73512	377 512
72906	465 154	72964	465 183	73329	375 829	73430	377 430	73513	377 513
72907	465 154	72965	465 183	73330	375 830	73431	377 431	73514	377 514
72908	465 155	72966	465 184	73331	375 901	73432	377 432	73515	377 515
72909	465 155	72967	465 184	73332	375 902	73433	377 433	73516	377 516
72910	465 156	72968	465 185	73333	375 903	73434	377 434	73517	377 517
72911	465 156	72969	465 185	73334	375 904	73435	377 435	73518	377 518
72912	465 157	72970	465 186	73335	375 905	73436	377 436	73519	377 519
72913	465 157	72971	465 186	73336	375 906	73437	377 437	73520	377 520
72914	465 158	72972	465 187	73337	375 907	73438	377 438	73521	377 521
72915	465 158	72973	465 187	73338	375 908	73439	377 439	73522	377 522
72916	465 159	72974	465 188	73339	375 909	73440	377 440	73523	377 523
72917	465 159	72975	465 188	73340	375 910	73441	377 441	73601	377 501
72918	465 160	72976	465 189	73341	375 911	73442	377 442	73602	377 502
72919	465 160	72977	465 189	73342	375 912	73443	377 443	73603	377 503
72920	465 161	72978	465 190	73343	375 913	73444	377 444	73604	377 504
72921	465 161	72979	465 190	73344	375 914	73445	377 445	73605	377 505
72922	465 162	72980	465 191	73345	375 915	73446	377 446	73606	377 506
72923	465 162	72981	465 191	73346	375 916	73447	377 447	73607	377 507
72924	465 163	72982	465 192	73347	375 917	73448	377 448	73608	377 508
72925	465 163	72983	465 192	73348	375 918	73449	377 449	73609	377 509
72926	465 164	72984	465 193	73349	375 919	73450	377 450	73610	377 510
72927	465 164	72985	465 193	73350	375 920	73451	377 451	73611	377 511
72928	465 165	72986	465 194	73351	375 921	73452	377 452	73612	377 512
72929	465 165	72987	465 194	73352	375 922	73453	377 453	73613	377 513
72930	465 166	72988	465 195	73353	375 923	73454	377 454	73614	377 514
72931	465 166	72989	465 195	73354	375 924	73455	377 455	73615	377 515
72932	465 167	72990	465 196	73355	375 925	73456	377 456	73616	377 516
72933	465 167	72991	465 196	73356	375 926	73457	377 457	73617	377 517
72934	465 168	72992	465 197	73357	375 927	73458	377 458	73618	377 518
72935	465 168	72993	465 197	73401	377 401	73459	377 459	73619	377 519
72936	465 169	73301	375 801	73402	377 402	73460	377 460	73620	377 520
72937	465 169	73302	375 802	73403	377 403	73461	377 461	73621	377 521
72938	465 170	73303	375 803	73404	377 404	73462	377 462	73622	377 522
72939	465 170	73304	375 804	73405	377 405	73463	377 463	73623	377 523
72940	465 171	73305	375 805	73406	377 406	73464	377 464	73701	375 801
72941	465 171	73306	375 806	73407	377 407	73465	377 465	73702	375 802
72942	465 172	73307	375 807	73408	377 408	73466	377 466	73703	375 803
72943	465 172	73308	375 808	73409	377 409	73467	377 467	73704	375 804
72944	465 173	73309	375 809	73410	377 410	73468	377 468	73705	375 805
72945	465 173	73310	375 810	73411	377 411	73469	377 469	73706	375 806
72946	465 174	73311	375 811	73412	377 412	73470	377 470	73707	375 807
72947	465 174	73312	375 812	73413	377 413	73471	377 471	73708	375 808
72948	465 175	73313	375 813	73414	377 414	73472	377 472	73709	375 809
72949	465 175	73314	375 814	73415	377 415	73473	377 473	73710	375 810
72950	465 176	73315	375 815	73416	377 416	73474	377 474	73711	375 811
72951	465 176	73316	375 816	73417	377 417	73475	377 475	73712	375 812
72952	465 177	73317	375 817	73418	377 418	73501	377 501	73713	375 813
72953	465 177	73318	375 818	73419	377 419	73502	377 502	73714	375 814
72954	465 178	73319	375 819	73420	377 420	73503	377 503	73715	375 815
72955	465 178	73320	375 820	73421	377 421	73504	377 504	73716	375 816

EMU/DEMU Car Index

73717	375 817	73818	377 418	74051	357 001	74113	458 513	74191	357 041
73718	375 818	73819	377 419	74052	357 002	74114	458 514	74192	357 042
73719	375 819	73820	377 420	74053	357 003	74115	458 515	74193	357 043
73720	375 820	73821	377 421	74054	357 004	74116	458 516	74194	357 044
73721	375 821	73822	377 422	74055	357 005	74117	458 517	74195	357 045
73722	375 822	73823	377 423	74056	357 006	74118	458 518	74196	357 046
73723	375 823	73824	377 424	74057	357 007	74119	458 519	74201	375 601
73724	375 824	73825	377 425	74058	357 008	74120	458 520	74202	375 602
73725	375 825	73826	377 426	74059	357 009	74121	458 521	74203	375 603
73726	375 826	73827	377 427	74060	357 010	74122	458 522	74204	375 604
73727	375 827	73828	377 428	74061	357 011	74123	458 523	74205	375 605
73728	375 828	73829	377 429	74062	357 012	74124	458 524	74206	375 606
73729	375 829	73830	377 430	74063	357 013	74125	458 525	74207	375 607
73730	375 830	73831	377 431	74064	357 014	74126	458 526	74208	375 608
73731	375 901	73832	377 432	74065	357 015	74127	458 527	74209	375 609
73732	375 902	73833	377 433	74066	357 016	74128	458 528	74210	375 610
73733	375 903	73834	377 434	74067	357 017	74129	458 529	74211	375 611
73734	375 904	73835	377 435	74068	357 018	74130	458 530	74212	375 612
73735	375 905	73836	377 436	74069	357 019	74151	357 001	74213	375 613
73736	375 906	73837	377 437	74070	357 020	74152	357 002	74214	375 614
73737	375 907	73838	377 438	74071	357 021	74153	357 003	74215	375 615
73738	375 908	73839	377 439	74072	357 022	74154	357 004	74216	375 616
73739	375 909	73840	377 440	74073	357 023	74155	357 005	74217	375 617
73740	375 910	73841	377 441	74074	357 024	74156	357 006	74218	375 618
73741	375 911	73842	377 442	74075	357 025	74157	357 007	74219	375 619
73742	375 912	73843	377 443	74076	357 026	74158	357 008	74220	375 620
73743	375 913	73844	377 444	74077	357 027	74159	357 009	74221	375 621
73744	375 914	73845	377 445	74078	357 028	74160	357 010	74222	375 622
73745	375 915	73846	377 446	74079	357 029	74161	357 011	74223	375 623
73746	375 916	73847	377 447	74080	357 030	74162	357 012	74224	375 624
73747	375 917	73848	377 448	74081	357 031	74163	357 013	74225	375 625
73748	375 918	73849	377 449	74082	357 032	74164	357 014	74226	375 626
73749	375 919	73850	377 450	74083	357 033	74165	357 015	74227	375 627
73750	375 920	73851	377 451	74084	357 034	74166	357 016	74228	375 628
73751	375 921	73852	377 452	74085	357 035	74167	357 017	74229	375 629
73752	375 922	73853	377 453	74086	357 036	74168	357 018	74230	375 630
73753	375 923	73854	377 454	74087	357 037	74169	357 019	74231	375 701
73754	375 924	73855	377 455	74088	357 038	74170	357 020	74232	375 702
73755	375 925	73856	377 456	74089	357 039	74171	357 021	74233	375 703
73756	375 926	73857	377 457	74090	357 040	74172	357 022	74234	375 704
73757	375 927	73858	377 458	74091	357 041	74173	357 023	74235	375 705
73801	377 401	73859	377 459	74092	357 042	74174	357 024	74236	375 706
73802	377 402	73860	377 460	74093	357 043	74175	357 025	74237	375 707
73803	377 403	73861	377 461	74094	357 044	74176	357 026	74238	375 708
73804	377 404	73862	377 462	74095	357 045	74177	357 027	74239	375 709
73805	377 405	73863	377 463	74096	357 046	74178	357 028	74240	375 710
73806	377 406	73864	377 464	74101	458 501	74179	357 029	74241	375 711
73807	377 407	73865	377 465	74102	458 502	74180	357 030	74242	375 712
73808	377 408	73866	377 466	74103	458 503	74181	357 031	74243	375 713
73809	377 409	73867	377 467	74104	458 504	74182	357 032	74244	375 714
73810	377 410	73868	377 468	74105	458 505	74183	357 033	74245	375 715
73811	377 411	73869	377 469	74106	458 506	74184	357 034	74251	375 601
73812	377 412	73870	377 470	74107	458 507	74185	357 035	74252	375 602
73813	377 413	73871	377 471	74108	458 508	74186	357 036	74253	375 603
73814	377 414	73872	377 472	74109	458 509	74187	357 037	74254	375 604
73815	377 415	73873	377 473	74110	458 510	74188	357 038	74255	375 605
73816	377 416	73874	377 474	74111	458 511	74189	357 039	74256	375 606
73817	377 417	73875	377 475	74112	458 512	74190	357 040	74257	375 607

EMU/DEMU Car Index

74258	375 608	74413	458 533	74481	333 005	74826	377 326	77011	317 509
74259	375 609	74414	458 534	74482	333 006	74827	377 327	77012	317 510
74260	375 610	74415	458 535	74483	333 007	74828	377 328	77013	317 714
74261	375 611	74416	458 536	74484	333 008	74901	377 501	77014	317 511
74262	375 612	74417	458 532	74485	333 009	74902	377 502	77015	317 512
74263	375 613	74418	458 531	74486	333 010	74903	377 503	77016	317 513
74264	375 614	74421	458 502	74487	333 011	74904	377 504	77018	317 719
74265	375 615	74422	458 525	74488	333 012	74905	377 505	77019	317 515
74266	375 616	74423	458 529	74489	333 013	74906	377 506	77020	317 881
74267	375 617	74424	458 522	74490	333 014	74907	377 507	77022	317 723
74268	375 618	74425	458 505	74491	333 015	74908	377 508	77023	317 882
74269	375 619	74426	458 517	74492	333 016	74909	377 509	77024	317 501
74270	375 620	74427	458 512	74551	360 101	74910	377 510	77025	317 884
74271	375 621	74428	458 507	74552	360 102	74911	377 511	77026	317 885
74272	375 622	74431	458 501	74553	360 103	74912	377 512	77027	317 886
74273	375 623	74432	458 518	74554	360 104	74913	377 513	77028	317 729
74274	375 624	74433	458 508	74555	360 105	74914	377 514	77029	317 344
74275	375 625	74434	458 523	74556	360 106	74915	377 515	77031	317 732
74276	375 626	74435	458 511	74557	360 107	74916	377 516	77035	317 892
74277	375 627	74436	458 506	74558	360 108	74917	377 517	77036	317 337
74278	375 628	74437	458 513	74559	360 109	74918	377 518	77037	317 338
74279	375 629	74438	458 521	74560	360 110	74919	377 519	77038	317 339
74280	375 630	74441	458 503	74561	360 111	74920	377 520	77039	317 340
74281	375 701	74442	458 526	74562	360 112	74921	377 521	77040	317 341
74282	375 702	74443	458 533	74563	360 113	74922	377 522	77041	317 342
74283	375 703	74444	458 534	74564	360 114	74923	377 523	77042	317 343
74284	375 704	74445	458 535	74565	360 115	75901	377 501	77044	317 345
74285	375 705	74446	458 531	74566	360 116	75902	377 502	77046	317 347
74286	375 706	74447	458 532	74567	360 117	75903	377 503	77047	317 348
74287	375 707	74448	458 536	74568	360 118	75904	377 504	77048	317 501
74288	375 708	74451	458 504	74569	360 119	75905	377 505	77049	317 502
74289	375 709	74452	458 509	74570	360 120	75906	377 506	77050	317 512
74290	375 710	74453	458 533	74571	360 121	75907	377 507	77051	317 504
74291	375 711	74454	458 534	74801	377 301	75908	377 508	77053	317 506
74292	375 712	74455	458 535	74802	377 302	75909	377 509	77054	317 507
74293	375 713	74456	458 536	74803	377 303	75910	377 510	77055	317 708
74294	375 714	74457	458 532	74804	377 304	75911	377 511	77056	317 709
74295	375 715	74458	458 531	74805	377 305	75912	377 512	77057	317 710
74351	375 301	74461	333 001	74806	377 306	75913	377 513	77058	317 508
74352	375 302	74462	333 002	74807	377 307	75914	377 514	77059	317 509
74353	375 303	74463	333 003	74808	377 308	75915	377 515	77060	317 510
74354	375 304	74464	333 004	74809	377 309	75916	377 516	77061	317 714
74355	375 305	74465	333 005	74810	377 310	75917	377 517	77062	317 511
74356	375 306	74466	333 006	74811	377 311	75918	377 518	77064	317 513
74357	375 307	74467	333 007	74812	377 312	75919	377 519	77066	317 719
74358	375 308	74468	333 008	74813	377 313	75920	377 520	77067	317 515
74359	375 309	74469	333 009	74814	377 314	75921	377 521	77068	317 881
74360	375 310	74470	333 010	74815	377 315	75922	377 522	77070	317 723
74401	458 520	74471	333 011	74816	377 316	75923	377 523	77071	317 882
74402	458 524	74472	333 012	74817	377 317	77000	317 883	77072	317 883
74403	458 519	74473	333 013	74818	377 318	77001	317 502	77073	317 884
74404	458 515	74474	333 014	74819	377 319	77003	317 504	77074	317 885
74405	458 510	74475	333 015	74820	377 320	77005	317 506	77075	317 886
74406	458 516	74476	333 016	74821	377 321	77006	317 507	77076	317 729
74407	458 514	74477	333 001	74822	377 322	77007	317 708	77079	317 732
74408	458 528	74478	333 002	74823	377 323	77008	317 709	77083	317 892
74411	458 530	74479	333 003	74824	377 324	77009	317 710	77084	317 337
74412	458 527	74480	333 004	74825	377 325	77010	317 508	77085	317 338

EMU/DEMU Car Index

77086	317 339	77151	377 151	77269	318 259	77337	769 424	77449	769 456
77087	317 340	77152	377 152	77270	318 260	77338	769 925	77450	319 457
77088	317 341	77153	377 153	77271	318 261	77339	769 925	77451	319 457
77089	317 342	77154	377 154	77272	318 262	77340	769 426	77452	769 458
77090	317 343	77155	377 155	77273	318 263	77341	769 426	77453	769 458
77091	317 344	77156	377 156	77274	318 264	77342	769 927	77454	769 959
77094	317 347	77157	377 157	77275	318 265	77343	769 927	77455	769 959
77095	317 348	77158	377 158	77276	318 266	77344	769 928	77456	319 460
77101	377 101	77159	377 159	77277	318 267	77345	769 928	77457	319 460
77102	377 102	77160	377 160	77278	318 268	77346	319 429	77458	319 361
77103	377 103	77161	377 161	77279	318 269	77347	319 429	77459	319 361
77104	377 104	77162	377 162	77288	318 270	77348	769 930	77460	319 362
77105	377 105	77163	377 163	77289	318 270	77349	769 930	77461	319 362
77106	377 106	77164	377 164	77290	799 001	77350	769 431	77462	319 363
77107	377 107	77171	377 201	77291	799 001	77351	769 431	77463	319 363
77108	377 108	77172	377 202	77292	769 002	77352	769 932	77464	319 364
77109	377 109	77173	377 203	77293	769 002	77353	769 932	77465	319 364
77110	377 110	77174	377 204	77294	769 003	77354	319 433	77466	319 365
77111	377 111	77175	377 205	77295	769 003	77355	319 433	77467	319 365
77112	377 112	77176	377 206	77298	319 005	77356	769 434	77468	319 366
77113	377 113	77177	377 207	77299	319 005	77357	769 434	77469	319 366
77114	377 114	77178	377 208	77300	769 006	77358	769 935	77470	319 367
77115	377 115	77179	377 209	77301	769 006	77359	769 935	77471	319 367
77116	377 116	77180	377 210	77302	769 007	77360	769 936	77472	319 368
77117	377 117	77181	377 211	77303	769 007	77361	769 936	77473	319 368
77118	377 118	77182	377 212	77304	769 008	77362	769 937	77474	319 369
77119	377 119	77183	377 213	77305	769 008	77363	769 937	77475	319 369
77120	377 120	77184	377 214	77306	768 002	77364	769 938	77476	319 370
77121	377 121	77185	377 215	77307	768 002	77365	769 938	77477	319 370
77122	377 122	77240	318 250	77308	768 001	77366	769 939	77478	319 371
77123	377 123	77241	318 251	77309	768 001	77367	769 939	77479	319 371
77124	377 124	77242	318 252	77310	319 011	77368	769 440	77480	319 372
77125	377 125	77243	318 253	77311	319 011	77369	769 440	77481	319 372
77126	377 126	77244	318 254	77312	319 012	77370	319 441	77482	319 373
77127	377 127	77245	318 255	77313	319 012	77371	319 441	77483	319 373
77128	377 128	77246	318 256	77314	319 013	77372	769 442	77484	319 374
77129	377 129	77247	318 257	77315	319 013	77373	769 442	77485	319 374
77130	377 130	77248	318 258	77316	319 214	77374	769 943	77486	319 375
77131	377 131	77249	318 259	77317	319 214	77375	769 943	77487	319 375
77132	377 132	77250	318 260	77318	319 215	77376	769 944	77488	319 376
77133	377 133	77251	318 261	77319	319 215	77377	769 944	77489	319 376
77134	377 134	77252	318 262	77320	319 216	77378	769 445	77490	319 377
77135	377 135	77253	318 263	77321	319 216	77379	769 445	77491	319 377
77136	377 136	77254	318 264	77322	319 217	77380	769 446	77492	319 378
77137	377 137	77255	318 265	77323	319 217	77381	769 446	77493	319 378
77138	377 138	77256	318 266	77324	319 218	77430	769 947	77494	319 379
77139	377 139	77257	318 267	77325	319 218	77431	769 947	77495	319 379
77140	377 140	77258	318 268	77326	319 219	77432	769 448	77496	319 380
77141	377 141	77259	318 269	77327	319 219	77433	769 448	77497	319 380
77142	377 142	77260	318 250	77328	319 220	77434	769 949	77579	455 825
77143	377 143	77261	318 251	77329	319 220	77435	769 949	77580	455 801
77144	377 144	77262	318 252	77330	769 421	77436	769 450	77581	455 802
77145	377 145	77263	318 253	77331	769 421	77437	769 450	77582	455 802
77146	377 146	77264	318 254	77332	769 922	77440	769 452	77583	455 803
77147	377 147	77265	318 255	77333	769 922	77441	769 452	77584	455 803
77148	377 148	77266	318 256	77334	769 923	77444	319 454	77585	455 804
77149	377 149	77267	318 257	77335	769 923	77445	319 454	77586	455 804
77150	377 150	77268	318 258	77336	769 424	77448	769 456	77587	455 805

EMU/DEMU Car Index

77588	455 805	77646	455 834	77704	5863	77762	5718	77820	5904
77589	455 806	77647	455 835	77705	5864	77763	5719	77821	5905
77590	455 806	77648	455 835	77706	5864	77764	5719	77822	5905
77591	455 807	77649	455 836	77707	5865	77765	5720	77823	5906
77592	455 807	77650	455 836	77708	5865	77766	5720	77824	5906
77593	455 824	77651	455 837	77709	5866	77767	5721	77825	5907
77594	455 808	77652	455 837	77710	5866	77768	5721	77826	5907
77595	455 812	77653	455 838	77711	5867	77769	5722	77827	5908
77596	455 823	77654	455 838	77712	5867	77770	5722	77828	5908
77597	455 810	77655	455 839	77713	5868	77771	5723	77829	5909
77598	455 810	77656	455 839	77714	5868	77772	5723	77830	5909
77599	455 811	77657	455 840	77715	5869	77773	5724	77831	5910
77600	455 811	77658	455 840	77716	5869	77774	5724	77832	5910
77601	455 823	77659	455 841	77717	5870	77775	5725	77833	5911
77602	455 809	77660	455 841	77718	5870	77776	5725	77834	5911
77603	455 813	77661	455 842	77719	5871	77777	5726	77835	5912
77604	455 813	77662	455 842	77720	5871	77778	5726	77836	5912
77605	455 814	77663	455 843	77721	5872	77779	5727	77837	5913
77606	455 814	77664	455 843	77722	5872	77780	5727	77838	5913
77607	455 815	77665	455 844	77723	5873	77781	5728	77839	5914
77608	455 815	77666	455 844	77724	5873	77782	5728	77840	5914
77609	455 816	77667	455 845	77725	5874	77783	5729	77841	5915
77610	455 827	77668	455 845	77726	5874	77784	5729	77842	5915
77611	455 817	77669	455 846	77727	5701	77785	5730	77843	5916
77612	455 817	77670	455 846	77728	5701	77786	5730	77844	5916
77613	455 818	77671	5847	77729	5702	77787	5731	77845	5917
77614	455 827	77672	5847	77730	5702	77788	5731	77846	5917
77615	455 819	77673	5848	77731	5703	77789	5732	77847	5918
77616	455 819	77674	5848	77732	5703	77790	5732	77848	5918
77617	455 820	77675	5849	77733	5704	77791	5733	77849	5919
77618	455 820	77676	5849	77734	5704	77792	5733	77850	5919
77619	455 821	77677	5850	77735	5705	77793	5734	77851	5920
77620	455 821	77678	5850	77736	5705	77794	5734	77852	5920
77621	455 822	77679	5851	77737	5706	77795	5735	77853	321 301
77622	455 822	77680	5851	77738	5706	77796	5735	77854	321 302
77623	455 809	77681	5852	77739	5707	77797	5736	77855	321 303
77624	455 824	77682	5852	77740	5707	77798	5736	77856	321 304
77625	455 830	77683	5853	77741	5708	77799	5737	77857	321 305
77626	455 812	77684	5853	77742	5708	77800	5737	77858	321 306
77627	455 801	77685	5854	77743	5709	77801	5738	77859	321 307
77628	455 825	77686	5854	77744	5709	77802	5738	77860	321 308
77629	455 826	77687	5855	77745	5710	77803	5739	77861	321 309
77630	455 826	77688	5855	77746	5710	77804	5739	77862	321 310
77631	455 828	77689	5856	77747	5711	77805	5740	77863	321 311
77632	455 818	77690	5856	77748	5711	77806	5740	77864	321 312
77633	455 816	77691	5857	77749	5712	77807	5741	77865	321 313
77634	455 828	77692	5857	77750	5712	77808	5741	77866	321 314
77635	455 829	77693	5858	77751	5713	77809	5742	77867	321 315
77636	455 829	77694	5858	77752	5713	77810	5742	77868	321 316
77637	455 808	77695	5859	77753	5714	77811	5750	77869	321 317
77638	455 830	77696	5859	77754	5714	77812	5750	77870	321 318
77639	455 831	77697	5860	77755	5715	77813	5901	77871	321 319
77640	455 831	77698	5860	77756	5715	77814	5901	77872	321 320
77641	455 832	77699	5861	77757	5716	77815	5902	77873	321 321
77642	455 832	77700	5861	77758	5716	77816	5902	77874	321 322
77643	455 833	77701	5862	77759	5717	77817	5903	77875	321 323
77644	455 833	77702	5862	77760	5717	77818	5903	77876	321 324
77645	455 834	77703	5863	77761	5718	77819	5904	77877	321 325

EMU/DEMU Car Index

77878	321 326	77939	320 319	78052	321 304	78113	321 419	78230	375 830
77879	321 327	77940	320 320	78053	321 305	78114	320 420	78250	456 001
77880	321 328	77941	320 321	78054	321 306	78115	321 421	78251	456 002
77881	321 329	77942	320 322	78055	321 307	78117	321 423	78252	456 003
77882	321 330	77943	320 401	78056	321 308	78118	321 424	78253	456 004
77883	321 331	77944	321 402	78057	321 309	78120	321 426	78254	456 005
77884	321 332	77945	320 403	78058	321 310	78121	321 427	78255	456 006
77885	321 333	77946	320 404	78059	321 311	78122	321 428	78256	456 007
77886	321 334	77947	321 405	78060	321 312	78123	321 429	78257	456 008
77887	321 335	77948	321 406	78061	321 313	78124	321 430	78258	456 009
77888	321 336	77949	321 407	78062	321 314	78125	321 443	78259	456 010
77889	321 337	77950	321 408	78063	321 315	78126	321 444	78260	456 011
77890	321 338	77951	321 409	78064	321 316	78127	321 445	78261	456 012
77891	321 339	77952	321 410	78065	321 317	78129	321 447	78262	456 013
77892	321 340	77953	320 411	78066	321 318	78130	600 001	78263	456 014
77893	321 341	77954	320 412	78067	321 319	78149	321 365	78264	456 015
77894	321 342	77955	320 413	78068	321 320	78151	321 431	78265	456 016
77895	321 343	77956	320 414	78069	321 321	78152	321 432	78266	456 017
77899	320 301	77957	320 415	78070	321 322	78153	321 433	78267	456 018
77900	320 302	77958	320 416	78071	321 323	78154	321 434	78268	456 019
77901	320 303	77959	320 417	78072	321 324	78156	321 436	78269	456 020
77902	320 304	77960	320 418	78073	321 325	78159	321 439	78270	456 021
77903	320 305	77961	321 419	78074	321 326	78160	321 440	78271	456 022
77904	320 306	77962	320 420	78075	321 327	78161	321 441	78272	456 023
77905	320 307	77963	321 421	78076	321 328	78163	322 481	78273	456 024
77906	320 308	77965	321 423	78077	321 329	78164	322 482	78274	321 443
77907	320 309	77966	321 424	78078	321 330	78165	322 483	78275	321 444
77908	320 310	77968	321 426	78079	321 331	78166	322 484	78276	321 445
77909	320 311	77969	321 427	78080	321 332	78167	322 485	78278	321 447
77910	320 312	77970	321 428	78081	321 333	78201	375 801	78279	600 001
77911	320 313	77971	321 429	78082	321 334	78202	375 802	78298	321 365
77912	320 314	77972	321 430	78083	321 335	78203	375 803	78300	321 431
77913	320 315	77973	319 381	78084	321 336	78204	375 804	78301	321 432
77914	320 316	77974	319 381	78085	321 337	78205	375 805	78302	321 433
77915	320 317	77975	799 201	78086	321 338	78206	375 806	78303	321 434
77916	320 318	77976	799 201	78087	321 339	78207	375 807	78305	321 436
77917	320 319	77977	319 383	78088	321 340	78208	375 808	78308	321 439
77918	320 320	77978	319 383	78089	321 341	78209	375 809	78309	321 440
77919	320 321	77979	319 384	78090	321 342	78210	375 810	78310	321 441
77920	320 322	77980	319 384	78091	321 343	78211	375 811	78312	466 001
77921	320 301	77981	319 385	78095	320 401	78212	375 812	78313	466 002
77922	320 302	77982	319 385	78096	321 402	78213	375 813	78314	466 003
77923	320 303	77983	319 386	78097	320 403	78214	375 814	78315	466 004
77924	320 304	77984	319 386	78098	320 404	78215	375 815	78316	466 005
77925	320 305	77985	322 481	78099	321 405	78216	375 816	78317	466 006
77926	320 306	77986	322 482	78100	321 406	78217	375 817	78318	466 007
77927	320 307	77987	322 483	78101	321 407	78218	375 818	78319	466 008
77928	320 308	77988	322 484	78102	321 408	78219	375 819	78320	466 009
77929	320 309	77989	322 485	78103	321 409	78220	375 820	78321	466 010
77930	320 310	77990	321 901	78104	321 410	78221	375 821	78322	466 011
77931	320 311	77991	321 902	78105	320 411	78222	375 822	78323	466 012
77932	320 312	77992	321 903	78106	320 412	78223	375 823	78324	466 013
77933	320 313	77993	321 901	78107	320 413	78224	375 824	78325	466 014
77934	320 314	77994	321 902	78108	320 414	78225	375 825	78326	466 015
77935	320 315	77995	321 903	78109	320 415	78226	375 826	78327	466 016
77936	320 316	78049	321 301	78110	320 416	78227	375 827	78328	466 017
77937	320 317	78050	321 302	78111	320 417	78228	375 828	78329	466 018
77938	320 318	78051	321 303	78112	320 418	78229	375 829	78330	466 019

78331	466 020	78475	333 013	78551	377 151	78630	377 430	78713	377 113
78332	466 021	78476	333 013	78552	377 152	78631	377 431	78714	377 114
78333	466 022	78477	333 014	78553	377 153	78632	377 432	78715	377 115
78334	466 023	78478	333 014	78554	377 154	78633	377 433	78716	377 116
78335	466 024	78479	333 015	78555	377 155	78634	377 434	78717	377 117
78336	466 025	78480	333 015	78556	377 156	78635	377 435	78718	377 118
78337	466 026	78481	333 016	78557	377 157	78636	377 436	78719	377 119
78338	466 027	78482	333 016	78558	377 158	78637	377 437	78720	377 120
78339	466 028	78501	377 101	78559	377 159	78638	377 438	78721	377 121
78340	466 029	78502	377 102	78560	377 160	78639	377 439	78722	377 122
78341	466 030	78503	377 103	78561	377 161	78640	377 440	78723	377 123
78342	466 031	78504	377 104	78562	377 162	78641	377 441	78724	377 124
78343	466 032	78505	377 105	78563	377 163	78642	377 442	78725	377 125
78344	466 033	78506	377 106	78564	377 164	78643	377 443	78726	377 126
78345	466 034	78507	377 107	78571	377 201	78644	377 444	78727	377 127
78346	466 035	78508	377 108	78572	377 202	78645	377 445	78728	377 128
78347	466 036	78509	377 109	78573	377 203	78646	377 446	78729	377 129
78348	466 037	78510	377 110	78574	377 204	78647	377 447	78730	377 130
78349	466 038	78511	377 111	78575	377 205	78648	377 448	78731	377 131
78350	466 039	78512	377 112	78576	377 206	78649	377 449	78732	377 132
78351	466 040	78513	377 113	78577	377 207	78650	377 450	78733	377 133
78352	466 041	78514	377 114	78578	377 208	78651	377 451	78734	377 134
78353	466 042	78515	377 115	78579	377 209	78652	377 452	78735	377 135
78354	466 043	78516	377 116	78580	377 210	78653	377 453	78736	377 136
78431	360 201	78517	377 117	78581	377 211	78654	377 454	78737	377 137
78432	360 202	78518	377 118	78582	377 212	78655	377 455	78738	377 138
78433	360 203	78519	377 119	78583	377 213	78656	377 456	78739	377 139
78434	360 204	78520	377 120	78584	377 214	78657	377 457	78740	377 140
78435	360 205	78521	377 121	78585	377 215	78658	377 458	78741	377 141
78441	360 201	78522	377 122	78601	377 401	78659	377 459	78742	377 142
78442	360 202	78523	377 123	78602	377 402	78660	377 460	78743	377 143
78443	360 203	78524	377 124	78603	377 403	78661	377 461	78744	377 144
78444	360 204	78525	377 125	78604	377 404	78662	377 462	78745	377 145
78445	360 205	78526	377 126	78605	377 405	78663	377 463	78746	377 146
78451	333 001	78527	377 127	78606	377 406	78664	377 464	78747	377 147
78452	333 001	78528	377 128	78607	377 407	78665	377 465	78748	377 148
78453	333 002	78529	377 129	78608	377 408	78666	377 466	78749	377 149
78454	333 002	78530	377 130	78609	377 409	78667	377 467	78750	377 150
78455	333 003	78531	377 131	78610	377 410	78668	377 468	78751	377 151
78456	333 003	78532	377 132	78611	377 411	78669	377 469	78752	377 152
78457	333 004	78533	377 133	78612	377 412	78670	377 470	78753	377 153
78458	333 004	78534	377 134	78613	377 413	78671	377 471	78754	377 154
78459	333 005	78535	377 135	78614	377 414	78672	377 472	78755	377 155
78460	333 005	78536	377 136	78615	377 415	78673	377 473	78756	377 156
78461	333 006	78537	377 137	78616	377 416	78674	377 474	78757	377 157
78462	333 006	78538	377 138	78617	377 417	78675	377 475	78758	377 158
78463	333 007	78539	377 139	78618	377 418	78701	377 101	78759	377 159
78464	333 007	78540	377 140	78619	377 419	78702	377 102	78760	377 160
78465	333 008	78541	377 141	78620	377 420	78703	377 103	78761	377 161
78466	333 008	78542	377 142	78621	377 421	78704	377 104	78762	377 162
78467	333 009	78543	377 143	78622	377 422	78705	377 105	78763	377 163
78468	333 009	78544	377 144	78623	377 423	78706	377 106	78764	377 164
78469	333 010	78545	377 145	78624	377 424	78707	377 107	78771	377 201
78470	333 010	78546	377 146	78625	377 425	78708	377 108	78772	377 202
78471	333 011	78547	377 147	78626	377 426	78709	377 109	78773	377 203
78472	333 011	78548	377 148	78627	377 427	78710	377 110	78774	377 204
78473	333 012	78549	377 149	78628	377 428	78711	377 111	78775	377 205
78474	333 012	78550	377 150	78629	377 429	78712	377 112	78776	377 206

EMU/DEMU Car Index

78777	377 207	78842	377 442	78917	377 117	78972	377 202	79036	375 906
78778	377 208	78843	377 443	78918	377 118	78973	377 203	79037	375 907
78779	377 209	78844	377 444	78919	377 119	78974	377 204	79038	375 908
78780	377 210	78845	377 445	78920	377 120	78975	377 205	79039	375 909
78781	377 211	78846	377 446	78921	377 121	78976	377 206	79040	375 910
78782	377 212	78847	377 447	78922	377 122	78977	377 207	79041	375 911
78783	377 213	78848	377 448	78923	377 123	78978	377 208	79042	375 912
78784	377 214	78849	377 449	78924	377 124	78979	377 209	79043	375 913
78785	377 215	78850	377 450	78925	377 125	78980	377 210	79044	375 914
78801	377 401	78851	377 451	78926	377 126	78981	377 211	79045	375 915
78802	377 402	78852	377 452	78927	377 127	78982	377 212	79046	375 916
78803	377 403	78853	377 453	78928	377 128	78983	377 213	79047	375 917
78804	377 404	78854	377 454	78929	377 129	78984	377 214	79048	375 918
78805	377 405	78855	377 455	78930	377 130	78985	377 215	79049	375 919
78806	377 406	78856	377 456	78931	377 131	79001	375 801	79050	375 920
78807	377 407	78857	377 457	78932	377 132	79002	375 802	79051	375 921
78808	377 408	78858	377 458	78933	377 133	79003	375 803	79052	375 922
78809	377 409	78859	377 459	78934	377 134	79004	375 804	79053	375 923
78810	377 410	78860	377 460	78935	377 135	79005	375 805	79054	375 924
78811	377 411	78861	377 461	78936	377 136	79006	375 806	79055	375 925
78812	377 412	78862	377 462	78937	377 137	79007	375 807	79056	375 926
78813	377 413	78863	377 463	78938	377 138	79008	375 808	79057	375 927
78814	377 414	78864	377 464	78939	377 139	79009	375 809	79061	375 901
78815	377 415	78865	377 465	78940	377 140	79010	375 810	79062	375 902
78816	377 416	78866	377 466	78941	377 141	79011	375 811	79063	375 903
78817	377 417	78867	377 467	78942	377 142	79012	375 812	79064	375 904
78818	377 418	78868	377 468	78943	377 143	79013	375 813	79065	375 905
78819	377 419	78869	377 469	78944	377 144	79014	375 814	79066	375 906
78820	377 420	78870	377 470	78945	377 145	79015	375 815	79067	375 907
78821	377 421	78871	377 471	78946	377 146	79016	375 816	79068	375 908
78822	377 422	78872	377 472	78947	377 147	79017	375 817	79069	375 909
78823	377 423	78873	377 473	78948	377 148	79018	375 818	79070	375 910
78824	377 424	78874	377 474	78949	377 149	79019	375 819	79071	375 911
78825	377 425	78875	377 475	78950	377 150	79020	375 820	79072	375 912
78826	377 426	78901	377 101	78951	377 151	79021	375 821	79073	375 913
78827	377 427	78902	377 102	78952	377 152	79022	375 822	79074	375 914
78828	377 428	78903	377 103	78953	377 153	79023	375 823	79075	375 915
78829	377 429	78904	377 104	78954	377 154	79024	375 824	79076	375 916
78830	377 430	78905	377 105	78955	377 155	79025	375 825	79077	375 917
78831	377 431	78906	377 106	78956	377 156	79026	375 826	79078	375 918
78832	377 432	78907	377 107	78957	377 157	79027	375 827	79079	375 919
78833	377 433	78908	377 108	78958	377 158	79028	375 828	79080	375 920
78834	377 434	78909	377 109	78959	377 159	79029	375 829	79081	375 921
78835	377 435	78910	377 110	78960	377 160	79030	375 830	79082	375 922
78836	377 436	78911	377 111	78961	377 161	79031	375 901	79083	375 923
78837	377 437	78912	377 112	78962	377 162	79032	375 902	79084	375 924
78838	377 438	78913	377 113	78963	377 163	79033	375 903	79085	375 925
78839	377 439	78914	377 114	78964	377 164	79034	375 904	79086	375 926
78840	377 440	78915	377 115	78971	377 201	79035	375 905	79087	375 927
78841	377 441	78916	377 116						

Loco Hauled Passenger Coaching Stock

Number	Depot	Name	Other Names & Numbers Carried	Coach Type
159(s)	CS		[99880]	Saloon
213	SL	Minerva	[99535]	PPF
239(s)	SL	Agatha		PPF
243	SL	Lucille	[99541]	PPF
245	SL	Ibis	[99534]	PKF
247(s)	CS	Leona		PPF
254	SL	Zena	[99536]	PPF
255	SL	Ione	[99539]	PKF
264(s)	SL	Ruth		PKC
278(s)	CS	Bertha		PPF
280	SL	Audrey	[99537]	PKF
281	SL	Gwen	[99546]	PKF
283(s)	SL	Mona		PKF
284	SL	Vera	[99543]	PKF
286(s)	SL	Car No. 86		PPT
292(s)	SL	Car No. 92		PBT
293(s)	SL	Car No. 93		PBT
301	SL	Perseus	[99530]	PPF
302	SL	Phoenix	[99531]	PPF
308	SL	Cygnus	[99532]	PPF
310	CD	Pegasus	[99107]	PFBar
311	TM	Eagle	[99971]	PKF
313	EGS		[99964 State Car No. 4]	PKF
315(s)	CS	Heron		PKF
317	EGS		[99967 Dining Car]	PKF
319	EGS		[99965 Observation Car]	PKF
321	EGS		[99960 Dining Car No.2]	PKF
324	EGS		[99961 State Car No. 1]	PKF
325	CS	Duart		AJ11 (RF)
99025	CS	Amber	[325]	PPF
326	CS	Emerald	[99402]	AJ11 (RF)
329	EGS		[99962 State Car No. 2]	PKF
331	EGS		[99963 State Car No. 3]	PKF
335	TM	Car No. 335	[99361]	PKS
337	EGS	Car No. 337	[99337 State Car Spa]	PPS
347	CS	Diamond	[99347]	PPS
348	CS	Topaz	[99348]	PPS
349	TM	Car No. 349	[99349]	PPS
350	CS	Tanzanite	[99350]	PPS
351	CS	Sapphire	[99351]	PPS
352	CS	Amethyst	[99352]	PPS
353	TM	Car No. 353	[99353]	PPS
354	CS	The Hadrian Bar	[99354]	PSBar
504	CS	Ullswater	[99678]	AP1Z (PFK)
506	CS	Windermere	[99679]	AP1Z (PFK)
546(s)	CS	City of Manchester	[99670]	AQ1Z (PFP)
548	CS	Grassmere	[99671]	AQ1Z (PFP)
549	CS	Bassenthwaite	[99672]	AQ1Z (PFP)
550	CS	Rydal Water	[99673]	AQ1Z (PFP)
551	CS	Buttermere	[99674]	AQ1Z (PFP)
552	CS	Ennerdale Water	[99675]	AQ1Z (PFP)
553	CS	Crummock Water	[99676]	AQ1Z (PFP)
586	CS	Derwent Water	[99677]	AR1Z (PFB)
807	CS		[99881]	Saloon

Number	Depot	Name	Other Names & Numbers Carried	Coach Type
1200	BU		[3287,6459]	AJIF (RFB)
1201(s)	TM		[3361,6445]	AJIF (RFB)
1203	CD		[3291]	AJIF (RFB)
1207(s)	CS		[3328,6422]	AJIF (RFB)
1211	CD	Snaefell	[3305]	AJIF (RFB)
1212	BU		[3427,6453]	AJIF (RFB)
1221(s)	CS		[3371]	AJIF (RFB)
1252(w)	SO		[3280]	AJIF (RFB)
1253(s)	SO		[3432]	AJIF (RFB)
1258(w)	CS		[3322]	AJIF (RFB)
1375	BT		[99803]	AJIF (RFB)
1566	CS	Caerdydd		AK51 (RKB)
1644(w)	CS			AJ41 (RBR)
1650(w)	CS			AJ41 (RBR)
1651	ZG			AJ41 (RBR)
1652(w)	CS			AJ41 (RBR)
1655(w)	CS			AJ41 (RBR)
1657	BU			AJ41 (RBR)
1658(s)	PEA			AJ41 (RBR)
1663(w)	CS			AJ41 (RBR)
1666	SO			AJ41 (RBR)
1670(w)	CS			AJ41 (RBR)
1671	ZG			AJ41 (RBR)
1679(s)	PEA			AJ41 (RBR)
1683	BU			AJ41 (RBR)
1691	BU			AJ41 (RBR)
1730	BT			AJ41 (RBR)
1800(s)	SO	Tintagel	[NIR546,5970]	AN2F (RSS)
1813	ZG			AN21 (RMB)
1832	ZG			AN21 (RMB)
1840	CS			AN21 (RMB)
1859	BT			AN21 (RMB)
1860	CS			AN21 (RMB)
1861	CS			AN21 (RMB)
1863(s)	CD			AN21 (RMB)
1882	CS		[99311]	AN21 (RMB)
1883(s)	CD			AN21 (RMB)
1953	CS	Car No 1953		AJ41 (RBR)
1954(s)	CD			AN21 (RMB)
1961	CS			AJ41 (RBR)
2127(w)	CS		[99887]	
2833	CS		[21270]	AU51
2903	ZN		[11001]	AT5G
2904	ZN		[12001]	AT5G
2915	ZN		[10735]	AT5G
2916	ZN		[40512]	AT5G
2917	ZN		[40514]	AT5G
2918(s)	ZN		[40515]	AT5G
2919(s)	ZN		[40518]	AT5G
2920	ZN		[17109,14109]	AT5B
2921	ZN		[17107,14107]	AT5B
2922	ZN			AT5H
2923	ZN			AT5H
3045	CD			AD11 (FO)
3058	CS	Florence		AD11 (FO)
3060(s)	CD	Gwilli		AD11 (FO)
3091(s)	PEA	Marguerite		AD11 (FO)

Number	Depot	Name	Other Names & Numbers Carried	Coach Type
3093	CS	Florence		AD11 (FO)
3096	BT		[99827]	AD11 (FO)
3097	ZG			AD11 (FO)
3098	ZG			AD11 (FO)
3100	CD			AD11 (FO)
3105	CS	Julia	[99121]	AD11 (FO)
3106	CS	Alexandra	[99122]	AD11 (FO)
3107(s)	ZG			AD11 (FO)
3110	ZG		[99124]	AD11 (FO)
3112	BU		[99357]	AD11 (FO)
3113	CS	Jessica	[99125]	AD11 (FO)
3115	BT			AD11 (FO)
3117	CS	Christina	[99127]	AD11 (FO)
3119	ZG			AD11 (FO)
3120	ZG			AD11 (FO)
3121	ZG			AD11 (FO)
3122	CD			AD11 (FO)
3123	ZG			AD11 (FO)
3125	CD			AD11 (FO)
3128	CS	Victoria	[99371]	AD11 (FO)
3130	CS	Pamela	[99128]	AD11 (FO)
3133(s)	BT			AD11 (FO)
3136	CS	Diana		AD11 (FO)
3140(s)	ZG			AD11 (FO)
3141	ZG			AD11 (FO)
3143	CS	Patricia		AD11 (FO)
3146	ZG			AD11 (FO)
3147	ZG			AD11 (FO)
3148	CD			AD11 (FO)
3149	ZG			AD11 (FO)
3150	BT			AD11 (FO)

AD1D/E/F (FO) - Mark 2^D/*E/F Open First

Number	Depot	Name	Number	Depot	Name	Number	Depot	Name
3174^	CS	Glamis	3313	CS		3359	CS	
3182^	CS(s)	Warwick	3314	BU		3360	CS	Car No 3360
3188^	CD	Caider Idris	3318	BU(s)		3362	CD	Car No 3362
3223*	CD(s)	Diamond	3325	BU		3364	BU	
3229*	CD	Snowdon	3326	CS		3379	BU(s)	
3231*	BU(s)		3330	CD		3384	CD	Pen-y-ghent
3232*	CS(s)		3331	BU(s)		3386	BU	
3241*	CS(s)		3333	BU		3390	BU	
3247*	CS	Chatsworth	3334	BU(s)		3392	CS	
3267*	CS	Belvior	3336	BU(s)		3395	CS	
3273*	CS	Alnwick	3340	BU		3397	BU	
3275*	CS	Harlech	3344	CD	Ben Crauchan	3400	BU(s)	
3277	PEA(s)		3345	BU		3408	CS(s)	
3278	BU		3348	CD	Ingleborough	3416	TM(s)	
3279	BU(s)		3350	CS		3417	BU	
3292	BU(s)		3351	TM		3424	BU(s)	Ben Nevis
3295	PEA(s)		3352	CS		3426	CD	
3304	BU		3356	BU		3431	CS	
3309	TM(s)		3358	BU(s)		3438	CD	Ben Lomond
3312	CD	Helvellyn						

AC21 (TSO) - Mark 1 Open Standard

4831	BT	(99824)	4927	ZG		4960	CS	
4832	BT	(99823)	4931	CS	(99329)	4973	CS	
4836	BT	(99831)	4932	CS(w)		4984	CS	
4849	CS(s)		4940	CS		4991	ZG	
4854	CS		4946	ZG		4994	CS	
4856	BT	(99829)	4949	TM		4997	CS(w)	
4860	CS(w)		4951	CS		4998	ZG	
4905	CS		4954	CS	(99326)	5009	BU	
4912	CS	(99318)	4959	ZG				

5028	BT	(99830)
5032	CS	
5033	CS	(99328)
5035	CS	
5044	CS	(99327)
5054	PEA(s) Sheila	
5067	CD	(99993)
	Club Car	

AC2 (TSO) - Mark 2 Open Standard

5125	BH(s)	5366	CD	5815	SO(s)	5958	CS(s)	6012	CS	6110	BU(s)
5157	TM	5419	CS	5876	CS(s)	5959	WP(s)	6021	CS	6115	CS
5171	CS	5453	CS(s)	5888	SO(s)	5961	BU	6022	CS	6117	CF(s)
5177	TM	5463	CS(s)	5910	BU(s)	5964	BU	6024	BU	6122	CF(s)
5179	TM(s)	5478	CS(s)	5912	CD	5965	BU(s)	6027	BU	6134	SO(s)
5183	TM(s)	5487	CS	5919	HQ	5971	CF(s)	6029	CS(s)	6137	BU(s)
5191	TM	5491	CS(s)	5921	BU	5976	BU(s)	6036	WP(s)	6139	BU(s)
5194	TM(s)	5569	CS(s)	5922	WP(s)	5978	CS	6041	CS(s)	6141	BU(s)
5198	TM	5631	BU(s)	5924	WP(s)	5985	BU	6042	BU	6151	SO(s)
5200	CS	5657	BU(s)	5925	SO(s)	5987	BU(s)	6045	CS(s)	6152	BU(s)
5212	TM	5687	KT(s)	5928	TM(s)	5991	CD	6046	HQ	6154	SO(s)
5216	CS	5710	ZK(s)	5929	BU	5995	CF(s)	6050	CS	6158	BU
5222	CS	5731	KT(s)	5937	ML(s)	5998	BU	6051	BU	6173	ML(s)
5229	CS	5737	CS(s)	5943	CS	6000	CS	6054	BU	6175	CS
5236	CS	5740	CS(s)	5945	BU(s)	6001	CF(s)	6064	KM(s)	6176	BU
5237	CS	5756	CS(s)	5950	BU	6006	CD	6067	BU	6177	BU(s)
5239	CS	5787	ML(s)	5952	BU	6008	CF(s)	6073	CS(s)	6179	CS(s)
5249	CD	5797	PEA(s)	5954	BU(s)	6009	CS(s)	6103	CS	6183	BU(s)
5278	CS	5810	HQ	5955	BU(s)						

AX51 - Mark 1 Generator Van

6310	TM		6311	CD		6312	CS	6313	SL Belmond

AZ51 - General Managers Saloon

6320	TM

AG2C (TSOT) - Mark 2 Open (Trolley)

6412	CD(s)	6528	CS

AN1F - Mark 2F Lounge / Bar

6705	CD	Ardnamurcan	6706	CD	Mount Mgahinga	6708	CD	Mount Helicon

AN1D (RMBF) - Mark 2 Miniature Buffet

6723	CS(s)	6724	CS

AE2/AH2(BSO) - Mark 2 Open Brake Standard (Micro-Buffet*)

9101*	TM	9440	SO(s)	9493	CS(s)	9509	BU	9525	HQ(s)	9529	WP(s)
9104*	CS	9479	CD	9502	SL	9513	CD(s)	9526	BU	9537	BU
9391	CS	9488	ML(s)	9504	BU	9520	BU	9527	BU(s)	9539	BU(s)
9392	CS	9489	CS(s)	9507	BU	9521	BU				

AF2F (DBSO) - Driving Open Brake Standard

9704	LT(s)	9705	KM(s)	9707	LT(s)	9709	LT(s)	9710	KM(s)

AJ1G (RFM) - Mark 3 Restaurant Buffet First

10211	TO	10222	BU(s)	10237	UKR	10245	CS(s)	10257	BU(s)	10271	AL
10217	PZ	10225	PZ	10241	IL(s)	10249	HQ	10259	HQ(s)	10272	AL
10219	PZ										

AJ2G (RSB) - Mark 4 Restaurant Buffet Standard

10300	NL	10306	NL	10311	NL	10315	NL	10324	NL	10330	CF
10301	CF	10307	HQ(s)	10312	CF	10318	CF	10325	CF	10332	HQ(s)
10305	ZB	10309	NL	10313	NL	10321	CF	10328	CF	10333	NL

AN2G (TSOB) - Mark 3 Mini-Buffet Standard

10406	HQ	10411	CD	10416	CD

AUG4G(SLEP) - Mark 3 Sleeping Car with Pantry (Disabled*)

10504	svr	10553	PZ(s)	10598	CS(s)	10661	ZN(s)
10513	svr	10556	EGS Service Car	10601	PZ	10675	svr
10519	CD	10563	PZ	10610	CS(s)	10683	svr
10520	CD	10584	PZ	10612	PZ	10688	CD
10532	PZ	10588	ZN(s)	10614	CS(s)	10703	CS(s)
10534	PZ	10589	PZ	10616	PZ	10718*	CS(s)
10541	EGS State Car 5	10590	PZ	10648	svr	10729	CS Crewe
10546	TO	10594	PZ	10650	svr	10734	CS Balmoral
10551	PZ(s)	10596	PZ				

AD1G*/H(FO) - Mark 3 Open First

11018*	UKR	11048*	UKR	11075	CD	11088	BU(s)	11092	HQ	11098	CD
11021*	LM(s)	11068	CD	11076	CD	11090	UKR	11093	HQ	11099	HQ
11028*	ZB(s)	11070	CD	11077	CD	11091	CD	11097	LM(s)	11101	HQ
11039*	TO	11074	UKR	11087	CD						

AD1J(FO/FOD*) - Mark 4 Open First (Disabled*)

11229	NL	11295	NL	11315*	NL	11321*	CF	11404	HQ(s)	11414	HQ(s)
11279	NL	11306*	NL	11316*	HQ(s)	11322*	CF	11406	NL	11415	NL
11284	NL	11308*	NL	11317*	NL	11323*	CF	11408	NL	11416	ZB
11285	NL	11312*	NL	11318*	ZB	11324*	CF	11409	HQ(s)	11417	NL
11287	NL	11313*	NL	11319*	ZB	11325*	CF	11412	NL	11418	ZB
11288	NL	11314*	HQ(s)	11320*	CF	11326*	NL	11413	NL	11426	NL
11289	NL										

Mark 5 TPExpress   *on test

TP01	HQ	11501	12701	12702	12703	12801
TP02*		11502	12704	12705	12706	12802
TP03*		11503	12707	12708	12709	12803
TP04	LG	11504	12710	12711	12712	12804
TP05	LG	11505	12713	12714	12715	12805
TP06	LG	11506	12716	12717	12718	12806
TP07	LG	11507	12719	12720	12721	12807
TP08	LG	11508	12722	12723	12724	12808
TP09	LG	11509	12725	12726	12727	12809
TP10	LG	11510	12728	12729	12730	12810
TP11	LG	11511	12731	12732	12733	12811
TP12	LG	11512	12734	12735	12736	12812
TP13	LG	11513	12737	12738	12739	12813
Spare						12814*

AC2G(TSO) - Mark 3 Open Standard

12032 UKR	12091 UKR	12125 HQ	12146 LM(s)	12171 CD	12180 HQ(s)
12061 LM(s)	12092 UKR	12133 UKR	12154 HQ	12176 HQ(s)	12181 HQ(s)
12064 UKR	12097 UKR	12137 LM(s)	12161 PZ	12177 HQ(s)	12182 HQ(s)
12078 UKR	12100 PZ	12138 UKR	12164 LM(s)	12178 HQ(s)	12184 HQ(s)
12079 LM(s)	12111 CD	12142 PZ	12167 LM(s)	12179 HQ(s)	12185 HQ(s)
12090 LM(s)	12122 UKR				

AI2J(TSOE) - Mark 4 Standard End

12202 ZB	12209 HQ(s)	12213 ZB	12219 CF	12224 CF	12228 NL
12203 HQ(s)	12210 CF	12214 NL	12220 NL	12225 CF	12229 HQ(s)
12205 NL	12211 CF	12215 ZB	12222 CF	12226 NL	12230 HQ(s)
12208 NL	12212 NL	12217 CF	12223 NL		

AL2J(TSOD) - Mark 4 Standard Disabled

12300 HQ(s)	12305 HQ(s)	12310 ZB	12313 NL	12323 CF	12326 CF
12303 NL	12308 HQ(s)	12311 NL	12315 ZB	12324 ZB	12328 NL
12304 ZB	12309 NL	12312 ZB	12316 CF	12325 NL	12330 NL

AC2J(TSO) - Mark 4 Standard

12404 NL	12421 HQ(s)	12431 NL	12446 CF	12468 HQ(s)	12485 NL
12406 NL	12422 NL	12432 NL	12447 CF	12469 NL	12486 HQ(s)
12407 NL	12423 HQ(s)	12433 ZB	12452 CF	12474 NL	12513 HQ(s)
12409 NL	12424 NL	12434 CF	12453 HQ(s)	12477 CF	12514 HQ(s)
12410 HQ(s)	12426 NL	12436 HQ(s)	12454 CF	12480 HQ(s)	12515 NL
12415 HQ(s)	12427 NL	12437 HQ(s)	12461 CF	12481 NL	12518 HQ(s)
12417 HQ(s)	12428 ZB	12442 NL	12465 NL	12483 HQ(s)	12520 HQ(s)
12419 HQ(s)	12429 NL	12443 HQ(s)	12467 ZB	12484 HQ(s)	12526 HQ(s)
12420 NL	12430 NL	12444 NL			

AC2G(TSO) - Mark 3 Open Standard

12602 AL	12606 AL	12610 AL	12616 AL	12619 AL	12623 AL
12603 AL	12607 AL	12613 AL	12617 AL	12620 AL	12625 AL
12604 AL	12608 AL	12614 AL	12618 AL	12621 AL	12627 AL
12605 AL	12609 AL	12615 AL			

AA11(FK) - Mark 1 Corridor First   * First Open

13227 CD	13230 BT (99828)	13320* CS Anna	13321 CS (99316)
13229 BT (99826)	13306* CS Joanna		

AA1A(FK) - Mark 2 Corridor First

13440 CS	13508 PEA(s)

Mark 5 Sleeping Car Seated - Caledonian Sleeper

15001 PO	15003 PO	15005 PO	15007 PO	15009 PO	15011 PO
15002 PO	15004 PO	15006 PO	15008 PO	15010 PO	

Mark 5 Sleeping Car Club - Caledonian Sleeper

15101 PO	15103 PO	15105 PO	15107 PO	15109 PO	15110 PO
15102 PO	15104 PO	15106 PO	15108 PO		

Mark 5 Sleeping Car (disabled access) - Caledonian Sleeper

15201 PO	15204 PO	15207 PO	15209 PO	15211 PO	15213 PO
15202 PO	15205 PO	15208 PO	15210 PO	15212 PO	15214 PO
15203 PO	15206 PO				

Mark 5 Sleeping Car - Caledonian Sleeper

15301 PO	15308 PO	15315 PO	15322 PO	15329 PO	15335 PO
15302 PO	15309 PO	15316 PO	15323 PO	15330 PO	15336 PO
15303 PO	15310 PO	15317 PO	15324 PO	15331 PO	15337 PO
15304 PO	15311 PO	15318 PO	15325 PO	15332 PO	15338 PO
15305 PO	15312 PO	15319 PO	15326 PO	15333 PO	15339 PO
15306 PO	15313 PO	15320 PO	15327 PO	15334 PO	15340 PO
15307 PO	15314 PO	15321 PO	15328 PO		

BFK - Mark 1/Mark 2* Corridor Brake First

14060 TM	17013 ZG(s) [99130]	17025 CS [99990]	17096* SL Mercator
14168 CS(s) [99319]	17015 TM	17056 CD	17102* CS [99680]
16204 BU(s)	17018 TM [99108]	17090* TM(s)	

AX5B - Mark 2B Couchette / Generator Vehicle

17105 BU

AB1D(BFK) - Mark 2D Corridor Brake First

17159 CD	17167 CS Mow Cop

AE1H(BFO) - Mark 3 Brake First

17173 PZ	17174 PZ	17175 PZ

AA21(SK) - Mark 1 Corridor Second

18756 CS [99722]	18808 CS(s) [99716]	18893 CS [99712]
18767 CS(s) [99710]	18862 CS(s) [99718]	

AB31(BCK) - Mark 1 Corridor Brake Composite

21232 MRC [99040]	21249 NRS [99355]	21268 PEA(s)
21241 BT	21256 CS [99304]	21269 ZG
21245 ZG [99356]	21266 CS	

AB21(BSK) - Mark 1 Corridor Brake Second

34525 CS(s) [99966]		35461 CD(s) [99720]
35185 BT		35463 CS [99312]
35317 CD		35465 CD [99991]
35322 CS [99035]		35467 CD(s) [99242]
35333 CD [99180]		35468 NRM [99953]
35407 CS [99886]	86 Service Car No.1	35469 ZG
35447 CS		35470 TM
35451 CD [99313]		35476 MRC [99041]
35453 SO		35479 SO
35457 MRC [99995]		35486 CS [99405]
35459 CS [99723]		

AB1C(BFK) - Mark 2C Corridor Declassified Brake First

35508 ELR

AB5C(BFK) - Mark 2C Brake / Power Kitchen

35511 CD

AB1A(BFK) - Mark 2A Corridor Brake First

35517 ELR	35518 CS

HST Coaching Stock

GN2G(TRSMB) - Trailer Standard Modular Buffet

40106 svr(s)

GN4G(TRFB) - Trailer First Buffet

40204 EY(s)	40205 EY(s)	40221 EY(s)

GH1G(TRFMB) - Trailer First Miniature Buffet

40601	IS	[41032]	40608	IS	[41122]	40614	IS	[41010]	40620	IS	[41158]
40602	IS	[41038]	40609	IS	[41020]	40615	IS	[41022]	40621	IS	[41146]
40603	IS	[41006]	40610	IS	[41103]	40616	IS	[41142]	40623	IS	[41180]
40604	IS	[41024]	40611	IS	[41130]	40617	IS	[41144]	40624	IS	[41116]
40605	IS	[41094]	40612	IS	[41134]	40618	IS	[41016]	40625	IS	[41137]
40606	IS	[41104]	40613	IS	[41135]	40619	IS	[41124]	40626	IS	[41012]
40607	IS	[41136]									

GK1G(TRFB) - Trailer First Buffet

40704	EY(s)	40720	EY(s)	40734	EY(s)	40750	EY(s)
40715	EY(s)	40728	UKR	40748	EY(s)		

GK1G(TRFB) - Trailer First Buffet

40801 CD	40802 CD	40804 CD	40808 svr(s)

GN4G(TRFB) - Trailer First Buffet

40900 LM(s)	40902 LM(s)	40904 LM(s)

GH1G(TF) - Trailer First

41026	LAx	41091	EY(s)	41149	svr(s)	41169	CD	41183	ZG	41204	EY(s)
41035	LAx	41100	EY(s)	41160	CD	41170	EY(s)	41187	CD	41205	EY(s)
41059	CD	41108	CD	41162	CD	41176	CD	41193	LAx	41206	EY(s)
41063	CD	41117	CD(s)	41166	CD	41180	ZB	41194	LAx	41208	EY(s)
41087	EY(s)	41118	EY(s)	41167	ZG(s)	41182	CD	41195	LAx	41209	EY(s)

GH2G(TS) - Trailer Standard

42004	IS	42046	IS	42144	IS	42245	IS	42292	IS	42360	IS
42009	IS	42047	IS	42167	LM(s)	42250	IS	42293	IS	42363	EY(s)
42010	IS	42051	LAx	42173	ZB(s)	42252	IS	42295	IS	42366	LAx
42012	IS	42052	LAx	42175	LA(s)	42253	IS	42296	IS	42367	LAx
42013	IS	42053	LAx	42176	LM(s)	42255	IS	42297	IS	42368	LAx
42014	IS	42054	IS	42179	EY(s)	42256	IS	42299	IS	42369	LAx
42019	IS	42055	IS	42183	IS	42257	IS	42300	IS	42370	LAx
42021	IS	42056	ZB	42184	IS	42259	IS	42301	IS	42371	LAx
42023	IS	42072	IS	42185	IS	42265	IS	42310	ZB	42372	LAx
42024	EY(s)	42075	IS	42195	ZB	42267	IS	42319	svr(s)	42373	LAx
42026	EY(s)	42077	IS	42200	IS	42268	IS	42325	IS	42374	LAx
42029	IS	42078	IS	42206	IS	42269	IS	42333	IS	42375	LAx
42030	IS	42094	LA(s)	42207	IS	42275	IS	42342	LAx	42376	LAx
42032	IS	42095	LA(s)	42208	IS	42276	IS	42343	IS	42377	LAx
42033	IS	42096	IS	42209	IS	42277	IS	42345	IS	42378	LAx
42034	IS	42097	LAx	42213	IS	42279	IS	42347	EY(s)	42379	LAx
42035	IS	42100	CD(s)	42217	ZB	42280	IS	42350	IS	42380	LAx
42036	LAx	42107	IS	42220	CD(s)	42281	IS	42351	IS	42401	EY(s)
42037	LAx	42110	BU(s)	42231	LM(s)	42288	IS	42353	ZB	42402	EY(s)
42038	LAx	42129	IS	42234	LAx	42290	LAx	42355	EY(s)	42404	EY(s)
42045	IS	42143	IS	42243	EY(s)	42291	IS	42357	EY(s)	42405	EY(s)

GH2G(TS) - Trailer Standard (cont)

42408	EY(s)	42555	IS	42562	IS	42568	IS	42576	IS	42581	IS
42503	ZB(s)	42557	IS	42563	LM(s)	42569	EY(s)	42577	IS	42583	svr(s)
42506	EY(s)	42558	IS	42565	LM(s)	42571	IS	42578	IS	42584	EY(s)
42551	IS	42559	IS	42566	PZ(s)	42574	IS	42579	IS	42585	EY(s)
42553	IS	42561	IS	42567	IS	42575	IS				

GJ2G(TGS) - Trailer Guard's Standard

44004	ZB(s)	44021	LAx	44040	ZB(s)	44063	EY(s)	44078	CD	44094	EY(s)
44012	LAx	44024	ZB(s)	44047	CD	44066	ZB(s)	44081	CD	44098	EY(s)
44017	LAx	44034	EY(s)	44052	LAx	44072	LAx	44086	ZB(s)	44100	PZ(s)
44020	ZB(s)	44035	ZB(s)	44061	EY(s)	44076	LM(s)	44089	YK(s)		

GH3G(TF) - Trailer Composite Catering

45001 LAx	45002 LAx	45003 LAx	45004 LAx	45005 LAx

GH2G(TC) - Trailer Composite

46006 ZG(s)	46012 svr(s)	46014 ZG(s)

GWR HST Coaching stock refurbished and been re-numbered

48101	[42093]	LA	48118	[42073]	LA	48134	[42264]	LA	49102	[44083]	LA
48102	[42218]	LA	48119	[42204]	LA	48135	[42251]	LA	49103	[44097]	LA
48103	[42168]	LA	48120	[42201]	LA	48136	[42570]	LA	49104	[44101]	LA
48104	[42365]	LA	48121	[42207]	LA	48137	[42582]	LA	49105	[44090]	LA
48105	[42266]	LA	48122	[42214]	LA	48140	[42005]	LA	49106	[44033]	LA
48106	[42258]	LA	48123	[42211]	LA	48141	[42015]	LA	49107	[44064]	LA
48107	[42101]	LA	48124	[42212]	LA	48142	[42016]	LA	49108	[44067]	LA
48108	[42174]	LA	48125	[42203]	LA	48143	[42050]	LA	49109	[44003]	LA
48109	[42085]	LA	48126	[42138]	LA	48144	[42066]	LA	49110	[44014]	LA
48110	[42315]	LA	48127	[42127]	LA	48145	[42048]	LA	49111	[44036]	LA
48111	[42224]	LA	48128	[42044]	LA	48146	[42074]	LA	49112	[44079]	LA
48112	[42222]	LA	48129	[42008]	LA	48147	[42081]	LA	49113	[44008]	LA
48113	[42177]	LA	48130	[42102]	LA	48148	[42071]	LA	49114	[44005]	LA
48114	[42317]	LA	48131	[42042]	LA	48149	[42087]	LA	49115	[44016]	LA
48115	[42285]	LA	48132	[42202]	LA	48150	[42580]	LA	49116	[44002]	LA
48116	[42273]	LA	48133	[42003]	LA	49101	[44055]	LA	49117	[44042]	LA
48117	[42271]	LA								

Notes

Loco Hauled Non-Passenger Coaching Stock

AK51(RK) - Mark 1 Kitchen Car

80041 ZG(s)	80042 BU	80043 CD (ex-1680)	80044 CD (ex-1659)

NNX - Mark 1 Courier Vehicle

80204 CS	80217 CS
80207 SL Baggage Car No.11 (99545)	80220 CS
80212 CS(s)	

NT(POT) - Mark 1 Post Office Stowage Van

80403 CS(w)	80404 CS(w)	80414 SL(s)

NZ(DLV) - Mark 3 Driving Luggage Van

Note: 82113 is being converted and renumbered to 19001

82101 LT(s)	82113 BT(s)	82126 LT(s)	82136 UKR	82139 CD
82107 BC(s)	82115 UKR	82127 CD	82138 UKR	82146 TO

NZ(DLV) - Mark 4 Driving Luggage Van

82200 CF	82208 NL	82213 NL	82220 ZB	82226 CF
82201 CF	82209 HQ(s)	82214 NL	82222 ZB	82227 CF
82204 HQ(s)	82210 HQ(s)	82215 ZB	82223 NL	82229 CF
82205 NL	82211 NL	82216 CF	82225 NL	82230 CF
82206 HQ(s)	82212 NL	82218 HQ(s)		

NZ(DLV) - Mark 3 Driving Luggage Van

82301 AL	82303 AL	82305 AL	82307 BC(s)	82309 AL
82302 AL	82304 AL	82306 HQ(s)	82308 BC(s)	

NB/NE/NH(BG) - Gangwayed Brake Van

92159 CS(w)	92904 CS	92908 CS(w)

NKA - High Security Van

94101 CS(w)	94153 WE(w)	94195 BU(w)	94214 CS(w)	94227 HM(w)
94106 BU(w)	94176 BU(w)	94196 CS(w)	94222 SO(w)	94229 CD(w)
94116 BU(w)	94177 CD(w)	94197 BU(w)	94225 CS	

NAA - Propelling Control Van

94302 HEL(w)	94308 CS(w)	94313 WE(w)	94332 CS(w)	94336 BU(w)
94303 HEL(w)	94310 WE(w)	94323 HEL(w)	94333 HEL(w)	94337 WE(w)
94304 MH(w)	94311 WE(w)	94326 HEL(w)	94335 BU(w)	94338 WE(w)
94306 HEL(w)				

NBA - Mark 1 High Security Brake Van

94401 CS(w)	94420 CS(w)	94429 HM(w)	94451 WE(w)	94492 WE(w)
94406 CS(w)	94423 BU(w)	94431 CS(w)	94482 CS(w)	94495 HEL(w)
94408 CS(w)	94427 WE(w)	94434 CD(w)	94488 BU(w)	94498 CS(w)
94410 WE(w)	94428 CS(w)	94445 WE(w)	94490 BU(w)	

NBA/NIA/NQA - Mark 1 High Security Brake Van

94504 HEL(w)	94520 BU(w)	94527 HEL(w)	94539 CS(w)	94545 HM(w)
94512 CS(w)	94525 CS(w)	94531 BU(w)	94540 TJ(w)	94546 HEL(w)
94515 ZG(w)	94526 CS(w)	94538 CD(s)	94542 CS(w)	94547 CS(w)
94517 BU(w)				

NAA - Propelling Control Van

95300 CS(w)	

NRA - Mark 1 BA Container Van

95400 CD(w)	95410 CS(w)

NOA - Mark 1 High Security Van

95727 WE(w)	95754 CS(w)	95761 WE(w)

NP/NX/NV(GUV) - Motorail Van

96100 TM	96135 CS(w)	96165 CS(w)	96175 CS	96191 CS(w)
96110 CS(w)	96164 CS(w)	96170 CS(w)	96178 CS(w)	96192 CS(w)
96132 CS(w)				

AX5G - Mark 3 Nightstar Generator Van

96372 LM(w)	96373 LM(w)	96375 LM(w)

NVA - Motorail Van

Note: Under conversion to universal barrier vehicles for use across Europe

96602	HQ	[96 70 0096 602-8]	Henry
96603	HQ	[96 70 0096 603-6]	Oliver
96605	HQ	[96 70 0096 605-1]	Ernest
96607	HQ	[96 70 0096 607-7]	Phillip

Private Owner Coaching Stock Cross Reference

99025	[325]	99347	[347]	99546	[281]	99827	[3096]
99035	[35322]	99348	[348]	99554	[92904]	99828	[13230]
99040	[21232]	99349	[349]	99670	[546]	99829	[4856]
99041	[35476]	99350	[350]	99671	[548]	99830	[5028]
99080	[21096]	99351	[351]	99672	[549]	99831	[4836]
99107	[310]	99352	[352]	99673	[550]	99880	[159]
99108	[17018]	99353	[353]	99674	[551]	99881	[807]
99121	[3105]	99354	[354]	99675	[552]	99884	[19208]
99122	[3106]	99355	[21249]	99676	[553]	99886	[35407]
99125	[3113]	99356	[21245]	99677	[586]	99887	[2127]
99127	[3117]	99357	[3112]	99678	[504]	99953	[35468]
99128	[3130]	99361	[335]	99679	[506]	99960	[321]
99130	[17013]	99368	[368]	99680	[17102]	99961	[324]
99131	[1999]	99371	[3128]	99710	[18767]	99962	[329]
99180	[35333]	99402	[326]	99712	[18893]	99963	[331]
99242	[35467]	99405	[35486]	99716	[18808]	99964	[313]
99304	[21256]	99530	[301]	99718	[18862]	99965	[319]
99311	[1882]	99531	[302]	99720	[35461]	99966	[34525]
99312	[35463]	99532	[308]	99721	[18806]	99967	[317]
99313	[35451]	99534	[245]	99722	[18756]	99968	[10541]
99316	[13321]	99535	[213]	99723	[35459]	99969	[10556]
99318	[4912]	99536	[254]	99803	[1375]	99971	[311]
99319	[14168]	99537	[280]	99822	[1859]	99990	[17025]
99326	[4954]	99539	[255]	99823	[4832]	99991	[35465]
99327	[5044]	99541	[243]	99824	[4831]	99993	[5067]
99328	[5033]	99543	[284]	99826	[13229]	99995	[35457]
99329	[4931]	99545	[80207]				

Departmental/Network Rail Stock

1256	Staff Coach		DF
5981	Staff Coach		DF
6260	Generator Van		DF
6261	Generator Van		DF
6262	Generator Van		DF
6263	Generator Van		DF
6264	Generator Van		DF
6324	Desiro EMU Barrier Vehicle		CP
6330	HST Barrier Vehicle		UKR
6336	HST Barrier Vehicle		LA
6338	HST Barrier Vehicle		UKR
6340	HST Barrier Vehicle		UKR
6344	HST Barrier Vehicle		UKR
6346	HST Barrier Vehicle		UKR
6348	HST Barrier Vehicle		LA
6352	Mark 4 Barrier Vehicle		WP
6353	Mark 4 Barrier Vehicle		WP
6364(s)	EMU Translator Vehicle		CF
6365(s)	EMU Translator Vehicle		CF
6376	EMU Translator Vehicle		UKR
6377	EMU Translator Vehicle		UKR
6378	EMU Translator Vehicle		UKR
6379	EMU Translator Vehicle		UKR
6392	Colas Brake Force Runner		DF
6393	HST Barrier Vehicle		UKR
6394	HST Barrier Vehicle		UKR
6397	Colas Brake Force Runner		DF
6398	HST Barrier Vehicle		DY
6399	HST Barrier Vehicle		NL
9419	Escort Coach		KM
9428	Escort Coach		KM
9481	Staff Coach		DF
9506	Escort Coach		KM
9508	Escort Coach		KM
9516	Brake force support vehicle		DF
9523	Brake force support vehicle		DF
9701	Driving Van Trailer [DBSO]		DF
9702	Driving Van Trailer [DBSO]		DF
9703	Driving Van Trailer [DBSO]		DF
9708	Driving Van Trailer [DBSO]		DF
9714	Driving Van Trailer [DBSO]		DF
9801	Network Rail Brake Force Runner		DF
9803	Network Rail Brake Force Runner		DF
9806	Network Rail Brake Force Runner		DF
9808	Network Rail Brake Force Runner		DF
9810	Network Rail Brake Force Runner		DF
62287	Ultrasonic Test Coach		DF
62384	Ultrasonic Test Coach		DF
62549	ERTMS Test Unit	[313 121]	ZG
62613	ERTMS Test Unit	[313 121]	ZG
64664	EMU Translator Vehicle	Liwet	ZG
64707	EMU Translator Vehicle	Labezerin	ZG
68501	Translator Vehicle		UKR
68504	Translator Vehicle		UKR
68505(s)	De-icing Coach		ZG

71233	ERTMS Test Unit	[313 121]	ZG
72612	Test Train Brake Force Runner	[910 002]	DF
72616	Test Train Brake Force Runner	[910 001]	DF
72630	Test Train Brake Force Runner		DF
72631	Test Train Brake Force Runner		DF
72639	Test Train Brake Force Runner		DF
82111(s)	Network Rail DVT		LM
82124(s)	Network Rail DVT		LM
82129(s)	Network Rail DVT		LM
82145(s)	Network Rail DVT		LM
96380	Eurostar Barrier Vehicle		TI
96381	Eurostar Barrier Vehicle		EMRK
96383	Eurostar Barrier Vehicle		EMRK
96384	Eurostar Barrier Vehicle		TI
96604	Network Rail Brake Force Runner		DF
96606	Network Rail Brake Force Runner		DF
96608	Network Rail Brake Force Runner		DF
96609	Network Rail Brake Force Runner		DF
99019(s)	Spray Coach		LM
99666	Ultrasonic Test Coach		DF
971001	Network Rail Support Coach		BS
971002	Network Rail Support Coach		SP
971003	Network Rail Support Coach		BS
971004	Network Rail Support Coach		SP
975025	General Managers Saloon	Caroline	DF
975081(s)	Structure Gauging Driving Trailer Coach		BU
975087	Support Coach		SP
975091	Overhead Line Equipment Test Coach		DF
975280(s)	Structure Gauging Train Dormitory and Generator Coach		DF
975454(s)	BTU Staff & Tool Van		TT
975464	Snowblower Train Coach		SP
975471	Staff & Tool Coach		BS
975477	Staff Coach		SP
975486	Snowblower Train Coach		SP
975814	Measurement Train Conference Coach		DF
975864	EMU Barrier Coach		BU
975875	EMU Barrier Coach		ZG
975920(s)	Cable Drum Carrier		PBO
975974	EMU Barrier Coach	Paschar	PG
975978	EMU Barrier Coach	Perpetiel	PG
975984	Measurement Train Lecture Coach		EC
977085(s)	Crewe Works Test Train Coach		BU
977087	Barrier Coach		UKR
977868	Radio Equipment Survey Coach		DF
977869	Snow Train Support Coach		IS
977969	Test Train Staff Coach		DF
977974	Laboratory Coach		DF
977983	Electrification Measurement Coach		DF
977984	Measurement Train Staff Coach		DF
977985	Structure Gauging Train Coach		DF
977986	Track Recording Train Coach		DF
977993	Measurement Train Overhead Line Equipment Test Coach		DF
977994	Measurement Train Track Recording Coach		DF
977995	Measurement Train Coach		DF
977997	Measurement Train Coach		DF
999550	Track Recording Coach		DF
999600	Track Recording Unit	[950001]	DF

		Departmental Coaching Stock (cont)			
999601	Track Recording Unit		[950001]		DF
999602	Ultrasonic Test Coach				DF
999605	Ultrasonic Test Coach				DF
999606	Ultrasonic Test Coach				DF

Internal Users & Miscellaneous

041989	87910	BR	Fish Van	Stores Van (Grounded)	TT
061202	93498	BR	GUV	Stores Van (Grounded)	LA
083439	94752	BR	CCT	Stores Van	BU
083602	94494	BR	CCT	Stores Van	TB
083637	99203	BR	Bullion Van	Stores Van	SL
	3101	Eurostar		High Speed College	Doncaster
	3102	Eurostar		High Speed College	Birmingham
	5636	BR	TSO	Instruction Coach	PM
	6360	BR		Barrier Vehicle	NL
	6361	BR		Barrier Vehicle	NL
	6396	BR	HSBV	Stores Van	LG
	6701	BR	RLO	Instruction Coach	ZK
	10231	BR	RFM	Rescue Training Vehicle	Moreton in the Marsh
	10256	BR	RFB	Instruction Coach	Yoker
	10260	BR	RFB	Instruction Coach	Yoker
	11043	BR	FO	Rescue Training Vehicle	Bury
	17156	BR	BFK	Instruction Coach	DY
	41165	BR	TF	Primary School Library	Waltham Abbey
	42109	BR	TS	Community Hub	Waltham Abbey
	42205	BR	TS	Rescue Training Vehicle	Cambuslang
	42210	BR	TS	Rescue Training Vehicle	Aberdeen
	55574	BR	DMU	Police Training Vehicle	Bridgend
	55584	BR	DMU	Police Training Vehicle	Uckfield
	55586	BR	DMU	Primary School Library	Kirk Merrington
	55624	BR	DMU	Police Training Vehicle	Bridgend
	55634	BR	DMU	Police Training Vehicle	Uckfield
	55636	BR	DMU	Primary School Library	Kirk Merrington
	55808	BR	DMU	School STEM Lab	Fagley, Bradford
	55809	BR	DMU	Rescue Training Vehicle	Manchester
	55832	BR	DMU	Rescue Training Vehicle	Manchester
	63400	BR	EMU	Training Vehicle	Siemens. Goole
	64649	BR	EMU	Rescue Training Vehicle	Seacombe
	64681	BR	EMU	Rescue Training Vehicle	Moreton in the Marsh
	64712	BR	EMU	Rescue Training Vehicle	Seacombe
	64724	BR	EMU	Rescue Training Vehicle	Moreton in the Marsh
	69633	BR	MSO	Rescue Training Vehicle	Moreton in the Marsh
	69733	BR	MSO	Rescue Training Vehicle	Moreton in the Marsh
	71515	BR	EMU	Rescue Training Vehicle	Moreton in the Marsh
	72412	BR	EMU	Training Vehicle	Siemens. Goole
	78400	BR	EMU	Training Vehicle	Siemens. Goole
	82143	BR	DLV	Rescue Training Vehicle	Bury
	93568	BR		Stores Van	CD
	94003	BR	NL	Stores Van	BU
	94170	BR	NK	Stores Van	CD
	94438	BR	NK	Stores Van	TT
	94522	BR	NA	Stores Van	CD
	96139	BR	GUV	Stores Van	LG
	889200	BR	Ferry Van	Stores Van	SL
	889202	BR	Ferry Van	Stores Van	SL

Large Plant Vehicles

DR 72211	Balfour Beatty		
DR 72213	Balfour Beatty		
DR 73105	Colas		
DR 73109	SB Rail		
DR 73111	SB Rail	Reading Panel	
DR 73113	SB Rail		
DR 73114	Network Rail	Ron Henderson	
DR 73115	Network Rail		
DR 73116	Network Rail		
DR 73117	Network Rail		
DR 73118	Network Rail		
DR 73120	Network Rail	99 70 9123 120-6	
DR 73121	Network Rail	99 70 9123 121-4	
DR 73122	Network Rail	99 70 9123 122-2	
DR 73502	Trackwork	99 70 9908 014-2	
DR 73503	XYZ Rail	99 70 9908 019-1	
		Grace	
DR 73803	SB Rail	Alexander G Bell	
DR 73806	Colas Rail	Katrine	
DR 73904	SB Rail	Thomas Telford	
DR 73905	Colas	Eddie King	
DR 73906	Colas	Panther	
DR 73907	Colas		
DR 73908	Colas		
DR 73909	Colas	Saturn	
DR 73910	Colas	Jupiter	
DR 73911	Colas	Puma	
DR 73913	Colas		
DR 73914	SB Rail	Robert McAlpine	
DR 73915	SB Rail	William Arrol	
DR 73916	SB Rail	First Engineering	
DR 73917	Balfour Beatty		
DR 73918	Balfour Beatty		
DR 73919	Colas		
DR 73920	Colas		
DR 73921	Colas		
DR 73922	Colas	John Snowdon	
DR 73923	Colas		
DR 73924	Colas	Atlas	
DR 73925	Colas	Europa	
DR 73927(s)	Balfour Beatty		
DR 73929	Colas Rail		
DR 73930	Colas Rail		
DR 73931	Colas Rail		
DR 73932	SB Rail		
DR 73933	SB Rail		
DR 73934	SB Rail		
DR 73935	Colas Rail		
DR 73936	Colas Rail		
DR 73937	Balfour Beatty		
DR 73938	Balfour Beatty		
DR 73939	Balfour Beatty	Pat Best	
DR 73940	SB Rail		
DR 73941	SB Rail		
DR 73942	Colas Rail		
DR 73943	Balfour Beatty		
DR 73944	Balfour Beatty		
DR 73945	Balfour Beatty		
DR 73946	Volker Rail	97 43 4450 117-2	
DR 73947	Colas		
DR 73948	Colas		
DR 73949	Balfour Beatty	99 70 9123 016-6	
DR 73950	Balfour Beatty	99 70 9123 017-4	
DR 74001	SB Rail	99 70 9128 001-9	
DR 74002	SB Rail	99 70 9128 002-1	
DR 75008	Colas	99 70 9123 008-3	
DR 75009	Colas	99 70 9123 009-1	
DR 75010	Colas	99 70 9123 010-9	
		Roger Nicholas	
DR 75011	Colas	99 70 9123 011-7	
		Andrew Smith	
DR 75012	SB Rail	99 70 9123 012-5	
DR 75013	SB Rail	99 70 9123 013-3	
DR 75014	SB Rail	99 70 9123 014-1	
DR 75015	SB Rail	99 70 9123 015-8	
DR 75204	Trackwork	99 70 9908 015-3	
DR 75301	Volker Rail		
DR 75302	Volker Rail	Gary Wright	
DR 75303	Volker Rail		
DR 75401	Volker Rail		
DR 75402	Volker Rail		
DR 75404	Volker Rail		
DR 75405	Volker Rail		
DR 75406	Colas Rail	Eric Machell	
DR 75407	Colas Rail	Gerry Taylor	
DR 75408	Balfour Beatty		
DR 75409	Balfour Beatty		
DR 75410(s)	Balfour Beatty		
DR 75411	Balfour Beatty		
DR 75501	Balfour Beatty		
DR 75502	Balfour Beatty		
DR 75503	Volker Rail	99 70 9124 001-7	
DR 75504	Volker Rail	99 70 9124 002-5	
DR 76003	XYZ Rail	99 70 9908 011-8	
DR 76501	Network Rail		
DR 76502	Network Rail		
DR 76503	Network Rail		
DR 76504	Network Rail	99 70 9314 504-0	
DR 76701	Network Rail		
DR 76703	Network Rail		
DR 76750	Network Rail		
DR 76751	Network Rail		
DR 76801	Network Rail		
DR 76802	Network Rail	99 70 9320 802-0	
DR 76901	Network Rail	99 70 9131 001-8	
DR 76903	Network Rail	99 70 9131 003-4	
DR 76905	Network Rail	99 70 9131 005-9	
DR 76906	Network Rail	99 70 9131 006-7	

Track Machines, Multi Purpose Vehicles, Stoneblowers & Cranes

No.	Operator	No./Name	No.	Operator	No./Name
DR 76910	Network Rail	99 70 9131 010-9	DR 79233	Loram	
DR 76911	Network Rail	99 70 9131 011-7	DR 79234(s)	Loram	
DR 76913	Network Rail	99 70 9131 013-3	DR 79235(s)	Loram	
DR 76914	Network Rail	99 70 9131 014-1	DR 79236	Loram	
DR 76915	Network Rail	99 70 9131 015-8	DR 79237	Loram	
DR 76918	Network Rail	99 70 9131 018-2	DR 79241	Network Rail	
DR 76920	Network Rail	99 70 9131 020-8	DR 79242	Network Rail	
DR 76921	Network Rail	99 70 9131 021-6	DR 79243	Network Rail	
DR 76922	Network Rail	99 70 9131 022-4	DR 79244	Network Rail	
DR 76923	Network Rail	99 70 9131 023-2	DR 79245	Network Rail	
DR 77001	SB Rail	Anthony Lou Phillips	DR 79246	Network Rail	
DR 77002	SB Rail		DR 79247	Network Rail	
DR 77010	Network Rail	99 70 9125 010-7	DR 79251	Network Rail	
DR 77322(s)	Balfour Beatty		DR 79252	Network Rail	
DR 77327	Colas Rail		DR 79253	Network Rail	
DR 77801	Volker Rail		DR 79254	Network Rail	
DR 77802	Volker Rail		DR 79255	Network Rail	
DR 77901	Colas		DR 79256	Network Rail	
DR 77903	SB Rail	99 70 9125 001-6	DR 79257	Network Rail	Martin Elwood
DR 77904	Network Rail		DR 79261	Network Rail	
DR 77905	Network Rail		DR 79262	Network Rail	
DR 77906	Network Rail		DR 79263	Network Rail	Chris Gibb
DR 77907	Network Rail		DR 79264	Network Rail	
DR 77909	Network Rail	99 70 9125 909-0	DR 79265	Network Rail	
DRB 78123(s)	Volker Rail		DR 79267	Network Rail	Bridget Rosewell
DRP 78213	Volker Rail		DR 79271	Network Rail	
DRP 78215	Balfour Beatty		DR 79272	Network Rail	
DRP 78216	Balfour Beatty		DR 79273	Network Rail	
DRP 78217(s)	SB Rail		DR 79274	Network Rail	
DRP 78219	Balfour Beatty		DR 79276	Network Rail	
DRP 78221	Balfour Beatty		DR 79277	Network Rail	Bridget Rosewell
DRP 78222	Balfour Beatty		DR 79301	Network Rail	99 70 9427 038-3
DRP 78223	Balfour Beatty		DR 79302	Network Rail	99 70 9427 039-1
DRC 78226	Colas		DR 79303	Network Rail	99 70 9427 040-9
DRC 78229	Network Rail		DR 79304	Network Rail	99 70 9427 041-7
DRC 78231	Network Rail		DR 79401	Network Rail	99 70 9427 042-5
DRC 78234	Network Rail		DR 79402	Network Rail	99 70 9427 043-3
DRC 78235	Colas		DR 79403	Network Rail	99 70 9427 044-1
DRC 78237(s)	Colas		DR 79404	Network Rail	99 70 9427 045-8
SLG 78490	Balfour Beatty		DR 79501	Network Rail	99 70 9427 046-6
DR 78701	Balfour Beatty		DR 79502	Network Rail	99 70 9427 047-4
DR 78702	Balfour Beatty		DR 79503	Network Rail	99 70 9427 048-2
DR 78801	Network Rail		DR 79504	Network Rail	99 70 9427 049-0
DR 78802	Network Rail		DR 79505	Network Rail	99 70 9427 050-8
DR 78811	Network Rail		DR 79506	Network Rail	99 70 9427 051-6
DR 78812	Network Rail		DR 79507	Network Rail	99 70 9427 052-4
DR 78821	Network Rail		DR 79602	Schweerbau	99 70 9427 064-9
DR 78822	Network Rail		DR 79603	Schweerbau	99 70 9427 065-6
DR 78831	Network Rail		DR 79604	Schweerbau	99 70 9527 005-1
DR 78832	Network Rail		DR 80201	Network Rail	
DR 79101	Crossrail	99 70 9127 006-3	DR 80202(s)	Harsco Rail	
DR 79102	Network Rail	99 70 9127 007-1	DR 80203(s)	Harsco Rail	
DR 79103	Network Rail	99 70 9327 001-2	DR 80205	Network Rail	
DR 79104	Network Rail	99 70 9127 008-9	DR 80206	Network Rail	
DR 79105	Network Rail	99 70 9327 002-0	DR 80208	Network Rail	
DR 79231	Loram	Pete Erwin	DR 80209	Network Rail	
DR 79232	Loram		DR 80210	Network Rail	

Track Machines, Multi Purpose Vehicles, Stoneblowers & Cranes

DR 80211	Network Rail		DR 97803	Network Rail	99 70 9580 003-0	
DR 80213	Network Rail		DR 97804	Network Rail	99 70 9580 004-8	
DR 80214	Network Rail		DR 97805	Network Rail	99 70 9580 005-5	
DR 80215	Network Rail		DR 97806	Network Rail	99 70 9580 006-3	
DR 80216	Network Rail				Andy King	
DR 80217	Network Rail		DR 97807	Network Rail	99 70 9580 007-1	
DR 80301	Network Rail	Stephen Cornish	DR 97808	Network Rail	99 70 9580 008-9	
DR 80302	Network Rail		DR 98001	Network Rail		
DR 80303	Network Rail		DR 98002	Network Rail		
DRP 81505	Balfour Beatty		DR 98003	Network Rail	Anthony Wrighton	
DRP 81508	Balfour Beatty		DR 98004	Network Rail	Phillip Cattrell	
DRP 81513	Balfour Beatty		DR 98005	Network Rail		
DRP 81517	Balfour Beatty		DR 98006	Network Rail	Jason McDonnell	
DRP 81519	Balfour Beatty		DR 98007	Network Rail		
DRP 81525	Balfour Beatty		DR 98008	Network Rail		
DRP 81532	Balfour Beatty		DR 98009	Network Rail	Melvyn Smith	
DRK 81601	Volker Rail	Nigel Chester	DR 98010	Network Rail	Benjamin Gautrey	
DRK 81602	Balfour Beatty		DR 98011	Network Rail		
DRK 81611	Balfour Beatty	Malcolm L Pearce	DR 98012	Network Rail	Terence Hand	
DRK 81612	Colas Rail		DR 98013	Network Rail	David Wood	
DRK 81613	Volker Rail		DR 98014	Network Rail	Wayne Imlach	
DRK 81621	Volker Rail		DR 98215	Balfour Beatty		
DRK 81622	Volker Rail		DR 98216	Balfour Beatty		
DRK 81623	SB Rail		DR 98217	Balfour Beatty		
DRK 81624	SB Rail		DR 98218	Balfour Beatty		
DRK 81625	SB Rail		DR 98219	Balfour Beatty		
DRK 81626	SB Rail	99 70 9319 012-9	DR 98220	Balfour Beatty		
ADRC 96715	Network Rail		DR 98901	Network Rail		
DR 97001	Network Rail		DR 98902	Network Rail		
DR 97011	Network Rail		DR 98903	Network Rail		
DR 97012	Network Rail	Geoff Bell	DR 98904	Network Rail		
DR 97013	Network Rail		DR 98905	Network Rail		
DR 97014	Network Rail		DR 98906	Network Rail		
DR 97501	Network Rail	99 70 9481 001-4	DR 98907	Network Rail		
DR 97502	Network Rail	99 70 9481 002-2	DR 98908	Network Rail		
DR 97503	Network Rail	99 70 9481 003-0	DR 98909	Network Rail		
DR 97504	Network Rail	99 70 9481 004-8	DR 98910	Network Rail		
DR 97505	Network Rail	99 70 9481 005-5	DR 98911	Network Rail		
DR 97506	Network Rail	99 70 9481 006-3	DR 98912	Network Rail		
		Andy King	DR 98913	Network Rail		
DR 97507	Network Rail	99 70 9481 007-1	DR 98914	Network Rail	Dick Preston	
DR 97508	Network Rail	99 70 9481 008-9	DR 98915	Network Rail	Nigel Cummins	
DR 97509	Crossrail	99 70 9481 009-7	DR 98916	Network Rail		
DR 97510	Crossrail	99 70 9481 010-5	DR 98917	Network Rail		
DR 97511	Crossrail	99 70 9481 011-3	DR 98918	Network Rail		
DR 97512	Crossrail	99 70 9481 012-1	DR 98919	Network Rail		
DR 97601	Network Rail	99 70 9559 001-1	DR 98920	Network Rail		
DR 97602	Network Rail	99 70 9559 002-9	DR 98921	Network Rail		
DR 97603	Network Rail	99 70 9559 003-7	DR 98922	Network Rail		
DR 97604	Network Rail	99 70 9559 004-5	DR 98923	Network Rail	Chris Lemon	
DR 97605	Network Rail	99 70 9559 005-2	DR 98924	Network Rail		
DR 97606	Network Rail	99 70 9559 006-0	DR 98925	Network Rail		
DR 97607	Network Rail	99 70 9559 007-8	DR 98926	Network Rail	John Denyer	
DR 97608	Network Rail	99 70 9559 008-6	DR 98927	Network Rail		
DR 97801	Network Rail	99 70 9580 001-4	DR 98928	Network Rail		
DR 97802	Network Rail	99 70 9580 002-2	DR 98929	Network Rail		

Track Machines, Multi Purpose Vehicles, Stoneblowers & Cranes

DR 98930	Network Rail		DR 98974	Network Rail		
DR 98931	Network Rail		DR 98975	Network Rail		
DR 98932	Network Rail		DR 98976	Network Rail	John Denyer	
DR 98951	Network Rail		DR 98977	Network Rail		
DR 98952	Network Rail		DR 98978	Network Rail		
DR 98953	Network Rail		DR 98979	Network Rail		
DR 98954	Network Rail		DR 98980	Network Rail		
DR 98955	Network Rail		DR 98981	Network Rail		
DR 98956	Network Rail		DR 98982	Network Rail		
DR 98957	Network Rail		968500	Network Rail		
DR 98958	Network Rail		968501	Network Rail		
DR 98959	Network Rail		999800	Network Rail	Richard Spoors	
DR 98960	Network Rail		999801	Network Rail		
DR 98961	Network Rail			ABC		99 70 9231 001-7
DR 98962	Network Rail			ABC		99 70 9231 002-5
DR 98963	Network Rail			ABC		99 70 9231 003-3
DR 98964	Network Rail	Dick Preston		ABC		99 70 9231 004-1
DR 98965	Network Rail	Nigel Cummins		ABC		99 70 9231 005-8
DR 98966	Network Rail			ABC		99 70 9231 006-6
DR 98967	Network Rail			ABC		99 70 9231 007-4
DR 98968	Network Rail			Network Rail		99 70 9319 013-7
DR 98969	Network Rail			Railcare		99 70 9515 002-2
DR 98970	Network Rail			Railcare		99 70 9515 003-0
DR 98971	Network Rail			Railcare		99 70 9515 004-8
DR 98972	Network Rail			Railcare		99 70 9515 005-5
DR 98973	Network Rail	Chris Lemon		Railcare		99 70 9515 006-3

Miscellaneous On-Track Plant

965	Schweerbau	97 43 4351 510-9	RGS	Schweerbau	
2797	Volker Rail		RGT	Schweerbau	
2834	Croydon Tram		RGU-2000	Schweerbau	
2865	SB Rail	99 70 9908 006-8	RG8	Schweerbau	
2866	TRS		RGM	Schweerbau	
2867	SB Rail	99 70 9908 007-6	SFU-04	Schweerbau	
2868	Volker Rail		TPB51001	Volker Rail	2620, GR5153
3012	Network Rail	99 70 9908 001-9	TPB51002	Volker Rail	2831
4013	Network Rail	99 70 9908 002-7	TSB51021	Volker Rail	2650, GR5156
4015	Network Rail	99 70 9908 003-5	TSB51022	Volker Rail	99 70 9908 009-2
5018	DB Schenker	99 70 9908 010-0	TSU51030	Volker Rail	2705, GR5142
LGRM1-2	Sheffield Tram	6063216 - AM16			

Tram, Light Rail & Underground

Birmingham Midland Metro

Built by CAF 2013-2023, 3 section car, Silver & Magenta — Built/On test *

17	22	27	32	37	42*	47 o/o	51 o/o	55 o/o
18	23	28	33	38*	43*	48 o/o	52 o/o	56 o/o
19	24	29	34	39*	44*	49 o/o	53 o/o	57 o/o
20	25	30	35	40*	45*	50 o/o	54 o/o	58 o/o
21	26	31(s)	36	41*	46 o/o			

Named Vehicles

28	Jasper Carrott	31	Cyrille Regis MBE 1958 - 2018	37	OZZY OSBOURNE

Blackpool Transport

Flexity 2 — 2011 - 2017* — Bombardier

001	004	007	009	011	013	015	017*
002	005	008	010	012	014	016	018*
003	006						

Preserved Vehicles

227	625(s)	648	685(s)	706(s)	715	724(s)	735(s)
230(s)	631	663(s)	686(s)	707	717	726(s)	736
259(s)	632(s)	671(s)	700	708(s)	718	732(s)	737
272(s)	634(s)	675(s)	701	709(s)	719	733	761(s)
600	642	676(s)	703(s)	711	720(s)	734	T2(s)
621	645(s)	681(s)	704(s)	713	723		

Vintage Cars

Bolton	66	1901	Blackpool	279	1935(s)	Blackpool	680	1960
Blackpool	OMO 8	1974(s)	Blackpool	290	1937(s)	Lytham	43	1924(s)
Blackpool	143	1924	Blackpool	304	1953(s)	Halle	902	1969(s)
Blackpool	147	1924	Blackpool	660	1953(s)			

Named Vehicles

002	Alderman E.E. Wynne		717	Walter luff
007	Alan Whitbread		719	Donna's Dream House
227	Charlie Cairoli		732	The Rocket
230	George Formby OBE		733	The Western Train Locomotive
600	Duchess of Cornwall		734	The Western Train Carriage
706	Princess Alice		736	The Frigate
711	Ray Roberts		737	The Trawler

Works Cars

260(s)	Rail Crane		938	Road/Rail Vehicle Q204 HFR
750	Reel Wagon		Crab	Shunter
754	Overhead Line Car			

Croydon Tramlink

Built by Bombardier (Vienna). 3 section car
Lime Green, Blue & White — Note:- 2535 named Stephen Parascandalo 1980-2007

2530	2535	2540	2545	2550	2554	2558	2562
2531	2536	2541	2546	2551(s)	2555	2559	2563
2532	2537	2542	2547	2552	2556	2560	2564
2533	2538	2543	2548	2553	2557	2561	2565
2534	2539	2544	2549				

Docklands Light Railway

Class *B90/B92	1991-1995/^2001-2002	BN Construction Brugge		2 Section Cars	750V DC 3rd				
01^	11^	26*	36*	46	55	64	73	82	91
02^	12^	27*	37*	47	56	65	74	83	92^
03^	13^	28*	38*	48	57	66	75	84	93^
04^	14^	29*	39*	49	58	67	76	85	94^
05^	15^	30*	40*	50	59	68	77	86	95^
06^	16^	31*	41*	51	60	69	78	87	96^
07^	22*	32*	42*	52	61	70	79	88	97^
08^	23*	33*	43*	53	62	71	80	89	98^
09^	24*	34*	44*	54	63	72	81	90	99^
10^	25*	35*	45						

Class B2007-B2009*			Bombardier Brugge			2 Section Cars		750V DC 3rd rail	
101	107	113	119	125*	131*	136*	141*	146*	151*
102	108	114	120	126*	132*	137*	142*	147*	152*
103	109	115	121	127*	133*	138*	143*	148*	153*
104	110	116	122	128*	134*	139*	144*	149*	154*
105	111	117	123	129*	135*	140*	145*	150*	155*
106	112	118	124	130*					

Works Vehicles			
992 CT30 Crane	993 Battery Locomotive	994 GEC Diesel	995 Ruston Diesel

LUAS Dublin Trams

3000 Class	2002-03		CITADIS TGA301				
3001	3005	3009	3012	3015	3018	3021	3024
3002	3006	3010	3013	3016	3019	3022	3025
3003	3007	3011	3014	3017	3020	3023	3026
3004	3008						

4000 Class	2003		CITADIS TGA401				
4001	4003	4005	4007	4009	4011	4013	4014
4002	4004	4006	4008	4010	4012		

5000 Class	2009-10/2017-22*		CITADIS TGA402/502*				
5001	5007	5012	5017	5022	5027*	5032*	5037*
5002	5008	5013	5018	5023	5028*	5033*	5038*
5003	5009	5014	5019	5024	5029*	5034*	5039*
5004	5010	5015	5020	5025	5030*	5035*	5040*
5005	5011	5016	5021	5026	5031*	5036*	5041*
5006							

Edinburgh Trams

1435mm			2010-2011			7 Section Trams	
251	255	259	263	266	269	272	275
252	256	260	264	267	270	273	276
253	257	261	265	268	271	274	277
254	258	262					

Glasgow Underground

Single Power Cars				1977-79		Metro-Cammell	
101	105	109	113	117	121	126	130
102	106	110	114	118	123	127	131
103	107	111	115	119	124	128	132
104	108	112	116	120	125	129	133

Intermediate Trailers				1992		Hunslet-Barclay	
201	202	203	204	205	206	207	208

New 4-Car Metro				2018-2020			Stadler
301	304	306	308	310	312	314	316
302	305	307	309	311	313	315	317
303							

Works Locomotives			1974-77		Clayton Equipment	
L2(s)	Lobey Dosser	L3(s)	Rank Bajin	L6		L7

Llandudno, Great Orme Tram System

Cable Tram		1902		Hurst Nelson
4		5	6	7

London Gatwick Track Transit System

Type				2006-2007			Bombardier	
01	03	04	05	06	07	08	09	
02								

London Heathrow Personal Rapid Transit Battery powered driverless pods

101	202	205	208	211	214	216	218
102	203	206	209	212	215	217	219
201	204	207	210	213			

London Underground

Bakerloo Line

1972 Tube Stock 4-car Single End Units

3231	4231	4331	3331	3243	4243	4343	3343	3256	4256	4356	3356
3232	4232	4332	3332	3244	4244	4344	3344	3258	4258	4358	3358
3233	4233	4333	3333	3245	4245	4345	3345	3259	4259	4359	3359
3234	4234	4334	3334	3246	4246	4346	3346	3260	4260	4360	3360
3235	4235	4335	3335	3247	4247	4347	3347	3261	4261	4361	3361
3236	4236	4336	3336	3248	4248	4348	3348	3262	4262	4362	3362
3237	4237	4337	3337	3250	4250	4350	3350	3263	4263	4363	3363
3238	4238	4338	3338	3251	4251	4351	3351	3264	4264	4364	3364
3239	4239	4339	3339	3252	4252	4352	3352	3265	4265	4365	3365
3240	4240	4340	3340	3253	4253	4353	3353	3266	4266	4366	3366
3241	4241	4341	3341	3254	4254	4354	3354	3267	4267	4367	3367
3242	4242	4342	3342	3255	4255	4355	3355	3299	4299	4399	3399

1972 Tube Stock 3-car Single End Units

3431	4531	3531	3441	4541	3541	3450	4550	3550	3459	4559	3559
3432	4532	3532	3442	4542	3542	3451	4551	3551	3460	4560	3560
3433	4533	3533	3443	4543	3543	3452	4552	3552	3461	4561	3561
3434	4534	3534	3444	4544	3544	3453	4553	3553	3462	4562	3562
3435	4535	3535	3445	4545	3545	3454	4554	3554	3463	4563	3563
3436	4536	3536	3446	4546	3546	3455	4555	3555	3464	4564	3564
3437	4537	3537	3447	4547	3547	3456	4556	3556	3465	4565	3565
3438	4538	3538	3448	4548	3548	3457	4557	3557	3466	4566	3566
3440	4540	3540	3449	4549	3549	3458	4558	3558	3467	4567	3567

Central Line

1992 Tube Stock 2-car Units

91001	92001	91071	92071	91141	92141	91211	92211	91281	92281
91003	92003	91073	92073	91143	92143	91213	92213	91283	92283
91005	92005	91075	92075	91145	92145	91215	92215	91285	92285
91007	92007	91077	92077	91147	92147	91217	92217	91287	92287
91009	92009	91079	92079	91149	92149	91219	92219	91289	92289
91011	92011	91081	92081	91151	92151	91221	92221	91291	92291
91013	92013	91083	92083	91153	92153	91223	92223	91293	92293
91015	92015	91085	92085	91155	92155	91225	92225	91295	92295
91017	92017	91087	92087	91157	92157	91227	92227	91297	92297
91019	92019	91089	92089	91159	92159	91229	92229	91299	92299
91021	92021	91091	92091	91161	92161	91231	92231	91301	92301
91023	92023	91093	92093	91163	92163	91233	92233	91303	92303
91025	92025	91095	92095	91165	92165	91235	92235	91305	92305
91027	92027	91097	92097	91167	92167	91237	92237	91307	92307
91029	92029	91099	92099	91169	92169	91239	92239	91309	92309
91031	92031	91101	92101	91171	92171	91241	92241	91311	92311
91033	92033	91103	92103	91173	92173	91243	92243	91313	92313
91035	92035	91105	92105	91175	92175	91245	92245	91315	92315
91037	92037	91107	92107	91177	92177	91247	92247	91317	92317
91039	92039	91109	92109	91179	92179	91249	92249	91319	92319
91041	92041	91111	92111	91181	92181	91251	92251	91321	92321
91043	92043	91113	92113	91183	92183	91253	92253	91323	92323
91045	92045	91115	92115	91185	92185	91255	92255	91325	92325
91047	92047	91117	92117	91187	92187	91257	92257	91327	92327
91049	92049	91119	92119	91189	92189	91259	92259	91329	92329
91051	92051	91121	92121	91191	92191	91261	92261	91331	92331
91053	92053	91123	92123	91193	92193	91263	92263	91333	92333
91055	92055	91125	92125	91195	92195	91265	92265	91335	92335
91057	92057	91127	92127	91197	92197	91267	92267	91337	92337
91059	92059	91129	92129	91199	92199	91269	92269	91339	92339
91061	92061	91131	92131	91201	92201	91271	92271	91341	92341
91063	92063	91133	92133	91203	92203	91273	92273	91343	92343
91065	92065	91135	92135	91205	92205	91275	92275	91345	92345
91067	92067	91137	92137	91207	92207	91277	92277	91347	92347
91069	92069	91139	92139	91209	92209	91279	92279	91349	92349

1992 Tube Stock 2-car Units

92002	93002	92038	93038	92074	93074	92110	93110	92146	93146
92004	93004	92040	93040	92076	93076	92112	93112	92148	93148
92006	93006	92042	93042	92078	93078	92114	93114	92150	93150
92008	93008	92044	93044	92080	93080	92116	93116	92152	93152
92010	93010	92046	93046	92082	93082	92118	93118	92154	93154
92012	93012	92048	93048	92084	93084	92120	93120	92156	93156
92014	93014	92050	93050	92086	93086	92122	93122	92158	93158
92016	93016	92052	93052	92088	93088	92124	93124	92160	93160
92018	93018	92054	93054	92090	93090	92126	93126	92162	93162
92020	93020	92056	93056	92092	93092	92128	93128	92164	93164
92022	93022	92058	93058	92094	93094	92130	93130	92166	93166
92024	93024	92060	93060	92096	93096	92132	93132	92168	93168
92026	93026	92062	93062	92098	93098	92134	93134	92170	93170
92028	93028	92064	93064	92100	93100	92136	93136	92172	93172
92030	93030	92066	93066	92102	93102	92138	93138	92174	93174
92032	93032	92068	93068	92104	93104	92140	93140	92176	93176
92034	93034	92070	93070	92106	93106	92142	93142	92178	93178
92036	93036	92072	93072	92108	93108	92144	93144	92180	93180

1992 Tube Stock 2-car Units

92182	93182	92200	93200	92218	93218	92236	93236	92252 93252
92184	93184	92202	93202	92220	93220	92238	93238	92254 93254
92186	93186	92204	93204	92222	93222	92240	93240	92256 93256
92188	93188	92206	93206	92224	93224	92242	93242	92258 93258
92190	93190	92208	93208	92226	93226	92244	93244	92260 93260
92192	93192	92210	93210	92228	93228	92246	93246	92262 93262
92194	93194	92212	93212	92230	93230	92248	93248	92264 93264
92196	93196	92214	93214	92232	93232	92250	93250	92266 93266
92198	93198	92216	93216	92234	93234			

1992 Tube Stock 2-car De-Icing Units

92402	93402	92416	93416	92430	93430	92442	93442	92454 93454
92404	93404	92418	93418	92432	93432	92444	93444	92456 93456
92406	93406	92420	93420	92434	93434	92446	93446	92458 93458
92408	93408	92422	93422	92436	93436	92448	93448	92460 93460
92410	93410	92424	93424	92438	93438	92450	93450	92462 93462
92412	93412	92426	93426	92440	93440	92452	93452	92464 93464
92414	93414	92428	93428					

District Line

D Stock 3-car

7526   17526   7527 (s)

D Stock Stored at Long Marston

7000	7026	7050	7078	7104	7502	7525	17029	17069	17104
7001	7028	7052	7079	7105	7503	7528	17035	17073	17106
7003	7029	7053	7080	7106	7504	7530	17036	17076	17110
7004	7030	7054	7081	7108	7505	7532	17043	17077	17112
7005	7031	7056	7082	7109	7506	7533	17045	17078	17113
7006	7033	7057	7084	7110	7507	7534	17047	17080	17114
7008	7034	7059	7085	7112	7509	7535	17049	17082	17116
7009	7035	7060	7087	7113	7512	7536	17052	17083	17117
7013	7038	7061	7088	7114	7513	7537	17053	17085	17118
7014	7039	7062	7089	7115	7514	7538	17054	17086	17119
7015	7041	7063	7091	7116	7515	7539	17055	17087	17120
7016	7042	7064	7092	7117	7516	17003	17056	17088	17124
7019	7043	7070	7094	7118	7517	17011	17059	17089	17127
7020	7044	7071	7095	7119	7518	17013	17062	17090	17129
7021	7045	7072	7096	7121	7519	17015	17064	17092	17510
7022	7046	7073	7097	7125	7520	17020	17065	17096	17520
7023	7047	7075	7099	7126	7521	17021	17067	17098	17522
7024	7048	7076	7101	7129	7522	17023	17068	17103	17528
7025	7049	7077	7102	7501	7524	17025			

Jubilee Line

1996 Tube Stock 4-car Single-ended Units

96001	96601	96201	96401	96043	96643	96243	96443	96085	96685	96285	96485
96003	96603	96203	96403	96045	96645	96245	96445	96087	96687	96287	96487
96005	96605	96205	96405	96047	96647	96247	96447	96089	96689	96289	96489
96007	96607	96207	96407	96049	96649	96249	96449	96091	96691	96291	96491
96009	96609	96209	96409	96051	96651	96251	96451	96093	96693	96293	96493
96011	96611	96211	96411	96053	96653	96253	96453	96095	96695	96295	96495
96013	96613	96213	96413	96055	96655	96255	96455	96097	96697	96297	96497
96015	96615	96215	96415	96057	96657	96257	96457	96099	96699	96299	96499
96017	96617	96217	96417	96059	96659	96259	96459	96101	96701	96301	96501
96019	96619	96219	96419	96061	96661	96261	96461	96103	96703	96303	96503
96021	96621	96221	96421	96063	96663	96263	96463	96105	96705	96305	96505
96023	96623	96223	96423	96065	96665	96265	96465	96107	96707	96307	96507
96025	96625	96225	96425	96067	96667	96267	96467	96109	96709	96309	96509
96027	96627	96227	96427	96069	96669	96269	96469	96111	96711	96311	96511
96029	96629	96229	96429	96071	96671	96271	96471	96113	96713	96313	96513
96031	96631	96231	96431	96073	96673	96273	96473	96115	96715	96315	96515
96033	96633	96233	96433	96075	96675	96275	96475	96117	96717	96317	96517
96035	96635	96235	96435	96077	96677	96277	96477	96119	96719	96319	96519
96037	96637	96237	96437	96079	96679	96279	96479	96121	96721	96321	96521
96039	96639	96239	96439	96081	96681	96281	96481	96123	96723	96323	96523
96041	96641	96241	96441	96083	96683	96283	96483	96125	96725	96325	96525

1996 Tube Stock 3-car Single-ended Units

96002	96202	96402	96034	96234	96434	96066	96266	96466	96098	96898	96498
96004	96204	96404	96036	96236	96436	96068	96268	96468	96100	96900	96500
96006	96206	96406	96038	96238	96438	96070	96270	96470	96102	96902	96502
96008	96208	96408	96040	96240	96440	96072	96272	96472	96104	96904	96504
96010	96210	96410	96042	96242	96442	96074	96274	96474	96106	96906	96506
96012	96212	96412	96044	96244	96444	96076	96276	96476	96108	96908	96508
96014	96214	96414	96046	96246	96446	96078	96278	96478	96110	96910	96510
96016	96216	96416	96048	96248	96448	96080	96880	96480	96112	96912	96512
96018	96218	96418	96050	96250	96450	96082	96882	96482	96114	96914	96514
96020	96220	96420	96052	96252	96452	96084	96884	96484	96116	96916	96516
96022	96222	96422	96054	96254	96454	96086	96886	96486	96118	96918	96518
96024	96224	96424	96056	96256	96456	96088	96888	96488	96120	96320	96520
96026	96226	96426	96058	96258	96458	96090	96890	96490	96122	96322	96522
96028	96228	96428	96060	96260	96460	96092	96892	96492	96124	96324	96524
96030	96230	96430	96062	96262	96462	96094	96894	96494	96126	96326	96526
96032	96232	96432	96064	96264	96464	96096	96896	96496			

Metropolitan, Circle, District and Hammersmith & City Lines

			S Tube Stock (De-Icing Units*)		2010-2013		
8 Car Units - two 4 Car Sets coupled together					DM+T+T+UNDM+UNDM+T+T+DM		

21001	22001	23001	24001	24002	25002	22002	21002*
21003	22003	23003	24003	24004	25004	22004	21004*
21005	22005	23005	24005	24006	25006	22006	21006*
21007	22007	23007	24007	24008	25008	22008	21008*
21009	22009	23009	24009	24010	25010	22010	21010*
21011	22011	23011	24011	24012	25012	22012	21012*
21013	22013	23013	24013	24014	25014	22014	21014*
21015	22015	23015	24015	24016	25016	22016	21016*
21017	22017	23017	24017	24018	25018	22018	21018*
21019	22019	23019	24019	24020	25020	22020	21020*
21021	22021	23021	24021	24022	25022	22022	21022*
21023	22023	23023	24023	24024	25024	22024	21024*
21025	22025	23025	24025	24026	25026	22026	21026*
21027	22027	23027	24027	24028	25028	22028	21028*
21029	22029	23029	24029	24030	25030	22030	21030*
21031	22031	23031	24031	24032	25032	22032	21032*
21033	22033	23033	24033	24034	25034	22034	21034*
21035	22035	23035	24035	24036	25036	22036	21036*
21037	22037	23037	24037	24038	25038	22038	21038*
21039	22039	23039	24039	24040	25040	22040	21040*
21041	22041	23041	24041	24042	25042	22042	21042*
21043	22043	23043	24043	24044	25044	22044	21044*
21045	22045	23045	24045	24046	25046	22046	21046*
21047	22047	23047	24047	24048	25048	22048	21048*
21049	22049	23049	24049	24050	25050	22050	21050*
21051	22051	23051	24051	24052	25052	22052	21052*
21053	22053	23053	24053	24054	25054	22054	21054*
21055	22055	23055	24055	24056	25056	22056	21056*
21057	22057	23057	24057	24058	23058	22058	21058
21059	22059	23059	24059	24060	23060	22060	21060
21061	22061	23061	24061	24062	23062	22062	21062
21063	22063	23063	24063	24064	23064	22064	21064
21065	22065	23065	24065	24066	23066	22066	21066
21067	22067	23067	24067	24068	23068	22068	21068
21069	22069	23069	24069	24070	23070	22070	21070
21071	22071	23071	24071	24072	23072	22072	21072
21073	22073	23073	24073	24074	23074	22074	21074
21075	22075	23075	24075	24076	23076	22076	21076
21077	22077	23077	24077	24078	23078	22078	21078
21079	22079	23079	24079	24080	23080	22080	21080
21081	22081	23081	24081	24082	23082	22082	21082
21083	22083	23083	24083	24084	23084	22084	21084
21085	22085	23085	24085	24086	23086	22086	21086
21087	22087	23087	24087	24088	23088	22088	21088
21089	22089	23089	24089	24090	23090	22090	21090
21091	22091	23091	24091	24092	23092	22092	21092
21093	22093	23093	24093	24094	23094	22094	21094
21095	22095	23095	24095	24096	23096	22096	21096
21097	22097	23097	24097	24098	23098	22098	21098
21099	22099	23099	24099	24100	23100	22100	21100
21101	22101	23101	24101	24102	23102	22102	21102
21103	22103	23103	24103	24104	23104	22104	21104
21105	22105	23105	24105	24106	23106	22106	21106

8 Car Units - two 4 Car Sets coupled together			DM+T+T+UNDM+UNDM+T+T+DM				(Cont)
21107	22107	23107	24107	24108	23108	22108	21108
21109	22109	23109	24109	24110	23110	22110	21110
21111	22111	23111	24111	24112	23112	22112	21112
21113	22113	23113	24113	24114	23114	22114	21114
21115	22115	23115	24115	24116	23116	22116	21116

S Tube Stock (De-Icing Units*)　　2010-2015
7 Car Units - One 3 Car Set and One 4 Car Set coupled together

21301	22301	24301	24302	25302	22302	21302*	
21303	22303	24303	24304	25304	22304	21304*	
21305	22305	24305	24306	25306	22306	21306*	
21307	22307	24307	24308	25308	22308	21308*	
21309	22309	24309	24310	25310	22310	21310*	
21311	22311	24311	24312	25312	22312	21312*	
21313	22313	24313	24314	25314	22314	21314*	
21315	22315	24315	24316	25316	22316	21316*	
21317	22317	24317	24318	25318	22318	21318*	
21319	22319	24319	24320	25320	22320	21320*	
21321	22321	24321	24322	25322	22322	21322*	
21323	22323	25384	24323	24324	25324	22324	21324*
21325	22325	24325	24326	25326	22326	21326*	
21327	22327	25386	24327	24328	25328	22328	21328*
21329	22329	24329	24330	25330	22330	21330*	
21331	22331	24331	24332	25332	22332	21332*	
21333	22333	24333	24334	25334	22334	21334*	
21335	22335	24335	24336	25336	22336	21336*	
21337	22337	24337	24338	25338	22338	21338*	
21339	22339	24339	24340	25340	22340	21340*	
21341	22341	24341	24342	25342	22342	21342*	
21343	22343	24343	24344	25344	22344	21344*	
21345	22345	24345	24346	25346	22346	21346*	
21347	22347	24347	24348	25348	22348	21348*	
21349	22349	24349	24350	25350	22350	21350*	
21351	22351	24351	24352	25352	22352	21352*	
21353	22353	24353	24354	25354	22354	21354*	
21355	22355	24355	24356	25356	22356	21356*	
21357	22357	24357	24358	25358	22358	21358*	
21359	22359	24359	24360	25360	22360	21360*	
21361	22361	24361	24362	25362	22362	21362*	
21363	22363	24363	24364	25364	22364	21364*	
21365	22365	24365	24366	25366	22366	21366*	
21367	22367	24367	24368	25368	22368	21368*	
21369	22369	24369	24370	25370	22370	21370*	
21371	22371	24371	24372	25372	22372	21372*	
21373	22373	24373	24374	25374	22374	21374*	
21375	22375	24375	24376	25376	22376	21376*	
21377	22377	24377	24378	25378	22378	21378*	
21379	22379	24379	24380	25380	22380	21380*	
21381	22381	24381	24382	25382	22382	21382*	
21383	22383	24383	24384	23384	22384	21384*	
21385	22385	24385	24386	23386	22386	21386*	
21387	22387	24387	24388	23388	22388	21388	
21389	22389	24389	24390	23390	22390	21390	
21391	22391	24391	24392	23392	22392	21392	
21393	22393	24393	24394	23394	22394	21394	

21395	22395	24395	24396	23396	22396	21396
21397	22397	24397	24398	23398	22398	21398
21399	22399	24399	24400	23400	22400	21400
21401	22401	24401	24402	23402	22402	21402
21403	22403	24403	24404	23404	22404	21404
21405	22405	24405	24406	23406	22406	21406
21407	22407	24407	24408	23408	22408	21408
21409	22409	24409	24410	23410	22410	21410
21411	22411	24411	24412	23412	22412	21412
21413	22413	24413	24414	23414	22414	21414
21415	22415	24415	24416	23416	22416	21416
21417	22417	24417	24418	23418	22418	21418
21419	22419	24419	24420	23420	22420	21420
21421	22421	24421	24422	23422	22422	21422
21423	22423	24423	24424	23424	22424	21424
21425	22425	24425	24426	23426	22426	21426
21427	22427	24427	24428	23428	22428	21428
21429	22429	24429	24430	23430	22430	21430
21431	22431	24431	24432	23432	22432	21432
21433	22433	24433	24434	23434	22434	21434
21435	22435	24435	24436	23436	22436	21436
21437	22437	24437	24438	23438	22438	21438
21439	22439	24439	24440	23440	22440	21440
21441	22441	24441	24442	23442	22442	21442
21443	22443	24443	24444	23444	22444	21444
21445	22445	24445	24446	23446	22446	21446
21447	22447	24447	24448	23448	22448	21448
21449	22449	24449	24450	23450	22450	21450
21451	22451	24451	24452	23452	22452	21452
21453	22453	24453	24454	23454	22454	21454
21455	22455	24455	24456	23456	22456	21456
21457	22457	24457	24458	23458	22458	21458
21459	22459	24459	24460	23460	22460	21460
21461	22461	24461	24462	23462	22462	21462
21463	22463	24463	24464	23464	22464	21464
21465	22465	24465	24466	23466	22466	21466
21467	22467	24467	24468	23468	22468	21468
21469	22469	24469	24470	23470	22470	21470
21471	22471	24471	24472	23472	22472	21472
21473	22473	24473	24474	23474	22474	21474
21475	22475	24475	24476	23476	22476	21476
21477	22477	24477	24478	23478	22478	21478
21479	22479	24479	24480	23480	22480	21480
21481	22481	24481	24482	23482	22482	21482
21483	22483	24483	24484	23484	22484	21484
21485	22485	24485	24486	23486	22486	21486
21487	22487	24487	24488	23488	22488	21488
21489	22489	24489	24490	23490	22490	21490
21491	22491	24491	24492	23492	22492	21492
21493	22493	24493	24494	23494	22494	21494
21495	22495	24495	24496	23496	22496	21496
21497	22497	24497	24498	23498	22498	21498
21499	22499	24499	24500	23500	22500	21500
21501	22501	24501	24502	23502	22502	21502
21503	22503	24503	24504	23504	22504	21504
21505	22505	24505	24506	23506	22506	21506

7 Car Units - One 3 Car Set and One 4 Car Set coupled together (cont)

21507	22507	24507	24508	23508	22508	21508
21509	22509	24509	24510	23510	22510	21510
21511	22511	24511	24512	23512	22512	21512
21513	22513	24513	24514	23514	22514	21514
21515	22515	24515	24516	23516	22516	21516
21517	22517	24517	24518	23518	22518	21518
21519	22519	24519	24520	23520	22520	21520
21521	22521	24521	24522	23522	22522	21522
21523	22523	24523	24524	23524	22524	21524
21525	22525	24525	24526	23526	22526	21526
21527	22527	24527	24528	23528	22528	21528
21529	22529	24529	24530	23530	22530	21530
21531	22531	24531	24532	23532	22532	21532
21533	22533	24533	24534	23534	22534	21534
21535	22535	24535	24536	23536	22536	21536
21537	22537	24537	24538	23538	22538	21538
21539	22539	24539	24540	23540	22540	21540
21541	22541	24541	24542	23542	22542	21542
21543	22543	24543	24544	23544	22544	21544
21545	22545	24545	24546	23546	22546	21546
21547	22547	24547	24548	23548	22548	21548
21549	22549	24549	24550	23550	22550	21550
21551	22551	24551	24552	23552	22552	21552
21553	22553	24553	24554	23554	22554	21554
21555	22555	24555	24556	23556	22556	21556
21557	22557	24557	24558	23558	22558	21558
21559	22559	24559	24560	23560	22560	21560
21561	22561	24561	24562	23562	22562	21562
21563	22563	24563	24564	23564	22564	21564
21565	22565	24565	24566	23566	22566	21566
21567	22567	24567	24568	23568	22568	21568

Northern Line

1995 Tube Stock 3-car Single-ended Units

51501	52501	53501	51521	52521	53521	51541	52541	53541	51561	52561	53561
51502	52502	53502	51522	52522	53522	51542	52542	53542	51562	52562	53562
51503	52503	53503	51523	52523	53523	51543	52543	53543	51563	52563	53563
51504	52504	53504	51524	52524	53524	51544	52544	53544	51564	52564	53564
51505	52505	53505	51525	52525	53525	51545	52545	53545	51565	52565	53565
51506	52506	53506	51526	52526	53526	51546	52546	53546	51566	52566	53566
51507	52507	53507	51527	52527	53527	51547	52547	53547	51567	52567	53567
51508	52508	53508	51528	52528	53528	51548	52548	53548	51568	52568	53568
51509	52509	53509	51529	52529	53529	51549	52549	53549	51569	52569	53569
51510	52510	53510	51530	52530	53530	51550	52550	53550	51570	52570	53570
51511	52511	53511	51531	52531	53531	51551	52551	53551	51571	52571	53571
51512	52512	53512	51532	52532	53532	51552	52552	53552	51572	52572	53572
51513	52513	53513	51533	52533	53533	51553	52553	53553	51573	52573	53573
51514	52514	53514	51534	52534	53534	51554	52554	53554	51574	52574	53574
51515	52515	53515	51535	52535	53535	51555	52555	53555	51575	52575	53575
51516	52516	53516	51536	52536	53536	51556	52556	53556	51576	52576	53576
51517	52517	53517	51537	52537	53537	51557	52557	53557	51577	52577	53577
51518	52518	53518	51538	52538	53538	51558	52558	53558	51578	52578	53578
51519	52519	53519	51539	52539	53539	51559	52559	53559	51579	52579	53579
51520	52520	53520	51540	52540	53540	51560	52560	53560	51580	52580	53580

1995 Tube Stock 3-car Single-ended Units

51581	52581	53581	51608	52608	53608	51635	52635	53635	51661	52661	53661
51582	52582	53582	51609	52609	53609	51636	52636	53636	51662	52662	53662
51583	52583	53583	51610	52610	53610	51637	52637	53637	51663	52663	53663
51584	52584	53584	51611	52611	53611	51638	52638	53638	51664	52664	53664
51585	52585	53585	51612	52612	53612	51639	52639	53639	51665	52665	53665
51586	52586	53586	51613	52613	53613	51640	52640	53640	51666	52666	53666
51587	52587	53587	51614	52614	53614	51641	52641	53641	51667	52667	53667
51588	52588	53588	51615	52615	53615	51642	52642	53642	51668	52668	53668
51589	52589	53589	51616	52616	53616	51643	52643	53643	51669	52669	53669
51590	52590	53590	51617	52617	53617	51644	52644	53644	51670	52670	53670
51591	52591	53591	51618	52618	53618	51645	52645	53645	51671	52671	53671
51592	52592	53592	51619	52619	53619	51646	52646	53646	51672	52672	53672
51593	52593	53593	51620	52620	53620	51647	52647	53647	51673	52673	53673
51594	52594	53594	51621	52621	53621	51648	52648	53648	51674	52674	53674
51595	52595	53595	51622	52622	53622	51649	52649	53649	51675	52675	53675
51596	52596	53596	51623	52623	53623	51650	52650	53650	51676	52676	53676
51597	52597	53597	51624	52624	53624	51651	52651	53651	51677	52677	53677
51598	52598	53598	51625	52625	53625	51652	52652	53652	51678	52678	53678
51599	52599	53599	51626	52626	53626	51653	52653	53653	51679	52679	53679
51600	52600	53600	51627	52627	53627	51654	52654	53654	51680	52680	53680
51601	52601	53601	51628	52628	53628	51655	52655	53655	51681	52681	53681
51602	52602	53602	51629	52629	53629	51656	52656	53656	51682	52682	53682
51603	52603	53603	51630	52630	53630	51657	52657	53657	51683	52683	53683
51604	52604	53604	51631	52631	53631	51658	52658	53658	51684	52684	53684
51605	52605	53605	51632	52632	53632	51659	52659	53659	51685	52685	53685
51606	52606	53606	51633	52633	53633	51660	52660	53660	51686	52686	53686
51607	52607	53607	51634	52634	53634						

1995 Tube Stock 3-car De-icing Units

51701	52701	53701	51708	52708	53708	51715	52715	53715	51721	52721	53721
51702	52702	53702	51709	52709	53709	51716	52716	53716	51722	52722	53722
51703	52703	53703	51710	52710	53710	51717	52717	53717	51723	52723	53723
51704	52704	53704	51711	52711	53711	51718	52718	53718	51724	52724	53724
51705	52705	53705	51712	52712	53712	51719	52719	53719	51725	52725	53725
51706	52706	53706	51713	52713	53713	51720	52720	53720	51726	52726	53726
51707	52707	53707	51714	52714	53714						

Piccadilly Line

1973 Tube Stock 3-car A Single-ended Units

100	500	300	117	517	317	133	533	333	149	549	349
101	501	301	118	518	318	134	534	334	150	550	350
102	502	302	119	519	319	135	535	335	151	551	351
103	503	303	120	520	320	136	536	336	152	552	352
104	504	304	121	521	321	137	537	337	153	553	353
105	505	305	122	522	322	138	538	338	154	554	354
106	506	306	123	523	323	139	539	339	155	555	355
107	507	307	124	524	324	140	540	340	156	556	356
108	508	308	125	525	325	141	541	341	157	557	357
109	509	309	126	526	326	142	542	342	158	558	358
110	510	310	127	527	327	143	543	343	159	559	359
111	511	311	128	528	328	144	544	344	160	560	360
112	512	312	129	529	329	145	545	345	161	561	361
113	513	313	130	530	330	146	546	346	162	562	362
115	515	315	131	531	331	147	547	347	163	563	363
116	516	316	132	532	332	148	548	348	164	564	364

1973 Tube Stock 3-car A Single-ended Units

165	565	365	188	588	388	211	611	411	233	633	433
167	567	367	189	589	389	212	612	412	234	634	434
168	568	368	190	590	390	213	613	413	235	635	435
169	569	369	191	591	391	214	614	414	236	636	436
170	570	370	192	592	392	215	615	415	237	637	437
171	571	371	193	593	393	216	616	416	238	638	438
172	572	372	194	594	394	217	617	417	239	639	439
173	573	373	195	595	395	218	618	418	240	640	440
174	574	374	196	596	396	219	619	419	241	641	441
175	575	375	197	597	397	220	620	420	242	642	442
176	576	376	198	598	398	221	621	421	243	643	443
177	577	377	199	599	399	222	622	422	244	644	444
178	578	378	200	600	400	223	623	423	245	645	445
179	579	379	201	601	401	224	624	424	246	646	446
180	580	380	202	602	402	225	625	425	247	647	447
181	581	381	203	603	403	226	626	426	248	648	448
182	582	382	205	605	405	227	627	427	249	649	449
183	583	383	206	606	406	228	628	428	250	650	450
184	584	384	207	607	407	229	629	429	251	651	451
185	585	385	208	608	408	230	630	430	252	652	452
186	586	386	209	609	409	231	631	431	253	653	453
187	587	387	210	610	410	232	632	432			

1973 Tube Stock 3-car Double-ended Units

854	654	855	866	666	867	876	676	877	886	686	887
856	656	857	868	668	869	878	678	879	890	690	891
858	658	859	870	670	871	880	680	881	892	692	893
860	660	861	872	672	873	882	682	883	894	694	895
862	662	863	874	674	875	884	684	885	896	696	897
864	664	865									

Notes

Victoria Line

2010 Tube Stock 4-car Units

11001	12001	13001	14001	11033	12033	13033	14033	11064	12064	13064	14064
11002	12002	13002	14002	11034	12034	13034	14034	11065	12065	13065	14065
11003	12003	13003	14003	11035	12035	13035	14035	11066	12066	13066	14066
11004	12004	13004	14004	11036	12036	13036	14036	11067	12067	13067	14067
11005	12005	13005	14005	11037	12037	13037	14037	11068	12068	13068	14068
11006	12006	13006	14006	11038	12038	13038	14038	11069	12069	13069	14069
11007	12007	13007	14007	11039	12039	13039	14039	11070	12070	13070	14070
11008	12008	13008	14008	11040	12040	13040	14040	11071	12071	13071	14071
11009	12009	13009	14009	11041	12041	13041	14041	11072	12072	13072	14072
11010	12010	13010	14010	11042	12042	13042	14042	11073	12073	13073	14073
11011	12011	13011	14011	11043	12043	13043	14043	11074	12074	13074	14074
11012	12012	13012	14012	11044	12044	13044	14044	11075	12075	13075	14075
11013	12013	13013	14013	11045	12045	13045	14045	11076	12076	13076	14076
11014	12014	13014	14014	11046	12046	13046	14046	11077	12077	13077	14077
11015	12015	13015	14015	11047	12047	13047	14047	11078	12078	13078	14078
11016	12016	13016	14016	11048	12048	13048	14048	11079	12079	13079	14079
11017	12017	13017	14017	11049	12049	13049	14049	11080	12080	13080	14080
11018	12018	13018	14018	11050	12050	13050	14050	11081	12081	13081	14081
11019	12019	13019	14019	11051	12051	13051	14051	11082	12082	13082	14082
11020	12020	13020	14020	11052	12052	13052	14052	11083	12083	13083	14083
11021	12021	13021	14021	11053	12053	13053	14053	11084	12084	13084	14084
11022	12022	13022	14022	11054	12054	13054	14054	11085	12085	13085	14085
11023	12023	13023	14023	11055	12055	13055	14055	11086	12086	13086	14086
11024	12024	13024	14024	11056	12056	13056	14056	11087	12087	13087	14087
11025	12025	13025	14025	11057	12057	13057	14057	11088	12088	13088	14088
11026	12026	13026	14026	11058	12058	13058	14058	11089	12089	13089	14089
11027	12027	13027	14027	11059	12059	13059	14059	11090	12090	13090	14090
11028	12028	13028	14028	11060	12060	13060	14060	11091	12091	13091	14091
11029	12029	13029	14029	11061	12061	13061	14061	11092	12092	13092	14092
11030	12030	13030	14030	11062	12062	13062	14062	11093	12093	13093	14093
11031	12031	13031	14031	11063	12063	13063	14063	11094	12094	13094	14094
11032	12032	13032	14032								

Waterloo & City Line

1992 Tube Stock 2-car Units

65501	67501	65503	67503	65505	67505	65507	67507	65509	67509
65502	67502	65504	67504	65506	67506	65508	67508	65510	67510

London Underground Departmental Locomotives

Diesel Locomotives Built by: Schoma (Germany)   1996

1	Britta Lotta	4	Pam	7	Annemarie	10	Clementine	13	Michele
2	Nikki	5	Sophie	8	Emma	11	Joan	14	Carol
3	Claire	6	Denise	9	Debora	12	Melanie		

Various Battery Locomotives

L15	L20	L24	L28	L32	L47	L51	L132
L16	L21	L25	L29	L44	L48	L52	L133
L17	L22	L26	L30	L45	L49	L53	L150
L18	L23	L27	L31	L46	L50	L54	L151
L19							

London Underground On-Track Plant

TMM771	Transplant	Plasser & Theurer 07-16 Tamper/Liner	1980
TMM772	Transplant	Plasser & Theurer 07-16 Tamper/Liner	1980
TMM773	Transplant	Plasser & Theurer 07-16 Tamper/Liner	1980
TMM774	Transplant	Plasser & Theurer 08-275/4ZW Tamper	
TMM775	Transplant	Matissa B45 Tamper (99-70-9128-003-9)	2015
TMM776	Transplant	Matissa B45 Tamper (99-70-9128-004-7)	2015
DHC 627	TransPlant	Cowans Boyd Self Propelled Twin Jib Crane	1985-1993
TRM 628	TransPlant	Cowans Boyd Self Propelled Twin Jib Crane	1985-1993
C 623	TransPlant	Cowans Sheldon 7.5 tonne Diesel Hydraulic Crane	1981-1983
C 624	TransPlant	Cowans Sheldon 7.5 tonne Diesel Hydraulic Crane	1981-1983
C 625	TransPlant	Cowans Sheldon 7.5 tonne Diesel Hydraulic Crane	1981-1983
C 626	TransPlant	Cowans Sheldon 7.5 tonne Diesel Hydraulic Crane	1981-1983
999666	LUL	Track Recording Car	1973
TCC1	LUL	Tunnel Cleaning Train [Acton Works]	1938-1972
TCC2	LUL	Tunnel Cleaning Train [Acton Works]	1938-1972
TCC3	LUL	Tunnel Cleaning Train [Acton Works]	1938-1972
TCC4	LUL	Tunnel Cleaning Train [Acton Works]	1938-1972
94801	W&C	Permaquip Track Maintenace Machine	1988
DISAB1	LUL	Railcare TubeVac 14000/330	
DISAB2	LUL	Railcare TubeVac 14000/330	
99 70 9319 014-5	Transplant	Kirow KRC250 LUL Multi task Crane	2019
99 70 9319 015-2	Transplant	Kirow KRC250 LUL Multi task Crane	2019
1570+9591+2440+9441+1441		Rail Adhesion Train	
7010+8123+17010+8010+7123		Rail Adhesion Train	
7040+8107+17040+8040+7107		Rail Adhesion Train	
1406+2682+9125+1681+1682+9577+2606+1407		Rail Adhesion Train	

Manchester Metrolink

Bombardier M5000 Flexity Swift			2009 -				Silver & Yellow	
3001	3020	3039	3058	3076	3094	3112	3130	
3002	3021	3040	3059	3077	3095	3113	3131	
3003	3022	3041	3060	3078	3096	3114	3132	o/o
3004	3023	3042	3061	3079	3097	3115	3133	o/o
3005	3024	3043	3062	3080	3098	3116	3134	o/o
3006	3025	3044	3063	3081	3099	3117	3135	o/o
3007	3026	3045	3064	3082	3100	3118	3136	o/o
3008	3027	3046	3065	3083	3101	3119	3137	o/o
3009	3028	3047	3066	3084	3102	3120	3138	o/o
3010	3029	3048	3067	3085	3103	3121	3139	o/o
3011	3030	3049	3068	3086	3104	3122	3140	o/o
3012	3031	3050	3069	3087	3105	3123	3141	o/o
3013	3032	3051	3070	3088	3106	3124	3142	o/o
3014	3033	3052	3071	3089	3107	3125	3143	o/o
3015	3034	3053	3072	3090	3108	3126	3144	o/o
3016	3035	3054	3073	3091	3109	3127	3145	o/o
3017	3036	3055	3074	3092	3110	3128	3146	o/o
3018	3037	3056	3075	3093	3111	3129	3147	o/o
3019	3038	3057						

Named Vehicles	
3009 Coronation Street 50th Anniversary 1960-2010	3022 Spirit of Manchester
3020 Lancashire Fusilier	3098 Gracie Fields

Nottingham Express Transit

Built by Bombardier Derby 2002 - 2003. 5 section car (62/128) / Dark Green, Silver & White

201	Torvill and Dean	206	Angela Alcock	211	Robin Hood
202	DH Lawrence	207	Mavis Worthington	212	William Booth
203	Bendigo Thompson	208	Dinah Minton	213	Mary Potter
204	Erica Beardsmore	209	Sydney Standard	214	Dennis McCarthy MBE
205	Lord Byron	210	Sir Jesse Boot	215	Brian Clough

Type 'Citadis'	2012 - 2014	Alstom

216	Dame Laura Knight	227	Sir Peter Mansfield
217	Carl Froch M.B.E	228	Local Armed Forces Heroes
218	Jim Taylor	229	Viv Anderson M.B.E
219	Alan Sillitoe	230	George Green
220	Sophie Robson	231	Rebecca Adlington O.B.E
221	Steven Lowe	232	William Ivory
222	David S Stewart O.B.E	233	Ava Lovelace
223	Colin Slater M.B.E	234	George Africanus
224	Vicky McClure	235	David Clarke
225	Doug Scott C.B.E	236	Sat Bains
226	Jimmy Sirrel & Jack Wheeler	237	Stuart Broad

South Yorkshire Supertram (Sheffield/Rotherham)

Built by Siemens (Duewag) 1993-94. 3 section car / Blue with Orange swirl and Red Cab Front

101	105	108	111	114	117	120	123
102	106	109	112	115	118	121	124
103	107	110	113	116	119	122	125
104							

Built by Siemens 2015 - 2016

Note: 399 202 is named "Theo in support of - The Children's Hospital Charity"

399 201	999001	999101	999201	399 205	999005	999105	999205
399 202	999002	999102	999202	399 206	999006	999106	999206
399 203	999003	999103	999203	399 207	999007	999107	999207
399 204	999004	999104	999204				

Tyne & Wear Metro

B-2-B	1978 - 1981	Metropolitan-Cammell

4001	4013	4025	4036	4047	4058	4069	4080
4002	4014	4026	4037	4048	4059	4070	4081
4003	4015	4027	4038	4049	4060	4071	4082
4004	4016	4028	4039	4050	4061	4072	4083
4005	4017	4029	4040	4051	4062	4073	4084
4006	4018	4030	4041	4052	4063	4074	4085
4007	4019	4031	4042	4053	4064	4075	4086
4008	4020	4032	4043	4054	4065	4076	4087
4009	4021	4033	4044	4055	4066	4077	4088
4010	4023	4034	4045	4056	4067	4078	4089
4011	4024	4035	4046	4057	4068	4079	4090
4012							

Battery Locos (now network rail registered)	1989-1990	Hunslet TPL

BL1	[97901]	BL2	[97902]	BL3	[97903]

Isle of Man

*   - Stored Unserviceable at Derby Castle
\#   - Stored Unserviceable at Laxey depot
(D)   - Disabled Access Car
Depots at Derby Castle, Douglas and Laxey

Snaefell Mountain Railway

Saloon built 1895/6 by G F Milnes, Birkenhead

1	2	3 (s)	4	5	6	

Manx Electric Railway

Power Cars

1	7	16	20	25#	29 *	32
2	9	17*	21	26#	30#	33
5	14	18*	22	27#	31#	34
6	15*	19	23#	28#		

Trailers

36#	42	47	50#	54	57	60
37	43	48	51	55*	58	61
40	44	49	53*	56 (D)	59	62
41	46					

Notes

IR/TranslinkNIR

Acknowledgements
With thanks to Nigel Farebrother, John Burdett, Downpatrick Railway Society, Martin Hall,
Irish Railway News, Irish Traction Group, RPSI, Wikipedia, Stradbally Railway, West Clare Railway
and www.heartland.ie
Note:- All preserved items of both Eire and Northern Ireland will be listed in our forthcoming updated
publication for European Preserved locos & units.

General Abbreviations

4w	4 wheel	**kW**	Kilowatts
6w	6 wheel	**m**	Metres
BE	Battery Electric	**mph**	Miles per hour
CE	Clayton Equipment	**MR**	Motor Rail Simplex
DE	Diesel Electric	**MS**	Motor Standard
DEMU	Diesel Electric Multiple Unit	**PM**	Petrol Mechanical
DH	Diesel Hydraulic	**PMR**	Petrol Mechanical Railcar
DHR	Diesel Hydraulic Railcar	**PMS**	Pantograph Motor Standard
DM	Diesel Mechanical	**ST**	Saddle Tank
DMF	Driving Motor First	**t**	Tons
DMS	Driving Motor Standard	**VBT**	Vertical Boiler Tank
DMR	Diesel Mechanical Railcar	**WR**	Wingrove & Rogers
DTS	Driving Trailer Standard	**WT**	Well Tank

Loco Status

(s)	Stored	**(w)**	Withdrawn

Depot Codes

CK	Cork		Dublin Connolly Station
DA	Drogheda		Dublin Heuston Station
DF	Dublin Fairview EMU depot	**LM**	Limerick
DN	Dublin North Wall yard	**LMS**	Limerick Station
DU	Dundalk	**PL**	Portlaoise
IW	Inchicore Depot & Works	**PY**	Portlaoise Yard

Translink/Northern Ireland Railways Depot Codes

BS	Ballymena Sidings		Belfast Fortwilliam
BY	Belfast York Road	**LIS**	Lisburn Station
	Belfast Adelaide		

Irish Rail

Diesel Locomotives

Class 071 — Co-Co — DE

Built by:	General Motors 1976	Weight:	99t
Power:	1360kW	Max Speed:	90mph
Length:	17.37m		

071	IW	[92 60 0117 071-7]	077	IW	[92 60 0117 077-4]	083	IW	[92 60 0117 083-2]
072	IW	[92 60 0117 072-5]	078	IW	[92 60 0117 078-2]	084	IW	[92 60 0117 084-0]
073	IW	[92 60 0117 073-3]	079	IW	[92 60 0117 079-0]	085	IW	[92 60 0117 085-7]
074	IW	[92 60 0117 074-1]	080	IW	[92 60 0117 080-8]	086	IW	[92 60 0117 086-5]
075	IW	[92 60 0117 075-8]	081	IW	[92 60 0117 081-6]	087	IW	[92 60 0117 087-3]
076	IW	[92 60 0117 076-6]	082	IW	[92 60 0117 082-4]	088	IW	[92 60 0117 088-1]

Named Locomotive

082   The Institution Of Engineers Of Ireland / Cumann Na Ninnealtoiri

Class 141B — Bo-Bo — DE

Built by:	General Motors 1962	Weight:	67t
Power:	530kW	Max Speed:	75mph
Length:	13.42m		

144	IW(s)	147	IW(s)	171	IW(s)	177	IW(s)

Class 201 — Co-Co — DE

Built by:	General Motors 1994 - 1995	Weight:	112t
Power:	2385kW	Max Speed:	100mph
Length:	20.94m		

* Push-pull equipment fitted	# TPWS fitted

Note: Locos 208 & 209 are run by NI Railways, see NIR section.
Note: When on service these locos can be found at DN or CK depots.

201	IW(s)	[92 60 0110 201-7]	River Shannon/Abhainn na Sionnaine
202	IW(s)	[92 60 0110 202-5]	River Lee/Abhainn na Laoi
203	IW(s)	[92 60 0110 203-3]	River Corrib/Abhainn na Coiribe
204	IW(s)	[92 60 0110 204-1]	River Barrow/Abhainn na Bearu
205	IW(s)	[92 60 0110 205-8]	River Nore/Abhainn na Feoire
206*#	IW	[92 60 0310 206-4]	Abhainn na Life
207*#	IW	[92 60 0310 207-2]	River Boyne/Abhainn na Boinne
210	IW(s)	[92 60 0110 210-8]	River Erne/Abhainn na Heirne
211	IW(s)	[92 60 0110 211-6]	River Suck/Abhainn na Suca
212	IW(s)	[92 60 0110 212-4]	River Slaney/Abhainn na Slaine
213	IW(s)	[92 60 0110 213-2]	River Moy/Abhainn na Muaide
214	IW(s)	[92 60 0110 214-0]	River Brosna/Abhainn na Brosani
215*	IW	[92 60 0210 215-6]	River Avonmore/Abhainn na Mhor
216*	IW	[92 60 0210 216-4]	River Dodder/Abhainn na Dothra
217*	IW	[92 60 0210 217-2]	River Flesk/Abhainn na Fleisce
218*	IW	[92 60 0210 218-0]	River Garavogue/Abhainn na Garbhoige
219*	IW	[92 60 0210 219-8]	River Tolka
220*	IW	[92 60 0210 220-6]	River Blackwater/Abhainn na Dhubh
221*	IW	[92 60 0210 221-4]	River Fealge/Abhainn na Feilge
222*	IW	[92 60 0210 222-2]	River Dargle
223*	IW	[92 60 0210 223-0]	River Anner/Abhainn na Hainnire
224*	IW	[92 60 0210 224-8]	Abhainn na Feile
225*	IW	[92 60 0210 225-6]	River Deel/Abhainn na Daoile
226*	IW	[92 60 0210 226-5]	Abhainn na Siuire

Class 201			Co-Co	DE
227*	IW(w)	[92 60 0310 227-3]	River Laune	
228*	IW	[92 60 0310 228-8]	An Abhainn Bhui	
229*	IW	[92 60 0210 229-7]	River Maine/Abhainn na Mainge	
230*	IW(s)	[92 60 0310 230-4]	Abhainn na Bandan	
231*	IW	[92 60 0310 231-2]	Abhainn na Maighe	
232*	IW	[92 60 0210 232-1]	River Cummeragh	
233*	IW	[92 60 0310 233-8]	River Clare/Abhainn na Chlair	
234*	IW	[92 60 0210 234-7]		

Diesel Multiple Units

Class 2600 — DMU-2 — DH

Built by:	Tokyu Car Corporation 1993	Weight:	DMS: 42t
Power:	260kW	Max Speed:	70mph
Length:	DMS: 20.26m		

Note: They run in pairs eg. 2601+2602 but not always in the correct order.

2601*	CK	[95 60 01 2601 0-1]	2610	CK	[95 60 02 2610 0-9]
2602	CK	[95 60 02 2602 0-9]	2611*	CK	[95 60 01 2611 0-9]
2603*	CK	[95 60 01 2603 0-9]	2612	CK	[95 60 02 2612 0-7]
2604	CK	[95 60 02 2604 0-7]	2613*	CK	[95 60 01 2613 0-7]
2605*	CK	[95 60 01 2605 0-7]	2614	CK	[95 60 02 2614 0-5]
2606	CK	[95 60 02 2606 0-5]	2615*	CK	[95 60 01 2615 0-5]
2607*	CK	[95 60 01 2607 0-5]	2616	CK	[95 60 02 2616 0-3]
2608	CK	[95 60 02 2608 0-3]	2617*	CK	[95 60 01 2617 0-3]
2609*	CK(w)	[95 60 01 2609 0-1]			

Class 2700 — DMU-2 — DH

Built by:	GEC Alstom 1998 - 1999	Weight:	DMS: 38.7t
Power:	260kW	Max Speed:	75mph
Length:	DMS: 20.55m		

Note: They run in pairs eg. 2701 + 2702 but not always in the correct order.

2701*	IW(s)	[95 60 01 2701 0-0]	2714	CK(s)	[95 60 02 2714 0-4]
2702	IW(s)	[95 60 02 2702 0-8]	2715*	IW(s)	[95 60 01 2715 0-4]
2703*	IW(s)	[95 60 01 2703 0-8]	2716	CK(s)	[95 60 04 2716 0-9]
2704	IW(s)	[95 60 02 2704 0-6]	2717*	CK(s)	[95 60 01 2717 0-2]
2705*	IW(s)	[95 60 01 2725 0-0]	2718	CK(s)	[95 60 02 2718 0-0]
2706	IW(s)	[95 60 02 2706 0-4]	2719*	CK(s)	[95 60 01 2719 0-0]
2707*	IW(s)	[95 60 01 2707 0-4]	2720	IW(s)	[95 60 02 2720 0-6]
2708	IW(s)	[95 60 02 2708 0-2]	2721*	IW(s)	[95 60 01 2721 0-6]
2709*	CK(s)	[95 60 01 2709 0-2]	2722	CK(s)	[95 60 02 2722 0-4]
2710	CK(s)	[95 60 02 2710 0-8]	2723*	IW(s)	[95 60 01 2723 0-4]
2711*	IW(s)	[95 60 01 2711 0-8]	2724	IW(s)	[95 60 02 2724 0-2]
2712	IW(s)	[95 60 02 2712 0-6]	2726	IW(s)	[95 60 02 2726 0-0]
2713*	CK(s)	[95 60 01 2713 0-6]			

Class 2750 — DMU-1 — DH

Built by:	GEC Alsthom 1998	Weight:	DMS:40.2t
Power:	260kW	Max Speed:	75mph
Length:	DMS: 21.59m		

2751	CK(s)	[95 60 03 2751 0-7]	2753	IW(s)	[95 60 03 2753 0-5]

Class 2800 DMU-2 DH

Built by:	Tokyu Car Corporation 2000	Weight:	DMS: 43.9t
Power:	260kW	Max Speed:	75mph
Length:	DMS: 20.73m	Run in pairs eg. 2801+2802 onwards	

2801	DA	[95 60 01 2801 0-9]	2811	DA	[95 60 01 2811 0-7]
2802	DA	[95 60 02 2802 0-7]	2812	DA	[95 60 02 2812 0-5]
2803	DA	[95 60 01 2803 0-7]	2813	DA	[95 60 01 2813 0-5]
2804	DA	[95 60 02 2804 0-5]	2814	DA	[95 60 02 2814 0-3]
2805	DA	[95 60 01 2805 0-5]	2815	DA	[95 60 01 2815 0-3]
2806	DA	[95 60 02 2806 0-3]	2816	DA	[95 60 02 2816 0-1]
2807	DA	[95 60 01 2807 0-3]	2817	DA	[95 60 01 2817 0-1]
2808	DA	[95 60 02 2808 0-1]	2818	DA	[95 60 02 2818 0-9]
2809	DA	[95 60 01 2809 0-1]	2819	DA	[95 60 01 2819 0-9]
2810	DA	[95 60 02 2810 0-7]	2820	DA	[95 60 02 2820 0-5]

Class 22000 DM+MS+DM DMU - 3 DH

Built by:-	Rotem, Korea/ Mitsui, Japan 2007-08	Max Speed:-	100mph
Power:-	360kW	UIC Number:-	95 60 09/03* 222xx-x /
Length:-	23.5m + 23.0m + 23.5m		95 60 04 224xx-x / 95 60 08/02* 223xx-x
Weight :-	49.4t + 47.1t + 50.0t		

22001	22201-3	22401-3	22301-0	DA	**22006**	22206-2	22406-2	22306-9	DA
22002	22202-1	22402-1	22302-8	DA	**22007**	22207-6*	22407-0	22307-3*	DA
22003	22203-9	22403-9	22303-6	DA	**22008**	22208-4	22408-8	22308-1	DA
22004	22204-7	22404-7	22304-4	DA	**22009**	22209-2	22409-6	22309-9	DA
22005	22205-4	22405-4	22305-1	DA	**22010**	22210-0	22410-4	22310-7	DA

Class 22000 DM+MS+MS+DM DMU - 4 DH

Built by:-	Rotem, Korea/ Mitsui, Japan 2007-08	Max Speed:-	100mph
Power:-	360kW	UIC Number:-	95 60 02 222xx-x / 95 60 04/06*
Length:-	23.5m + 23.0m + 23.0m + 23.5m		22xxx-x /95 60 04 224xx-x / 95 60 03 223xx-x
Weight :-	49.4t + 47.1t + 47.1t + 50.0t		

22011	22211-8	22531-7	22411-2	22311-5	DA
22012	22212-6	22532-5	22412-0	22312-3	DA
22013	22213-4	22533-3	22413-8	22313-1	DA
22014	22214-2	22534-1	22414-6	22314-9	DA
22015	22215-9	22535-8	22415-3	22315-6	DA
22016	22216-7	22536-6	22416-1	22316-4	DA
22017	22217-5	22537-4	22417-9	22317-2	DA
22018	22218-3	22538-2	22418-7	22318-0	DA
22019	22219-1	22539-0	22419-5	22319-8	DA
22020	22220-9	22540-8	22420-3	22320-6	DA
22021	22221-7	22641-2*	22421-1	22321-4	DA
22022	22222-5	22741-2	22422-9	22322-2	DA
22023	22223-3	22642-0	22423-7	22323-0	DA
22024	22224-1	22742-0	22424-5	22324-8	DA
22025	22225-8	22643-8	22425-2	22325-5	DA
22026	22226-6	22743-8	22426-0	22326-3	DA
22027	22227-4	22644-6	22427-8	22327-1	DA
22028	22228-2	22744-6	22428-6	22328-9	DA
22029	22229-0	22645-3	22429-4	22329-7	DA
22030	22230-8	22745-3	22430-2	22330-5	DA

Class 22000 DM+MS+MS+MS+DM   DMU - 5   DH

Built by:-	Rotem, Korea/ Mitsui, Japan 2007-08	Max Speed:- 100mph
Power:-	360kW	UIC Number:- 95 60 01/07* 221xx-x /
Length:-	23.5m+23.0m+23.0m+23.0m+23.5m	95 60 04 227xx-x / 95 60 06 226xx-x /
Weight :-	49.4t + 47.1t + 47.1t + 47.1t + 50.0t	95 60 04 224xx-x / 95 60 03/09* 223xx-x

22031	22131-9	22731-3	22631-3	22431-0	22331-3 DA
22032	22132-7	22732-1	22632-1	22432-8	22332-1 DA
22033	22133-5	22733-9	22633-9	22433-6	22333-9 DA
22034	22134-3	22734-7	22634-7	22434-4	22334-7 DA
22035	22135-0	22735-4	22635-4	22435-1	22335-4 DA
22036	22136-2*	22736-2	22636-2	22436-9	22336-6* DA
22037	22137-0	22737-0	22637-0	22437-7	22337-4 DA
22038	22138-8	22738-8	22638-8	22438-5	22338-2 DA
22039	22139-6	22739-6	22639-6	22439-3	22339-0 DA
22040	22140-0	22740-4	22640-4	22440-1	22340-4 DA

Class 22000 DM+MS+MS+DM   DMU - 4   DH

Built by:-	Rotem, Korea/ Mitsui, Japan 2007-08	Max Speed:- 100mph
Power:-	360kW	UIC Number:- 95 60 02 222xx-x /
Length:-	23.5m + 23.0m + 23.0m + 23.5m	95 60 04 224xx-x / 95 04 225xx-x /
Weight :-	49.4t + 47.1t + 47.3t + 50.0t	95 60 03 223xx-x

22041	22241-5	22441-9	22541-6	22341-2 DA
22042	22242-3	22442-7	22542-4	22342-0 DA
22043	22243-1	22443-5	22543-2	22343-8 DA
22044	22244-9	22444-3	22544-0	22344-6 DA
22045	22245-6	22445-0	22545-7	22345-3 DA

Class 22000 DM+MS+DM   DMU - 3   DH

Built by:-	Rotem, Korea/ Mitsui, Japan 2007-08	Max Speed:- 100mph
Power:-	360kW	UIC Number:- 95 60 09/03* 222xx-x /
Length:-	23.5m + 23.0m + 23.5m	95 60 04 224xx-x / 95 60 08/02* 223xx-x
Weight :-	49.4t + 47.1t + 50.0t	

22046	22246-4	22446-8	22346-1	DA	22055	22255-5	22455-9	22355-2	DA
22047	22247-2	22447-6	22347-9	DA	22056	22256-3	22456-7	22356-0	DA
22048	22248-0	22448-4	22348-7	DA	22057	22257-1	22457-5	22357-8	DA
22049	22249-8	22449-2	22349-5	DA	22058	22258-9	22458-3	22358-6	DA
22050	22250-6	22450-0	22350-3	DA	22059	22259-7	22459-1	22359-4	DA
22051	22251-4	22451-8	22351-1	DA	22060	22260-5	22460-9	22360-2	DA
22052	22252-2	22452-6	22352-9	DA	22061	22261-3	22461-7	22361-0	DA
22053	22253-0	22453-4	22353-7	DA	22062	22262-1	22462-5	22362-8	DA
22054	22254-8	22454-2	22354-5	DA	22063	22263-9	22463-3	22363-6	DA

Class 29000   DMU - 4   DH

Built by:-	CAF 2001 - 2006	Max Speed:-75mph
Power:-	294kW	UIC Number:- 95 60 01 291xx-x /
Length:-	20.4m + 20.2m + 20.2m + 20.4m	95 60 02 292xx-x / 95 60 03 293xx-x /
Weight :-	43.56t + 41.36t + 42.07t + 43.52t	95 60 04 294xx-x

29001	29101-5	29201-2	29301-9	29401-6	DA	**29011**	29111-5	29211-1	29311-8	29411-5	DA
29002	29102-3	29202-0	29302-7	29402-4	DA	**29012**	29112-3	29212-9	29312-6	29412-3	DA
29003	29103-1	29203-8	29303-5	29403-2	DA	**29013**	29113-1	29213-7	29313-4	29413-1	DA
29004	29104-9	29204-6	29304-3	29404-0	DA	**29014**	29114-9	29214-5	29314-2	29414-9	DA
29005	29105-6	29205-3	29305-0	29405-7	DA	**29015**	29115-6	29215-2	29315-9	29415-6	DA
29006	29106-4	29206-1	29306-8	29406-5	DA	**29016**	29116-4	29216-0	29316-7	29416-4	DA
29007	29107-2	29207-9	29307-6	29407-3	DA	**29017**	29117-2	29217-8	29317-5	29417-2	DA
29008	29108-0	29208-7	29308-4	29408-1	DA	**29018**	29118-0	29218-6	29318-3	29418-0	DA
29009	29109-9	29209-5	29309-2	29409-9	DA	**29019**	29119-8	29219-4	29319-1	29419-8	DA
29010	29110-7	29210-3	29310-0	29410-7	DA	**29020**	29120-6	29220-2	29320-9	29420-6	DA

Class 29000			DMU - 4							DH
29021	29121-4	29221-0	29321-7	29421-4	DA	**29026**	29126-3	29226-9	29326-6	29426-3 DA
29022	29122-2	29222-8	29322-5	29422-2	DA	**29027**	29127-1	29227-7	29327-4	29427-1 DA
29023	29123-0	29223-6	29323-3	29423-0	DA	**29028**	29128-9	29228-5	29328-2	29428-9 DA
29024	29124-8	29224-4	29324-1	29424-8	DA	**29029**	29129-7	29229-3	29329-0	29429-7 DA
29025	29125-5	29225-1	29325-8	29425-5	DA					

Electric Multiple Units

Class 8100 DMS+DTS   EMU-2   1500V DC

Built by:-	Linke-Hofmann-Busch 1983	Max Speed:-	62mph
Length:-	20.490m	UIC Number:-	94 60 01 81xx 0-x /
Weight :-	40.34t / 25.43t		94 60 02 83xx 0-x

8101 0-4	8301 0-1	DF	8115 0-8	8315 0-5	DF	8128 0-3	8328 0-0	DF
8102 0-3	8302 0-0	DF	8116 0-7	8316 0-4	DF	8129 0-2	8329 0-9	DF
8103 0-2	8303 0-9	DF	8117 0-6	8317 0-3	DF	8130 0-9	8330 0-6	DF
8104 0-1	8304 0-8	DF	8118 0-5	8318 0-2	DF	8131 0-8	8331 0-5	DF
8105 0-0	8305 0-7	DF	8119 0-4	8319 0-1	DF	8132 0-7	8332 0-4	DF
8106 0-9	8306 0-6	DF	8120 0-0	8320 0-8	DF	8133 0-6	8333 0-3	DF
8107 0-8	8307 0-5	DF	8121 0-0	8321 0-7	DF	8134 0-5	8334 0-2	DF
8108 0-7	8308 0-4	DF	8122 0-9	8322 0-6	DF	8135 0-4	8335 0-1	DF
8109 0-6	8309 0-3	DF	8123 0-8	8323 0-5	DF	8137 0-2	8337 0-9	DF
8111 0-2	8311 0-9	DF	8124 0-7	8324 0-4	DF	8138 0-1	8338 0-8	DF
8112 0-1	8312 0-8	DF	8125 0-6	8325 0-3	DF	8139 0-0	8339 0-7	DF
8113 0-0	8313 0-7	DF	8126 0-5	8326 0-2	DF	8140 0-7	8340 0-4	DF
8114 0-9	8314 0-6	DF	8127 0-4	8327 0-1	DF			

Class 8200   EMU-2   1500V DC

Built by:-	Linke-Hofmann-Busch 1983	Max Speed:-	62mph
Length:-	20.490m	UIC Number:-	94 60 01 82xx 0-x /
Weight :-	40.34t/ 25.43t		94 60 02 84xx 0-x

8201 0-3	8401 0-0	IW(s)	8203 0-1	8403 0-8	IW(s)	8205 0-9	8405 0-6	IW(s)
8202 0-2	8402 0-9	IW(s)	8204 0-0	8404 0-7	IW(s)			

Class 8500 DTS+PMS+PMS+DTS   EMU-4   1500V DC

Built by:-	Tokyu Car Corporation 2000	Max Speed:-	68mph
Length:-	20.00m / 20.13m	UIC Number:-	94 60 02 86xx 0-x / 94 60 01
Weight :-	39.00t / 32.67t		85xx 0-x / 94 60 01 85xx 0-x / 94 60 02 86xx 0-x

8601 0-8	8501 0-0	8502 0-9	8602 0-7	DF	8605 0-4	8505 0-6	8506 0-5	8606 0-3	DF
8603 0-6	8503 0-8	8504 0-7	8604 0-5	DF	8607 0-2	8507 0-4	8508 0-3	8608 0-1	DF

Class 8510 DTS+PMS+PMS+DTS   EMU-4   1500V DC

Built by:-	Tokyu Car Corporation 2001	Max Speed:-	68mph
Length:-	20.00m / 20.13m	UIC Number:-	94 60 12 86xx 0-x / 94 60 11
Weight :-	39.00t / 32.67t		85xx 0-x / 94 60 11 85xx 0-x / 94 60 12 86xx 0-x

8611 0-4	8511 0-6	8512 0-5	8612 0-3	DF	8615 0-0	8515 0-2	8516 0-1	8616 0-9	DF
8613 0-2	8513 0-4	8514 0-3	8614 0-1	DF					

Class 8520 DTS+PMS+PMS+DTS   EMU-4   1500V DC

Built by:-	Tokyu Car Corporation 2003-04	Max Speed:-	68mph
Length:-	20.00m / 20.13m	UIC Number:-	94 60 22 86xx 0-x / 94 60 21
Weight :-	39.00t / 32.67t		85xx 0-x / 94 60 21 85xx 0-x / 94 60 22 86xx 0-x

8621 0-0	8521 0-2	8522 0-1	8622 0-9	DF	8631 0-8	8531 0-0	8532 0-9	8632 0-7	DF
8623 0-8	8523 0-0	8524 0-9	8624 0-7	DF	8633 0-6	8533 0-8	8534 0-7	8634 0-5	DF
8625 0-6	8525 0-8	8526 0-7	8626 0-5	DF	8635 0-4	8535 0-6	8536 0-5	8636 0-3	DF
8627 0-4	8527 0-6	8528 0-5	8628 0-3	DF	8637 0-2	8537 0-4	8538 0-3	8638 0-1	DF
8629 0-2	8529 0-4	8530 0-1	8630 0-9	DF	8639 0-0	8539 0-2	8540 0-9	8640 0-7	DF

Coaching Stock

Belmond Grand Hibernian Coaching Stock

87001	[7116, 55 60 76 87001-8]	FERMANAGH
87002	[7158, 55 60 76 87002-6]	LEITRIM
87003	[7129, 55 60 76 87003-4]	WATERFORD
87004	[7149, 55 60 76 87004-2]	DOWN
87005	[7137, 55 60 76 87005-9]	KERRY
87101	[7171, 55 60 88 87101-2]	SLIGO
87102	[7169, 55 60 88 87102-0]	WEXFORD
87103	[7104, 55 60 89 87103-7]	KILDARE
87104	[7601, 55 60 99 87104-3]	CARLOW
87110	[7130, 55 60 89 87110-2]	DONEGAL
7122(sp)		

Mark 4 CAF Built stock for Dublin - Cork service

4001	4102	4111	4120	4128	4136	4201	4401
4002	4103	4112	4121	4129	4137	4202	4402
4003	4104	4113	4122	4130	4138	4203	4403
4004	4105	4114	4123	4131	4139	4204	4404
4005	4106	4115	4124	4132	4140	4205	4405
4006	4107	4116	4125	4133	4141	4206	4406
4007	4108	4117	4126	4134	4142	4207	4407
4008	4109	4118	4127	4135	4143	4208	4408
4101	4110	4119					

ON-TRACK PLANT MACHINES

700	Plasser & Theurer EM50	Recording Car	1974
703	Plasser & Theurer USB4000	Regulator	1994
704	Plasser & Theurer USB4001	Regulator	1994
708	Plasser & Theurer SSP108	Regulator	1980
710	Plasser & Theurer DTS62N	Dynamic Track Stabiliser	1988
721	Hugh Phillips	Inspection Car	1993
722	Matisa VM100ST	Inspection Car	1994
723	Matisa VM100ST	Inspection Car	1994
739	Plasser & Theurer 08-16	Tamper	1992
740	Plasser & Theurer 09-16CAT-5/IR	Tamper	1991
741	Plasser & Theurer 09-16CAT	Tamper	1994
742	Plasser & Theurer 08-16/4x4C	Tamper	1999
743	Plasser & Theurer 08-16/4x4C	Tamper	1999
744	Plasser & Theurer 09-2X	Tamper	2010
751	Plasser & Theurer	Tamper	2008
770	Geismar PD350	2xRelaying Gantries	1977
772	Geismar PTH350	2xRelaying Gantries	1979
774	Geismar PTH350	2xRelaying Gantries	1979
776	Geismar PTH500	2xRelaying Gantries	1979
778	Geismar PTH500	2xRelaying Gantries	1979
780	Plasser & Theurer RM76UHR	Ballast Cleaner	1979
781	Plasser & Theurer RM90	Ballast Cleaner	2011
790	Giesmar MPV	Multi-Purpose Vehicle	2008
99 60 9419 900-6		Kirow Crane	2021

DEPARTMENTAL STOCK

639A	Dormitory Coach	(w)		656A	Flat wagon	(w)
654A	Flat wagon	(w)		657A	Flat wagon	(w)
655A	Flat wagon	(w)		658A	Flat wagon	(w)

Translink Northern Ireland Railways

Diesel Locomotives

Class 111   Co-Co   DE

Built by:	General Motors 1980/84"	Weight:	99t
Power:	1360kW	Max Speed:	90mph
Length:	17.37m		

8111	BY	Great Northern	8113*	BY	Belfast & Co Down	
8112	BY	Northern Counties				

Class 201   Co-Co   DE

Built by:	General Motors 1994 - 1995	Weight:	112t
Power:	2385kW	Max Speed:	100mph
Length:	20.94m		

8208	BY	[NIR 208]	[92 70 0382 080-4]	RIVER LAGAN	
8209	BY	[NIR 209]	[92 70 0382 090-3]		

Diesel Multiple Units

Class 3000   DMS+MS+DMS   DMU-3   DH

Built by:	CAF 2004 - 2005	Weight:	DMS: 49.5t, MS: 45.5t
Power:	338kW	Max Speed:	90mph
Length:	DMS: 23.74m, MS: 23.14m		

Note: *Fitted with signal and radio systems for use in the Irish Republic

3001*	3301	3501	3401	BY		3013	3313	3513	3413	BY
3002*	3302	3502	3402	BY		3014	3314	3514	3414	BY
3003*	3303	3503	3403	BY		3015	3315	3515	3415	BY
3004*	3304	3504	3404	BY		3016	3316	3516	3416	BY
3005*	3305	3505	3405	BY		3017	3317	3517	3417	BY
3006*	3306	3506	3406	BY		3018	3318	3518	3418	BY
3007	3307	3507	3407	BY		3019	3319	3519	3419	BY
3008	3308	3508	3408	BY		3020	3320	3520	3420	BY
3009	3309	3509	3409	BY		3021	3321	3521	3421	BY
3010	3310	3510	3410	BY		3022	3322	3522	3422	BY
3011	3311	3511	3411	BY		3023	3323	3523	3423	BY
3012	3312	3512	3412	BY						

Class 4000 DMS+MS+DMS   DMU-3/6   DH

Built by:	CAF 2010 - 2012	Weight:	DMS: 48.1t, MS: 46.5t
Power:	390kW	Max Speed:	90mph
Length:	DMS: 23.74m, MS: 23.14m		

4001	4301	4501	4401	BY		4008	4308	4508	4408	BY
4002	4302	4502	4402	BY		4009	4309	4509	4409	BY
4003	4303	4503	4403	BY		4010	4310	4510	4410	BY
4004	4304	4504	4404	BY		4011	4311	4511	4411	BY
4005	4305	4505	4405	BY		4012	4312	4512	4412	BY
4006	4306	4506	4406	BY		4013	4313	4513	4413	BY
4007	4307	4507	4407	BY						

4014	4314	4514	4414	4614	4714	4814	BY
4015	4315	4515	4415	4615	4715	4815	BY
4016	4316	4516	4416	4616	4716	4816	BY
4017	4317	4517	4417	4617	4717	4817	BY
4018	4318	4518	4418	4618	4718	4818	BY
4019	4319	4519	4419	4619	4719	4819	BY
4020	4320	4520	4420	4620	4720	4820	BY

Cross Border Coaching Stock

9001	[55 60 80 8 9001-6]	9204	[50 70 28 9204 0-7]	9215*	[55 60 298 9215-6]
9002	[50 60 80 8 9002 0-6]	9205	[55 60 298 9205-7]	9216*	[50 70 28 9216 0-3]
9003	[55 60 80 8 9003-2]	9206	[50 70 28 9206 0-5]	9401	[55 60 888 9401-0]
9004	[50 60 80 8 9004 0-4]	9207	[55 60 298 9207-7]	9402	[50 70 88 9402 0-4]
9101	[55 60 188 9101-1]	9208	[50 70 28 9208 0-3]	9403	[55 60 888 9403-6]
9102	[55 70 18 9102 0-2]	9209	[55 60 298 9209-9]	9404	[50 70 88 9404 0-2]
9103	[55 60 188 9103-7]	9210	[50 70 28 9210 0-9]	9602	[55 70 89 9602 0-6]
9104	[55 70 18 9104 0-0]	9211	[55 60 298 9211-5]	9604	[55 70 89 9604 0-4]
9201	[55 60 298 9201-6]	9212	[50 70 28 9212 0-7]	9606	[55 70 89 9606 0-2]
9202	[50 70 28 9202 0-9]	9213*	[55 60 298 9213-1]	9608	[55 70 89 9608 0-0]
9203	[55 60 298 9203-2]	9214*	[50 70 28 9214 0-5]		

On-Track Plant Machines & Road Rail

315	Plasser & Theurer USP3000	Ballast Regulator	1978
558	Donelli VMT850GR	Formation Repair Machine	1988
780	Plasser & Theurer RM76UHR	Ballast Cleaner	1979
1165	Donelli	Hopper Trailer	1988
1166	Donelli	Tipping Trailer	1988
7005	Plasser & Theurer MU07-16	Tamper & Liner	1976
7007	Plasser & Theurer MU07-16	Tamper & Liner	1978
7008	Plasser & Theurer MU08-165P4	Tamper & Liner	1994
7009 [73926]	Plasser & Theurer 08-16/4x4C80RT	Tamper	2003
7010	Plasser & Theurer USP5000RT	Ballast Regulator	2003
7015	Plasser & Theurer K355APT	Rail Welder	1986
7017	Giesmar VMT 850 GR	Multi-Purpose Vehicle	
83018	Donelli	Sleeper Space Beam	1983
F83282	Donelli PD350	Relaying Gantry	1983
F83283	Donelli PD351	Relaying Gantry	1983
402783	Donelli PRD6	Sleeper Positioner & Rail Threader	1983
?	Donelli	Water Tank Trailer	2001
KGT1	Giesmar		
KGT2	Giesmar		
99 70 9428 011-9	Windhoff	Multi-Purpose Vehicle	2018
TOI 882	Atlas 1302D R/R Excavator	[132S20603]	
YOI 8544	Atlas 1302E R/R Excavator	[132S22224]	
YXI 4404	Atlas 1304K R/R Excavator	[132S38697]	
YXI 4405	Atlas 1304K R/R Excavator	[132S38743]	

Notes